POETS' QUAIR

POETS' QUAIR

AN ANTHOLOGY
FOR SCOTTISH SCHOOLS

EDITED BY

DAVID RINTOUL

AND

J. B. SKINNER

OLIVER AND BOYD
EDINBURGH AND LONDON

FIRST PUBLISHED 1950
SEVENTH IMPRESSION 1964

Embellishment on the title page
by Joan Hassall

PRINTED IN GREAT BRITAIN BY
OLIVER AND BOYD LTD., EDINBURGH

INTRODUCTION

Our aim in presenting this anthology is to provide in one book as large and comprehensive a selection of poetry as can conveniently be studied in the last two or three years of a Scottish secondary school course. It includes therefore short lyrical poems, long poems such as are often read in separate editions, Scottish poems from the time of the Makars, and Scottish and English poems representative of the best of the twentieth century.

The selection is in keeping with the recommendations in the report of the Advisory Council on Education in Scotland, that 'at every stage of the secondary school there should be included in the scheme of work in English provision for the study of appropriate examples of Scottish literature' and that 'senior pupils should be at least as familiar with Dunbar and Henryson as they are with Chaucer'.

We have chosen to present rather the major poets than the best individual poems from Chaucer to our own day, and to illustrate as many different aspects of the work of each author as possible. Only complete poems are included, unless they are lyrics from longer poems or something similar. We have not tried to be markedly original in our choice, believing that the consensus of informed opinion in poetry to the end of last century has very largely selected for us the best poems to give to school pupils. In the modern section we have tried to represent fairly fully the poets whom we consider to have been most influential in shaping the modern style, but none is represented who was not well known before 1939—though more recent poems are included—partly because later reputations do not seem to us fully established, and partly because the last war seems to have opened another chasm across a developing tradition. We must emphasise that these poems are chosen specifically for a school anthology and do not necessarily, especially in the twentieth century section, reflect our own predilections in verse. This is one reason that Matthew Arnold, who is represented by three long poems running to 36 pages, may seem, if poetic stature be measured by volume, to be worshipped hardly this side idolatry.

We have spoken of 'our' selection; and indeed we accept the final responsibility for everything in—and not in—the book; but we acknowledge with gratitude the assistance of a group of Scottish headmasters and teachers, many of whom sent us lists of the poems they regularly handle in class, and who, at a meeting in Edinburgh, subjected our proposals to a very thorough examination and considered many poems both for inclusion and exclusion. Some of this criticism inevitably cancelled itself out, but in other cases we accepted correction, or differed from our critics only after much heartsearching. In particular, we felt unable to include much of what is called 'Georgian' poetry. We do not deny the existence of good poems in the period covered by the term, but we find ourselves in cordial agreement with Mr Herbert Read and Professor Bonamy Dobrée when they write of 'the pathological condition of sentimentality' which characterised the years before 1914. Similarly, we have chosen to include poems which some tell us are too hard, remembering our own happy experience in showing them to pupils, and admitting our debt to the many good books on modern verse, such as those on T. S. Eliot by Professor Matthiessen and Miss Helen Gardner. But the points on which we differed were few in comparison with the great measure of agreement we secured. The members of the advisory panel were: Miss A. E. Foster and Messrs A. Banks, A. S. Cairncross, J. D. Cairns, J. Caldwell, J. Collie, N. Dixon, A. Gillespie, E. M. Heron, J. F. Houstoun, W. G. Laird, G. More, J. W. Oliver, H. J. L. Robbie, A. B. Russell, C. H. Simpson and E. Smart.

We wish to thank, too, Mr Sam Stewart, educational editor to our publishers, whose guidance and help in a multiplicity of technical matters have ever been at our disposal, and whose courage and initiative are primarily responsible for this book's having existence outside the minds of its editors.

DAVID RINTOUL
JAMES B. SKINNER

Daniel Stewart's College,
    Edinburgh, 1950

ACKNOWLEDGMENTS

The editors gratefully acknowledge their indebtedness to the following authors, publishers and agents, for permission to include copyright material: M. Angus, *Think Lang* (from *The Turn of the Day*), Faber and Faber Ltd.; W. H. Auden, *It's no use raising a Shout, Get there if you can, A. E. Housman* and *Look, Stranger* (from *Poems and Another Time*), Faber and Faber Ltd.; R. Bridges, *A Passer-by, Nightingales, London Snow, Awake my Heart to be loved, I never shall love the Snow again, When first we met* and *All Women Born* (from *Poetical Works*), The Clarendon Press, Oxford; R. Brooke, *Grantchester, Heaven* and *The Dead* (from *Collected Poems*), Sidgwick and Jackson Ltd.; J. Buchan, *Fisher Jamie* (from *Poems Scots and English*), Thomas Nelson & Sons Ltd.; C. Day Lewis, *Cornet Solo, Will it be so again? Sketches for a Portrait, Seen from the Train* (from *Word Over All* and *Poems 1943-1947*), Jonathan Cape Ltd., and *The Conflict* (from *A Time to Dance*), the Hogarth Press Ltd.; T. S. Eliot, *Journey of the Magi, Preludes, Morning at the Window, La Figlia che Piange, The Hollow Men* and *Marina* (from *Collected Poems*), Faber and Faber Ltd.; J. E. Flecker, *The Old Ships*, Martin Secker Ltd.; T. Hardy, *The Oxen, When I set out for Lyonnesse, Snow in the Suburbs, In Time of 'The Breaking of Nations', The Darkling Thrush* and *We Field Women* (from *Collected Poems*), Trustees of the Hardy Estate and Macmillan & Co. Ltd.; G. M. Hopkins, *Inversnaid* and *Pied Beauty* (from *Collected Poems*), Oxford University Press and Mr Hopkins' family; A. E. Housman, *The Chestnut casts his Flambeaux, Bredon Hill, Loveliest of Trees the Cherry now, Yonder see the Morning blink* and *On Wenlock Edge* (from *Collected Poems* and *A Shropshire Lad*); The Society of Authors as Literary Representative of the Trustees of the Estate of the late A. E. Housman, and Jonathan Cape Ltd., publishers of A. E. Housman's *Collected Poems*; V. Jacob, *Tam i' the Kirk* (from *Songs of Angus*), John Murray; H. McDiarmid, *Frae anither Window in Thrums, The Bonnie Broukit Bairn, The Watergaw, Crowdieknowe* and *Munestruck*, Blackwood and Sons Ltd.; L. Macneice, *Autumn Journal—X, Rugby Football Excursion, Spring Voices* and *The Conscript* (from *The Earth Compels* and *Poems*), Faber and Faber Ltd.; W. Owen, *Anthem for Doomed Youth* and *Greater Love* (from *Poems of Wilfred Owen*), Chatto and Windus; W. Soutar, *The Gowk* (from *Collected Poems*), Andrew Dakers; S. Spender, *Landscape near an Aerodrome, I think continually of those, The Pylons* and *An Elementary School Classroom in a Slum* (from *Poems* and *The Still Centre*), Faber and Faber Ltd.; W. B. Yeats, *The Wild Swans at Coole, Easter, 1916, A Prayer for my Daughter, An Irish Airman foresees his Death* and *Sailing to Byzantium* (from *The Collected Poems of W. B. Yeats*, by kind permission of Mrs Yeats), A. P. Watt and Son.

CONTENTS

GEOFFREY CHAUCER

1340-1400

The Prologue

Whan that Aprille with his shoures sote
The droghte of Marche hath perced to the roote,
And bathed every veyne in swich licour,
Of which vertu engendred is the flour;
Whan Zephirus eek with his swete breeth
Inspired hath in every holt and heeth
The tendre croppes, and the yonge sonne
Hath in the Ram his halfe cours y-ronne,
And smale fowles maken melodye,
That slepen al the night with open ye,
(So priketh hem nature in hir corages):
Than longen folk to goon on pilgrimages,
And palmers for to seken straunge strondes,
To ferne halwes, couthe in sondry londes;
And specially, from every shires ende
Of Engelond, to Caunterbury they wende,
The holy blisful martir for to seke,
That hem hath holpen, whan that they were seke.
　　Bifel that, in that seson on a day,
In Southwerk at the Tabard as I lay
Redy to wenden on my pilgrimage
To Caunterbury with ful devout corage,
At night was come in-to that hostelrye
Wel nyne and twenty in a compagnye,
Of sondry folk, by aventure y-falle
In felawshipe, and pilgrims were they alle,
That towards Caunterbury wolden ryde;
The chambres and the stables weren wyde,
And wel we weren esed atte beste.
And shortly, whan the sonne was to reste,
So hadde I spoken with hem everichon,

sote, *sweet*　　eek, *also*　　y-ronne, *run*　　priketh, *urges*　　corages, *hearts*
ferne halwes, *distant shrines*　　couthe, *known*　　everichon, *every one*

1

That I was of hir felawshipe anon,
And made forward erly for to ryse,
To take our wey, ther as I yow devyse.

But natheles, whyl I have tyme and space,
Er that I ferther in this tale pace,
Me thinketh it accordaunt to resoun,
To telle yow al the condicioun
Of ech of hem, so as it semed me,
And whiche they weren, and of what degree;
And eek in what array that they were inne:
And at a knight than wol I first biginne.

A KNIGHT ther was, and that a worthy man,
That fro the tyme that he first bigan
To ryden out, he loved chivalrye,
Trouthe and honour, fredom and curteisye.
Ful worthy was he in his lordes werre,
And thereto hadde he riden (no man ferre)
As wel in Cristendom as hethenesse,
And ever honoured for his worthinesse.
At Alisaundre he was, whan it was wonne;
Ful ofte tyme he hadde the bord bigonne
Aboven alle naciouns in Pruce.
In Lettow hadde he reysed and in Ruce,
No Cristen man so ofte of his degree.
In Gernade at the sege eek hadde he be
Of Algezir, and riden in Belmarye.
At Lyeys was he, and at Satalye,
Whan they were wonne; and in the Grete See
At many a noble armee hadde he be.
At mortal batailles hadde he been fiftene,
And foughten for our feith at Tramissene
In listes thryes, and ay slayn his fo.
This ilke worthy knight hadde been also
Somtyme with the lord of Palatye,
Ageyn another hethen in Turkye:
And evermore he hadde a sovereyn prys.
And though that he were worthy, he was wys,
And of his port as meek as is a mayde.
He nevere yet no vileinye ne sayde

ferre, *farther*   the bord bigonne, *sat at the head of the table*
    armee, *expedition*   prys, *reputation*
        port, *deportment*

In al his lyf, un-to no maner wight.
He was a verray parfit gentil knight.
But for to tellen yow of his array,
His hors were gode, but he was nat gay.
Of fustian he wered a gipoun
Al bismotered with his habergeoun.
For he was late y-come from his viage,
And wente for to doon his pilgrimage.

  With him ther was his sone, a yong SQUYER,
A lovyer, and a lusty bacheler,
With lokkes crulle, as they were leyd in presse.
Of twenty yeer of age he was, I gesse.
Of his stature he was of evene lengthe,
And wonderly deliver, and greet of strengthe.
And he hadde been somtyme in chivachye,
In Flaundres, in Artoys, and Picardye,
And born him wel, as of so litel space,
In hope to stonden in his lady grace.
Embrouded was he, as it were a mede
Al ful of fresshe floures, whyte and rede.
Singinge he was, or floytinge, al the day;
He was as fresh as is the month of May.
Short was his goune, with sleves longe and wyde.
Well coude he sitte on hors, and faire ryde.
He coude songes make and wel endyte,
Juste and eek daunce, and wel purtreye and wryte.
So hote he lovede, that by nightertale
He sleep namore than doth a nightingale.
Curteys he was, lowly, and servisable,
And carf biforn his fader at the table.

  A YEMAN hadde he, and servaunts namo
At that tyme, for him liste ryde so;
And he was clad in cote and hood of grene;
A sheef of pecok arwes brighte and kene
Under his belt he bar ful thriftily,
(Wel coude he dresse his takel yemanly:
His arwes drouped noght with fetheres lowe),
And in his hand he bar a mighty bowe.

3

A not-heed hadde he, with a broun visage.
Of wode-craft wel coude he al the usage.
Upon his arm he bar a gay bracer,
And by his syde a swerd and a bokeler,
And on that other syde a gay daggere,
Harneised wel, and sharp as point of spere;
A Cristofre on his brest of silver shene.
An horn he bar, the bawdrik was of grene;
A forster was he, soothly, as I gesse.

Ther was also a Nonne, a PRIORESSE,
That of hir smyling was ful simple and coy;
Hir gretteste ooth was but by seynt Loy;
And she was cleped madame Eglentyne.
Ful wel she song the service divyne,
Entuned in hir nose ful semely;
And Frensh she spak ful faire and fetisly,
After the scole of Stratford atte Bowe,
For Frensh of Paris was to hir unknowe.
At mete wel y-taught was she with-alle;
She leet no morsel from hir lippes falle,
Ne wette hir fingres in hir sauce depe.
Wel coude she carie a morsel, and wel kepe,
That no drope ne fille up-on hir brest.
In curteisye was set ful moche hir lest.
Hir over lippe wyped she so clene,
That in hir coppe was no ferthing sene
Of grece, whan she dronken hadde hir draughte.
Ful semely after hir mete she raughte,
And sikerly she was of greet disport,
And ful plesaunt, and amiable of port,
And peyned hir to countrefete chere
Of court, and been estatlich of manere,
And to ben holden digne of reverence.
But, for to speken of hir conscience,
She was so charitable and so pitous,
She wolde wepe, if that she sawe a mous
Caught in a trappe, if it were deed or bledde.

not-heed, *head with cropped hair*		bracer, *arm-guard*
harneised, *mounted*	bawdrik, *cross-belt*	cleped, *called*
semely, *agreeably*	fetisly, *properly*	lest, *desire*
ferthing, *trace*	raughte, *stretched*	sikerly, *certainly*
of greet disport, *affable*	peyned hir, *took pains*	chere, *manner*
	estatlich, *stately*	

4

Of smale houndes had she, that she fedde
With rosted flesh, or milk and wastel breed.
But sore weep she if oon of hem were deed,
Or if men smoot it with a yerde smerte:
And al was conscience and tendre herte.
Ful semely hir wimpel pinched was;
Hir nose tretys; hir eyen greye as glas;
Hir mouth ful smal, and ther-to softe and reed;
But sikerly she hadde a fair forheed.
It was almost a spanne brood, I trowe;
For, hardily, she was nat undergrowe.
Ful fetis was hir cloke, as I was war.
Of smal coral aboute hir arm she bar
A peire of bedes, gauded al with grene;
And ther-on heng a broche of gold ful shene,
On which there was first write a crowned A,
And after, *Amor vincit omnia.*

Another NONNE with hir hadde she,
That was hir chapeleyne, and PREESTES THREE.

A MONK ther was, a fair for the maistrye,
An out-rydere, that lovede venerye;
A manly man, to been an abbot able.
Ful many a deyntee hors hadde he in stable:
And, whan he rood, men mighte his brydel here
Ginglen in a whistling wynd as clere,
And eek as loude as doth the chapel-belle,
Ther as this lord was keper of the celle.
The reule of seint Maure or of seint Beneit,
By-cause that it was old and som-del streit,
This ilke monk leet olde thinges pace,
And held after the newe world the space.
He yaf nat of that text a pulled hen,
That seith, that hunters been nat holy men;
Ne that a monk, whan he is cloisterlees,
Is lykned til a fish that is waterlees;
This is to seyn, a monk out of his cloistre.
But thilke text held he nat worth an oistre.
And I seyde his opinioun was good.
What sholde he studie, and make himselven wood,

wastel, *finest*	yerde, *stick*	wimpel, *headkerchief*
tretys, *shapely*	peire, *string*	gauded, *with large beads*
crowned, *capital*	out-rydere, *overseer*	yaf, *gave* wood, *mad*

Upon a book in cloistre alwey to poure,
Or swinken with his handes, and laboure,
As Austin bit? How shal the world be served?
Lat Austin have his swink to him reserved.
Therfore he was a pricasour aright;
Grehoundes he hadde, as swifte as fowel in flight;
Of priking and of hunting for the hare
Was al his lust, for no cost wolde he spare.
I seigh his sleves purfiled at the hond
With grys, and that the fyneste of a lond;
And, for to festne his hood under his chin,
He hadde of gold y-wroght a curious pin:
A love-knot in the gretter ende ther was.
His heed was balled, that shoon as any glas,
And eek his face, as he hadde been anoint.
He was a lord ful fat and in good point;
His eyen stepe, and rollinge in his heed,
That stemed as a forneys of a leed;
His botes souple, his hors in greet estat.
Now certeinly he was a fair prelat;
He was nat pale as a for-pyned goost.
A fat swan loved he best of any roost.
His palfrey was as broun as is a berye.

   A Frere ther was, a wantown and a merye,
A limitour, a ful solempne man.
In alle the ordres foure is noon that can
So moche of daliaunce and fair langage.
He hadde maad ful many a mariage
Of yonge wommen, at his owne cost.
Un-to his ordre he was a noble post.
Ful wel biloved and famulier was he
With frankeleyns over-al in his contree,
And eek with worthy wommen of the toun:
For he had power of confessioun,
As seyde him-self, more than a curat,
For of his ordre he was licenciat.
Ful swetely herde he confessioun,
And plesaunt was his absolucioun;
He was an esy man to yive penaunce

swinken, *work*   bit, *bade*   pricasour, *hard rider*
purfiled, *trimmed*   grys, *grey fur*   stepe, *bright*
  leed, *cauldron* limitour, *licensed to beg within certain limits*   yive, *give*

6

Ther as he wiste to han a good pitaunce;
For unto a povre ordre for to yive
Is signe that a man is wel y-shrive.
For if he yaf, he dorste make avaunt,
He wiste that a man was repentaunt.
For many a man so hard is of his herte,
He may nat wepe al-thogh him sore smerte.
Therfore, in stede of weping and preyeres,
Men moot yive silver to the povre freres.
His tipet was ay farsed ful of knyves
And pinnes, for to yeven faire wyves.
And certeinly he hadde a mery note;
Wel coude he singe and pleyen on a rote.
Of yeddinges he bar utterly the prys.
His nekke whyt was as the flour-de-lys.
Ther-to he strong was as a champioun.
He knew the tavernes wel in every toun,
And everich hostiler and tappestere
Bet than a lazar or a beggestere;
For un-to swich a worthy man as he
Acorded nat, as by his facultee,
To have with seke lazars aqueyntaunce.
It is nat honest, it may nat avaunce
For to delen with no swich poraille,
But al with riche and sellers of vitaille.
And over-al, ther as profit sholde aryse,
Curteys he was, and lowly of servyse.
Ther was no man nowher so vertuous.
He was the beste beggere in his hous;
For thogh a widwe hadde noght a sho,
So plesaunt was his *In principio*,
Yet wolde he have a ferthing, er he wente.
His purchas was wel bettre than his rente.
And rage he coude as it were right a whelpe.
In love-dayes ther coude he mochel helpe.
For ther he was nat lyk a cloisterer,
With a thredbare cope, as is a povre scoler,

---

tipet, *end of cowl*   farsed, *stuffed*   yeddinges, *songs*
lazar, *leper*   poraille, *rabble*   purchas, *occasional gains*
rente, *fixed income*   rage, *romp*
love-dayes, *days for settling disputes*
cope, *cloak*

7

But he was lyk a maister or a pope.
Of double worsted was his semi-cope,
That rounded as a belle out of the presse.
Somwhat he lipsed, for his wantownesse,
To make his English swete up-on his tonge;
And in his harping, whan that he had songe,
His eyen twinkled in his heed aright,
As doon the sterres in the frosty night.
This worthy limitour was cleped Huberd.

A MARCHANT was ther with a forked berd,
In mottelee, and hye on horse he sat,
Up-on his heed a Flaundrish bever hat;
His botes clasped faire and fetisly.
His resons he spak ful solempnely,
Sowninge alway th'encrees of his winning.
He wolde the see were kept for any thing
Bitwixe Middelburgh and Orewelle.
Wel coude he in eschaunge sheeldes selle.
This worthy man ful wel his wit bisette;
Ther wiste no wight that he was in dette,
So estatly was he of his governaunce,
With his bargaynes, and with his chevisaunce.
For sothe he was a worthy man with-alle,
But sooth to seyn, I noot how men him calle.

A CLERK ther was of Oxenford also,
That un-to logik hadde longe y-go.
As lene was his hors as is a rake,
And he nas nat right fat, I undertake;
But loked holwe, and ther-to soberly.
Ful thredbar was his overest courtepy;
For he had geten him yet no benefice,
Ne was so worldly for to have office.
For him was levere have at his beddes heed
Twenty bokes, clad in blak or reed
Of Aristotle and his philosophye,
Than robes riche, or fithele, or gay sautrye.
But al be that he was a philosophre,
Yet hadde he but litel gold in cofre;
But al that he mighte of his frendes hente,

wantownesse, *affectation*	Sowninge, *dwelling upon*	sheeldes, *crowns*
bisette, *employed*	chevisaunce, *borrowing*	courtepy, *short cloak*
levere, *rather*	sautrye, *psaltery*	hente, *obtain*

On bokes and on lerninge he it spente,
And bisily gan for the soules preye
Of hem that yaf him wher-with to scoleye.
Of studie took he most cure and most hede.
Noght o word spak he more than was nede,
And that was seyd in forme and reverence,
And short and quik, and ful of hy sentence.
Sowninge in moral vertu was his speche,
And gladly wolde he lerne, and gladly teche.

A SERGEANT OF THE LAWE, war and wys,
That often hadde been at the parvys,
Ther was also, ful riche of excellence.
Discreet he was, and of greet reverence:
He semed swich, his wordes weren so wyse.
Justice he was ful often in assyse,
By patente, and by pleyn commissioun;
For his science, and for his heigh renoun
Of fees and robes hadde he many oon.
So greet a purchasour was nowher noon.
Al was fee simple to him in effect,
His purchasing mighte nat been infect.
Nowher so bisy a man as he ther nas,
And yet he semed bisier than he was.
In termes hadde he caas and domes alle,
That from the tyme of king William were falle
Therto he coude endyte, and make a thing,
Ther coude no wight pinche at his wryting;
And every statut coude he pleyn by rote.
He rood but hoomly in a medlee cote
Girt with a ceint of silk, with barres smale;
Of his array telle I no lenger tale.

A FRANKELEYN was in his compagnye;
Whyt was his berd, as is the dayesye.
Of his complexioun he was sangwyn.
Wel loved he by the morwe a sop in wyn.
To liven in delyt was evere his wone,
For he was Epicurus owne sone,
That heeld opinioun that pleyn delyt
Was verraily felicitee parfyt.

sentence, *thought*	parvys, *church-porch*	science, *knowledge*
purchasour, *buyer of land*	fee simple, *unentailed*	infect, *invalid*
termes, *precise wording*	pinche, *find fault with*	ceint, *girdle*

9

An householdere, and that a greet, was he;
Seynt Julian he was in his contree.
His breed, his ale, was alwey after oon;
A bettre envyned man was nowher noon.
With-oute bake mete was nevere his hous,
Of fish and flesh, and that so plentevous,
It snewed in his hous of mete and drinke,
Of alle deyntees that men coude thinke.
After the sondry sesons of the yeer,
So chaunged he his mete and his soper.
Ful many a fat partrich hadde he in mewe,
And many a breem and many a luce in stewe.
Wo was his cook, but-if his sauce were
Poynaunt and sharp, and redy al his gere.
His table dormant in his halle alway
Stood redy covered al the longe day.
At sessiouns ther was he lord and sire.
Ful ofte tyme he was knight of the shire.
An anlas and a gipser al of silk
Heng at his girdel, whyt as morne milk.
A shirreve hadde he been, and a countour;
Was nowher such a worthy vavasour.

  An HABERDASSHER and a CARPENTER,
A WEBBE, a DYERE and a TAPICER,
And they were clothed alle in o liveree,
Of a solempne and greet fraternitee.
Ful fresh and newe hir gere apyked was;
Hir knyves were y-chaped noght with bras,
But al with silver wroght ful clene and weel,
Hir girdles and hir pouches everydeel.
Wel semed ech of hem a fair burgeys,
To sitten in a yeldhalle on a deys.
Everich, for the wisdom that he can,
Was shapely for to been an alderman.
For catel hadde they ynogh and rente,
And eek hir wyves wolde it wel assente;
And elles certein were they to blame.
It is ful fair to been y-clept *ma dame,*

after oon, *alike*	mewe, *coop*	luce, *pike*
stewe, *fish-pond*	anlas, *knife*	gipser, *purse*
vavasour, *small landowner*	webbe, *weaver*	Tapicer, *upholsterer*
apyked, *fashioned*	**y-**chaped, *mounted*	catel, *property*

And goon to vigilyes al bifore,
And have a mantel roialliche y-bore.
A COOK they hadde with hem for the nones,
To boille the chiknes with the mary-bones,
And poudre-marchant tart, and galingale.
Wel coulde he knowe a draughte of London ale.
He coude roste, and sethe, and broille, and frye,
Maken mortreux, and wel bake a pye.
But greet harm was it, as it thoughte me,
That on his shine a mormal hadde he;
For blankmanger, that made he with the beste.

A SHIPMAN was ther, woning fer by weste:
For aught I woot, he was of Dertemouthe.
He rood up-on a rouncy, as he couthe,
In a gowne of falding to the knee.
A daggere hanging on a laas hadde he
Aboute his nekke under his arm adoun.
The hote somer had maad his hewe al broun;
And, certeinly, he was a good felawe.
Ful many a draughte of wyn had he y-drawe
From Burdeux-ward, whyl that the chapman sleep.
Of nyce conscience took he no keep.
If that he faught, and hadde the hyer hond,
By water he sente hem hoom to every lond.
But of his craft to rekene wel his tydes,
His stremes and his daungers him bisydes,
His herberwe and his mone, his lodemenage,
Ther was noon swich from Hulle to Cartage.
Hardy he was, and wys to undertake;
With many a tempest hadde his berd been shake.
He knew wel alle the havenes, as they were,
From Gootlond to the cape of Finistere,
And every cryke in Britayne and in Spayne;
His barge y-cleped was the Maudelayne.

With us ther was a DOCTOUR OF PHISYK,
In al this world ne was ther noon him lyk
To speke of phisik and of surgerye;

---

mary-bones, *marrow bones*	poudre-marchant, *spicy*
galingale, *a sweet root* mortreux, *dish*	mormal, *running sore*
woning, *dwelling* rouncy, *hack*	falding, *coarse stuff*
laas, *lanyard* chapman, *merchant*	nyce, *scrupulous*
herberwe, *harbour*	lodemenage, *pilotage*

11

For he was grounded in astronomye.
He kepte his pacient a ful greet del
In houres, by his magik naturel.
Wel coude he fortunen the ascendent
Of his images for his pacient.
He knew the cause of everich maladye,
Were it of hoot or cold, or moiste, or drye,
And where engendred, and of what humour;
He was a verrey parfit practisour.
The cause y-knowe, and of his harm the rote,
Anon he yaf the seke man his bote.
Ful redy hadde he his apothecaries,
To sende him drogges, and his letuaries,
For ech of hem made other for to winne;
Hir frendschipe was nat newe to biginne.
Wel knew he the olde Esculapius,
And Deiscorides, and eek Rufus;
Old Ypocras, Haly, and Galien;
Serapion, Razis, and Avicen;
Averrois, Damascien, and Constantyn;
Bernard, and Gatesden, and Gilbertyn.
Of his diete mesurable was he,
For it was of no superfluitee,
But of greet norissing and digestible.
His studie was but litel on the Bible.
In sangwin and in pers he clad was al,
Lyned with taffata and with sendal;
And yet he was but esy of dispence;
He kepte that he wan in pestilence.
For gold in phisik is a cordial,
Therfore he lovede gold in special.

    A good WYF was ther of bisyde BATHE,
But she was som-del deef, and that was scathe.
Of cloth-making she hadde swiche an haunt,
She passed hem of Ypres and of Gaunt.
In al the parisshe wyf ne was ther noon
That to the offring bifore hir sholde goon;
And if ther dide, certeyn, so wrooth was she,

grounded, *instructed*	kepte, *watched*	bote, *remedy*
letuaries, *remedies*	mesurable, *moderate*	sangwin, *red material*
pers, *dark blue*	sendal, *thin silk*	esy of dispence, *close-fisted*
	scathe, *a pity*	

12

That she was out of alle charitee.
Hir coverchiefs ful fyne were of ground;
I dorste swere they weyeden ten pound
That on a Sonday were upon hir heed.
Hir hosen weren of fyn scarlet reed,
Ful streite y-teyd, and shoos ful moiste and newe.
Bold was hir face, and fair, and reed of hewe.
She was a worthy womman al hir lyve,
Housbondes at chirche-dore she hadde fyve,
Withouten other compagnye in youthe;
But thereof nedeth nat to speke as nouthe.
And thryes hadde she been at Jerusalem;
She hadde passed many a straunge streem;
At Rome she hadde been, and at Boloigne,
In Galice at seint Jame, and at Coloigne.
She coude moche of wandring by the weye.
Gat-tothed was she, soothly for to seye.
Up-on an amblere esily she sat,
Y-wimpled wel, and on hir heed an hat
As brood as is a bokeler or a targe;
A foot-mantel aboute hir hipes large,
And on hir feet a paire of spores sharpe.
In felaweschip wel coude she laughe and carpe.
Of remedies of love she knew per-chaunce,
For she coude of that art the olde daunce.

    A good man was ther of religioun,
And he was a povre PERSOUN of a toun;
But riche he was of holy thoght and werk.
He was also a lerned man, a clerk,
That Cristes gospel trewely wolde preche;
His parisshens devoutly wolde he teche.
Benigne he was, and wonder diligent,
And in adversitee ful pacient;
And swich he was y-preved ofte sythes.
Ful looth were him to cursen for his tythes,
But rather wolde he yeven, out of doute,
Un-to his povre parisshens aboute
Of his offring, and eek of his substaunce.

---

streite, *tightly*   moiste, *supple*   as nouthe, *at present*
coude, *knew*   gat-tothed, *with teeth far apart*   amblere, *ambling horse*
carpe, *talk*   the olde daunce, *all the tricks*   sythes, *times*
cursen, *excommunicate*   offring, *alms*

He coude in litel thing han suffisaunce.
Wyd was his parisshe, and houses fer a-sonder,
But he ne lafte nat, for reyn ne thonder,
In siknes nor in meschief to visyte
The ferreste in his parisshe, muche and lyte,
Up-on his feet, and in his hand a staf.
This noble ensample to his sheep he yaf,
That first he wroghte, and afterward he taughte;
Out of the gospel he tho wordes caughte;
And this figure he added eek ther-to,
That if gold ruste, what shal yren do?
For if a preest be foul, on whom we truste,
No wonder is a lewed man to ruste;
And shame it is, if a preest take keep,
A shiten shepherde and a clene sheep.
Wel oghte a preest ensample for to yive,
By his clennesse, how that his sheep shold live.
He sette nat his benefice to hyre,
And leet his sheep encombred in the myre,
And ran to London, un-to seynt Poules,
To seken him a chaunterie for soules,
Or with a bretherhed to been withholde;
But dwelte at hoom, and kepte wel his folde,
So that the wolf ne made it nat miscarie;
He was a shepherde and no mercenarie.
And though he holy were, and vertuous,
He was to sinful man nat despitous,
Ne of his speche daungerous ne digne,
But in his teching discreet and benigne.
To drawen folk to heven by fairnesse
By good ensample, this was his bisinesse:
But it were any persone obstinat,
What so he were, of heigh or lowe estat,
Him wolde he snibben sharply for the nones.
A bettre preest, I trowe that nowher noon is.
He wayted after no pompe and reverence,
Ne maked him a spyced conscience,
But Cristes lore, and his apostles twelve,
He taughte, but first he folwed it himselve.
    With him ther was a PLOWMAN, was his brother,

| muche and lyte, *high and low* | lewed, *lay* | despitous, *cruel* |
| daungerous, *domineering* | digne, *haughty* | spyced, *over-scrupulous* |

14

That hadde y-lad of dong ful many a fother,
A trewe swinkere and a good was he,
Livinge in pees and parfit charitee.
God loved he best with al his hole herte
At alle tymes, thogh him gamed or smerte,
And thanne his neighebour right as himselve.
He wolde thresshe, and ther-to dyke and delve,
For Cristes sake, for every povre wight,
Withouten hyre, if it lay in his might.
His tythes payed he ful faire and wel,
Bothe of his propre swink and his catel.
In a tabard he rood upon a mere.

   Ther was also a Reve and a Millere,
A Somnour and a Pardoner also,
A Maunciple, and myself; ther were namo.

   The MILLER was a stout carl, for the nones,
Ful big he was of braun, and eek of bones;
That proved wel, for over-al ther he cam,
At wrastling he wolde have alwey the ram.
He was short-sholdred, brood, a thikke knarre,
Ther nas no dore that he nolde heve of harre,
Or breke it, at a renning, with his heed.
His berd as any sowe or fox was reed,
And ther-to brood, as though it were a spade.
Up-on the cop right of his nose he hade
A werte, and ther-on stood a tuft of heres,
Reed as the bristles of a sowes eres;
His nose-thirles blake were and wyde.
A swerd and bokeler bar he by his syde;
His mouth as greet was as a greet forneys.
He was a janglere and a goliardeys,
And that was most of sinne and harlotryes.
Wel coude he stelen corn, and tollen thryes;
And yet he hadde a thombe of gold, pardee.
A whyt cote and a blew hood wered he.
A baggepype wel coude he blowe and sowne,
And therwithal he broghte us out of towne.

   A gentil MAUNCIPLE was ther of a temple,

---

fother, *cart-load* thogh him gamed or smerte, *in all circumstances*
dyke, *ditch* knarre, *stocky fellow* harre, *hinge*
cop, *top* janglere, *babbler* goliardeys, *coarse buffoon*
harlotryes, *ribaldries* Maunciple, *steward* temple, *Inn of Court*

15

Of which achatours mighte take exemple
For to be wyse in bying of vitaille.
For whether that he payde, or took by taille,
Algate he wayted so in his achat,
That he was ay biforn and in good stat.
Now is nat that of God a ful fair grace,
That swich a lewed mannes wit shal pace
The wisdom of an heep of lerned men?
Of maistres hadde he mo than thryes ten,
That were of lawe expert and curious;
Of which ther were a doseyn in that hous,
Worthy to been stiwardes of rente and lond
Of any lord that is in Engelond,
To make him live by his propre good,
In honour dettelees, but he were wood,
Or live as scarsly as him list desire;
And able for to helpen al a shire
In any cas that mighte falle or happe;
And yit this maunciple sette hir aller cappe.

  The REVE was a sclendre colerik man,
His berd was shave as ny as ever he can.
His heer was by his eres round y-shorn.
His top was dokked lyk a preest biforn.
Ful longe were his legges, and ful lene,
Y-lyk a staf, ther was no calf y-sene.
Wel coude he kepe a gerner and a binne;
Ther was noon auditour coude on him winne.
Wel wiste he, by the droghte, and by the reyn,
The yeldyng of his seed, and of his greyn.
His lordes sheep, his neet, his dayerye,
His swyn, his hors, his stoor, and his pultrye,
Was hooly in this reves governing,
And by his covenaunt yaf the rekening,
Sin that his lord was twenty yeer of age;
Ther coude no man bringe him in arrerage.
Ther nas baillif, ne herde, ne other hyne,
That he ne knew his sleighte and his covyne;
They were adrad of him, as of the deeth.

achatours, *caterers*		by taille, *on account*
Algate he wayted, *always he watched*		scarsly, *economically*
sette hir aller cappe, *befooled them all*		Reve, *farm-bailiff*
neet, *cattle*	hyne, *farm-servant*	sleighte, *trickery* covyne, *deceit*

His woning was ful fair up-on an heeth,
With grene trees shadwed was his place.
He coude bettre than his lord purchase.
Ful riche he was astored prively,
His lord wel coude he plesen subtilly,
To yeve and lene him of his owne good,
And have a thank, and yet a cote and hood.
In youthe he lerned hadde a good mister;
He was a wel good wrighte, a carpenter.
This reve sat up-on a ful good stot,
That was al pomely grey, and highte Scot.
A long surcote of pers up-on he hade,
And by his syde he bar a rusty blade.
Of Northfolk was this reve, of which I telle,
Bisyde a toun men clepen Baldeswelle.
Tukked he was, as is a frere, aboute,
And evere he rood the hindreste of our route.

A SOMNOUR was ther with us in that place,
That hadde a fyr-reed cherubinnes face,
For sawceflem he was, with eyen narwe.
As hoot he was, and lecherous as a sparwe,
With scalled browes blake, and piled berd;
Of his visage children were aferd.
Ther nas quik-silver, litarge, ne brimstoon,
Boras, ceruce, ne oille of tartre noon,
Ne oynement that wolde clense and byte,
That him mighte helpen of his whelkes whyte,
Nor of the knobbes sittinge on his chekes.
Wel loved he garleek, oynons, and eek lekes,
And for to drinken strong wyn, reed as blood.
Thanne wolde he speke, and crye as he were wood.
And whan that he wel dronken hadde the wyn,
Than wolde he speke no word but Latyn.
A fewe termes hadde he, two or three,
That he had lerned out of som decree;
No wonder is, he herde it al the day;
And eek ye knowen wel, how that a jay

lene, *lend*   mister, *trade*   stot, *horse*   pomely, *dappled*
highte, *was called*   surcote, *coat worn above another*   clepen, *call*
sawceflem, *having a red pimpled face*   scalled, *scurfy*   piled, *thin*
litarge, *ointment*   ceruce, *white lead*   whelkes, *pimples*
knobbes, *boils*

Can clepen 'Watte', as well as can the pope.
But who-so coude in other thing him grope,
Thanne hadde he spent al his philosophye;
Ay *Questio quid iuris* wolde he crye.
He was a gentil harlot and a kynde;
A bettre felawe sholde men noght fynde.
He wolde suffre for a quart of wyn
A good felawe to have his concubyn
A twelf-month, and excuse him atte fulle:
And prively a finch eek coude he pulle.
And if he fond owher a good felawe,
He wolde techen him to have non awe,
In swich cas, of the erchedeknes curs,
But-if a mannes soule were in his purs;
For in his purs he sholde y-punisshed be.
'Purs is the erchedeknes helle,' seyde he.
But wel I woot he lyed right in dede;
Of cursing oghte ech gulty man him drede—
For curs wol slee right as assoilling saveth—
And also war him of a *significavit*.
In daunger hadde he at his owne gyse
The yonge girles of the diocyse,
And knew hir counseil, and was al hir reed.
A gerland hadde he set up-on his heed,
As greet as it were for an ale-stake;
A bokeler hadde he maad him of a cake.
    With him ther rood a gentil PARDONER
Of Rouncival, his frend and his compeer,
That streight was comen fro the court of Rome.
Ful loude he song, 'Com hider, love, to me'.
This somnour bar to him a stif burdoun,
Was nevere trompe of half so greet a soun.
This pardoner hadde heer as yelow as wex,
But smothe it heng, as doth a strike of flex;
By ounces henge his lokkes that he hadde,
And ther-with he his shuldres overspradde;

grope, *test*   harlot, *fellow*
    a finch coude he pulle, *he could swindle an ignorant person*
assoilling, *absolution*   significavit, *opening word of a decree of excommunication*
    daunger, *jurisdiction*   girles, *young people*   reed, *adviser*
    compeer, *comrade*   burdoun, *accompaniment*   strike, *hank*
                ounces, *locks*

18

But thinne it lay, by colpons oon and oon;
But hood, for jolitee, ne wered he noon,
For it was trussed up in his walet.
Him thoughte, he rood al of the newe jet;
Dischevele, save his cappe, he rood al bare.
Swiche glaringe eyen hadde he as an hare.
A vernicle hadde he sowed on his cappe.
His walet lay biforn him in his lappe,
Bret-ful of pardoun come from Rome al hoot.
A voys he hadde as smal as hath a goot.
No berd hadde he, ne nevere sholde have,
As smothe it was as it were late y-shave;
I trowe he were a gelding or a mare.
But of his craft, fro Berwik into Ware,
Ne was ther swich another pardoner.
For in his male he hadde a pilwe-beer,
Which that, he seyde, was our lady veyl:
He seyde, he hadde a gobet of the seyl
That seynt Peter hadde, whan that he wente
Up-on the see, til Jesu Crist him hente.
He hadde a croys of latoun, ful of stones,
And in a glas he hadde pigges bones.
But with thise relikes, whan that he fond
A povre person dwelling up-on lond,
Up-on a day he gat him more moneye
Than that the person gat in monthes tweye.
And thus with feyned flaterye and japes,
He made the person and the peple his apes.
But trewely to tellen, atte laste,
He was in chirche a noble ecclesiaste.
Wel coude he rede a lessoun or a storie,
But alderbest he song an offertorie;
For wel he wiste, whan that song was songe,
He moste preche, and wel affyle his tonge,
To winne silver, as he ful wel coude;
Therefore he song so meriely and loude.
    Now have I told you shortly, in a clause,
Th'estat, th'array, the nombre, and eek the cause
Why that assembled was this compagnye

colpons, *strips*   jet, *fashion*   vernicle, *portrait of Christ*
    Bret-ful, *brimful*   pilwe-beer, *pillow-case*   gobet, *piece*
latoun, *alloy*   apes, *dupes*   affyle, *smooth*

In Southwerk, at this gentil hostelrye,
That highte the Tabard, faste by the Belle.
But now is tyme to yow for to telle
How that we baren us that ilke night,
Whan we were in that hostelrye alight.
And after wol I telle of our viage,
And al the remenaunt of our pilgrimage.
But first I pray yow of your curteisye,
That ye n'arette it nat my vileinye,
Thogh that I pleynly speke in this matere,
To telle yow hir wordes and hir chere;
Ne thogh I speke hir wordes properly.
For this ye knowen al-so well as I,
Who-so shal telle a tale after a man,
He moot reherce, as ny as evere he can,
Everich a word, if it be in his charge,
Al speke he never so rudeliche and large;
Or elles he moot telle his tale untrewe,
Or feyne thing, or fynde wordes newe.
He may nat spare, al-thogh he were his brother;
He moot as wel seye o word as another.
Crist spak himself ful brode in holy writ,
And wel ye woot, no vileinye is it.
Eek Plato seith, who-so that can him rede,
The wordes mote be cosin to the dede.
Also I prey yow to foryeve it me,
Al have I nat set folk in hir degree
Here in this tale, as that they sholde stonde;
My wit is short, ye may wel understonde.

Greet chere made our hoste us everichon,
And to the soper sette he us anon;
And served us with vitaille at the beste.
Strong was the wyn, and wel to drinke us leste.
A semely man our hoste was with-alle
For to han been a marshal in an halle;
A large man he was with eyen stepe,
A fairer burgeys was ther noon in Chepe:
Bold of his speche, and wys, and wel y-taught,
And of manhod him lakkede right naught.
Eek thereto he was right a mery man,
And after soper pleyen he bigan,

And spak of mirthe amonges othere thinges,
Whan that we hadde maad our rekeninges;
And seyde thus: 'Now, lordinges, trewely
Ye ben to me right welcome hertely:
For by my trouthe, if that I shal nat lye,
I ne saugh this yeer so mery a compagnye
At ones in this herberwe as is now.
Fayn wolde I doon yow mirthe, wiste I how.
And of a mirthe I am right now bithoght,
To doon yow ese, and it shal coste noght.

    Ye goon to Caunterbury; God yow spede,
The blisful martir quyte yow your mede.
And wel I woot, as ye goon by the weye,
Ye shapen yow to talen and to pleye;
For trewely, confort ne mirthe is noon
To ryde by the weye doumb as a stoon;
And therefore wol I maken yow disport,
As I seyde erst, and doon yow som confort.
And if yow lyketh alle, by oon assent,
Now for to stonden at my jugement,
And for to werken as I shal yow seye,
To-morwe, whan ye ryden by the weye,
Now, by my fader soule, that is deed,
But ye be merye, I wol yeve yow myn heed.
Hold up your hond, withoute more speche.'
Our counseil was nat longe for to seche;
Us thoughte it was noght worth to make it wys,
And graunted him withouten more avys,
And bad him seye his verdit, as him leste.

    'Lordinges,' quod he, 'now herkneth for the beste;
But tak it not, I prey yow, in desdeyn;
This is the poynt, to speken short and pleyn,
That ech of yow, to shorte with your weye,
In this viage, shal telle tales tweye,
To Caunterbury-ward, I mene it so,
And hom-ward he shal tellen othere two,
Of aventures that whylom han bifalle.
And which of yow that bereth him best of alle,
That is to seyn, that telleth in this cas

quyte yow your mede, *pay you your reward*   shapen, *plan*
talen, *to tell stories*   disport, *diversion*   make it wys, *reflect*
             avys, *consideration*

Tales of best sentence and most solas,
Shal have a soper at our aller cost
Here in this place, sitting by this post,
Whan that we come agayn fro Caunterbury.
And for to make yow the more mery,
I wol myselven gladly with yow ryde,
Right at myn owne cost, and be your gyde.
And who-so wol my jugement withseye
Shall paye al that we spenden by the weye.
And if ye vouche-sauf that it be so,
Tel me anon, with-outen wordes mo,
And I wol erly shape me therfore.'
  This thing was graunted, and our othes swore
With ful glad herte, and preyden him also
That he wold vouch-sauf for to do so,
And that he wolde been our governour,
And of our tales juge and reportour,
And sette a soper at a certeyn prys;
And we wold reuled been at his devys,
In heigh and lowe; and thus, by oon assent,
We been acorded to his jugement.
And ther-up-on the wyn was fet anon;
We dronken, and to reste wente echon,
With-outen any lenger taryinge.
A-morwe, whan that day bigan to springe,
Up roos our host, and was our aller cok,
And gadrede us togidre, alle in a flok,
And forth we riden, a litel more than pas,
Un-to the watering of seint Thomas.
And there our host bigan his hors areste,
And seyde; 'Lordinges, herkneth if yow leste.
Ye woot your forward, and I it yow recorde.
If even-song and morwe-song acorde,
Lat se now who shal telle the firste tale.
As ever mote I drinke wyn or ale,
Who-so be rebel to my jugement
Shal paye for al that by the weye is spent.
Now draweth cut, er that we ferrer twinne;
He which that hath the shortest shal biginne.

at his devys, *according to his direction*
pas, *walking pace*   forward, *bargain*
twinne, *go on*

22

Sire knight,' quod he, 'my maister and my lord,
Now draweth cut, for that is myn acord.
Cometh neer,' quod he, 'my lady prioresse;
And ye, sir clerk, lat be your shamfastnesse,
Ne studieth noght; ley hond to, every man.'
    Anon to drawen every wight bigan,
And shortly for to tellen, as it was,
Were it by aventure, or sort, or cas,
The sothe is this, the cut fil to the knight,
Of which ful blythe and glad was every wight;
And telle he moste his tale, as was resoun,
By forward and by composicioun,
As ye han herd; what nedeth wordes mo?
And whan this gode man saugh it was so,
As he that wys was and obedient
To kepe his forward by his free assent,
He seyde: 'Sin I shall biginne the game,
What, welcome be the cut, a Goddes name!
Now lat us ryde, and herkneth what I seye.'
    And with that word we riden forth our weye;
And he bigan with right a mery chere
His tale anon, and seyde in this manere.

The Prologue of the Pardoner's Tale

'Lordinges,' quod he, 'in chirches whan I preche,
I peyne me to han an hauteyn speche,
And ringe it out as round as gooth a belle,
For I kan al by rote that I telle.
My theme is alwey oon, and ever was,—
Radix malorum est Cupiditas.
    'First, I pronounce whennes that I come,
And thanne my bulles shewe I, alle and somme;
Oure lige lordes seel on my patente,
That shewe I first, my body to warente,
That no man be so boold, ne preest, ne clerk,
Me to destourbe of Cristes holy werk;
And, after that, thanne telle I forth my tales.
Bulles of popes and of cardinales,

sort, *destiny*   cas, *accident*   hauteyn, *stately*
        Radix, etc., *The love of money is the root of evil*

23

Of patriarkes and bishoppes I shewe,
And in Latyn I speke a wordes fewe
To saffron with my predicacioun,
And for to stire men to devocioun;
Thanne shew I forth my longe cristal stones
Y-crammed ful of cloutes and of bones,—
Relikes been they, as wenen they echoon;
Thanne have I in latoun a sholder boon
Which that was of an holy Jewes sheepe.
  ' "Good men," seye I, "tak of my wordes keepe,—
If that this boon be wasshe in any welle,
If cow, or calf, or sheepe, or oxe swelle
That any worm hath ete, or worm y-stonge,
Tak water of that welle and wash his tonge,
And it is hool anon; and forthermoor
Of pokkes, and of scabbe, and every sore,
Shal every sheepe be hool that of this welle
Drinketh a draughte. Tak kepe eek what I telle:
If that the good-man that the beestes oweth
Wol every wike, er that the cok hym croweth,
Fastinge, drinken of this welle a draughte,
As thilke holy Jew oure eldres taughte,
His beestes and his stoor shal multiplye.
And, sires, also it heeleth jalousye,
For though a man be falle in jalous rage,
Lat maken with this water his potage,
And nevere shal he moore his wyf mistriste,
Though he the soothe of hir defaute wiste,—

.   .   .   .

Heer is a miteyn eek, that ye may se;
He that his hand wol putte in this miteyn,
He shal have multiplying of his greyn,
Whan he hath sowen, be it whete or otes,
So that he offre pens, or elles grotes.
  ' "Good men and wommen, o thyng warne I yow,
If any wight be in this chirche now
That hath doon sinne horrible, that he
Dar nat for shame of it y-shriven be,
Or any woman, be she young or old,
That hath y-maad hir housbond cokewold,

saffron, *colour*	predicacioun, *preaching*
wenen, *suppose*	pens, *pence*

24

Swich folk shal have no power ne no grace
To offren to my relikes in this place;
And whoso fyndeth hym out of swich blame
They wol come up and offre in goddes name,
And I assoille hem by the auctoritee
Which that by bulle y-graunted was to me."
    'By this gaude have I wonne, yeer by yeer,
An hundred mark sith I was Pardoner.
I stonde lyk a clerk in my pulpet,
And whan the lewed peple is doun y-set,
I preche, so as ye han herd bifore,
And telle an hundred false japes more;
Thanne peyne I me to strecche forth the nekke,
And est and west upon the peple I bekke,
As dooth a dowve, sittynge on a berne;
Myne hondes and my tonge goon so yerne,
That it is joye to se my bisinesse.
Of avaryce and of swich cursednesse
Is al my preching, for to make hem free
To yeven her pens, and namely unto me;
For my entente is nat but for to winne,
And no thyng for correccioun of sinne.
I rekke nevere, whan that they been beried,
Though that hir soules goon a-blakeberied;
For certes many a predicacioun
Comth ofte tyme of yvel entencioun;
Som for pleasaunce of folk and flaterye,
To been avaunced by ipocrisye;
And som for veyne glorie, and som for hate,
For whan I dar non other weyes debate,
Thanne wol I stinge hym with my tonge smerte
In preching, so that he shall nat asterte
To been defamed falsly, if that he
Hath trespased to my brethren or to me;
For though I telle noght his propre name,
Men shal wel knowe that it is the same,
By signes and by othere circumstances.
Thus quyte I folk that doon us displesances;
Thus spitte I out my venim under hewe

         assoille, *absolve*   gaude, *trick*
         a-blakeberyed, *astray*   asterte, *escape*
              displesances, *ill turns*

25

Of holynesse, to semen holy and trewe.
  'But, shortly, myn entente I wol devyse,—
I preche of no thyng but for coveityse;
Therfor my theme is yet and ever was,
Radix malorum est Cupiditas.
Thus can I preche agayn that same vice
Which that I use, and that is avaryce;
But though myself be gilty in that sinne
Yet can I maken oother folk to twinne
From avaryce, and sore to repente;
But that is nat my principal entente;
I preche no thyng but for coveityse.
Of this mateere it oghte ynogh suffyse.
  'Than telle I hem ensamples many oon
Of olde stories longe tyme agoon:
For lewed peple loven tales olde;
Swiche thinges kan they wel reporte and holde.
What! trowe ye, the whyles I may preche,
And winne gold and silver for I teche,
That I wol lyve in poverte wilfully?
Nay, nay, I thoghte it nevere, trewely!
For I wol preche and begge in sondry londes;
I wol nat do no labour with myne hondes,
Ne make baskettes and lyve therby,
Because I wol nat beggen ydelly.
I wol non of the Apostles countrefete;
I wol have money, wolle, chese and whete,
Al were it yeven of the povrest page,
Or of the povrest widwe in a village,
Al sholde hir children sterve for famyne.
Nay, I wol drinke licour of the vyne,
And have a joly wenche in every toun;
But herkneth, lordynges, in conclusioun.
  'Your lyking is that I shal telle a tale.
Now have I dronke a draughte of corny ale,
By god, I hope I shal yow telle a thing
That shal by resoun been at youre lyking;
For though myself be a ful vicious man,
A moral tale yet I yow telle kan,
Which I am wont to preche, for to winne.
Now holde your pees, my tale I wol beginne.'

sterve, *die*

The Pardoner's Tale

In Flaundres whylom was a companye
Of yonge folk, that haunteden folye,
As ryot, hasard, stewes, and tavernes,
Wher-as, with harpes, lutes, and giternes,
They daunce and pleye at dees bothe day and night,
And ete also and drinken over hir might,
Thurgh which they doon the devel sacrifyse
With-in that develes temple, in cursed wyse,
By superfluitee abhominable;
Hir othes been so grete and so dampnable,
That it is grisly for to here hem swere;
Our blissed lordes body they to-tere;
Hem thoughte Jewes rente him noght y-nough;
And ech of hem at otheres sinne lough.
And right anon than comen tombesteres
Fetys and smale, and yonge fruytesteres,
Singers with harpes, baudes, wafereres,
Whiche been the verray develes officeres
To kindle and blowe the fyr of lecherye,
That is annexed un-to glotonye;
The holy writ take I to my witnesse,
That luxurie is in wyn and dronkenesse.

> . . . . .

  Thise ryotoures three, of whiche I telle,
Longe erst er pryme rong of any belle,
Were set hem in a taverne for to drinke;
And as they satte, they herde a belle clinke
Biforn a cors, was caried to his grave;
That oon of hem gan callen to his knave,
'Go bet,' quod he, 'and axe redily,
What cors is this that passeth heer forby;
And look that thou reporte his name wel.'
  'Sir,' quod this boy, 'it nedeth never-a-del.
It was me told, er ye cam heer, two houres;
He was, pardee, an old felawe of youres;
And sodeynly he was y-slayn to-night,
For-dronke, as he sat on his bench upright;
Ther cam a privee theef, men clepeth Deeth,

haunteden, *practised*   dees, *dice*   fetys, *neat*
fruytesteres, *female fruitsellers*   pryme, 9 *a.m.*   clepeth, *call*

27

That in this contree al the peple sleeth,
And with his spere he smoot his herte a-two,
And wente his wey with-outen wordes mo.
He hath a thousand slayn this pestilence:
And, maister, er ye come in his presence,
Me thinketh that it were necessarie
For to be war of swich an adversarie:
Beth redy for to mete him evermore.
Thus taughte me my dame, I sey na-more.'
'By seinte Marie,' seyde this taverner,
'The child seith sooth, for he hath slayn this yeer,
Henne over a myle, with-in a greet village,
Both man and womman, child and hyne, and page.
I trowe his habitacioun be there;
To been avysed greet wisdom it were,
Er that he dide a man a dishonour,'
'Ye goddes armes,' quod this ryotour,
'Is it swich peril with him for to mete?
I shal him seke by wey and eek by strete,
I make avow to goddes digne bones!
Herkneth, felawes, we three been al ones;
Lat ech of us holde up his hond til other,
And ech of us bicomen otheres brother,
And we wol sleen this false traytour Deeth;
He shal be slayn, which that so many sleeth,
By goddes dignitee, er it be night.'

Togidres han thise three her trouthes plight,
To live and dyen ech of hem for other,
As though he were his owene y-boren brother.
And up they sterte al dronken, in this rage,
And forth they goon towardes that village,
Of which the taverner had spoke biforn,
And many a grisly ooth than han they sworn,
And Cristes blessed body they to-rente—
'Deeth shal be deed, if that they may him hente.'

Whan they han goon nat fully half a myle,
Right as they wolde han troden over a style,
An old man and a povre with hem mette.
This olde man ful mekely hem grette,
And seyde thus, 'now, lordes, god yow see!'
The proudest of thise ryotoures three

child, *fellow*   hente, *seize*

28

Answerde agayn, 'what? carl, with sory grace,
Why artow al forwrapped save thy face?
Why livestow so longe in so greet age?'

This olde man gan loke in his visage,
And seyde thus, 'for I ne can nat finde
A man, though that I walked in-to Inde,
Neither in citee nor in no village,
That wolde chaunge his youthe for myn age;
And therfore moot I han myn age stille,
As longe time as it is goddes wille.

Ne deeth, allas! ne wol nat han my lyf;
Thus walke I, lyk a restlelees caityf,
And on the ground, which is my modres gate,
I knokke with my staf, bothe early and late,
And seye, "leve moder, leet me in!
Lo, how I vanish, flesh, and blood, and skin!
Allas! whan shul my bones been at reste?
Moder, with yow wolde I chaunge my cheste,
That in my chambre longe tyme hath be,
Ye! for an heyre clout to wrappe me!"
But yet to me she wol nat do that grace,
For which ful pale and welked is my face.

But, sirs, to yow it is no curteisye
To speken to an old man vileinye,
But he trespasse in worde, or elles in dede.
In holy writ ye may your-self wel rede,
"Agayns an old man, hoor upon his heed,
Ye sholde aryse"; wherfor I yeve yow reed,
Ne dooth un-to an old man noon harm now,
Na-more than ye wolde men dide to yow
In age, if that ye so longe abyde;
And god be with yow, wher ye go or ryde.
I moot go thider as I have to go.'

'Nay, olde cherl, by god, thou shalt nat so,'
Seyde this other hasardour anon;
'Thou partest nat so lightly, by seint John!
Thou spak right now of thilke traitour Deeth,
That in this contree alle our frendes sleeth.
Have heer my trouthe, as thou art his aspye,
Tel wher he is, or thou shalt it abye,

---

sory grace, *ill favour*	caityf, *wretch*	leve, *dear*
welked, *withered*	reed, *advice*	abye, *pay for*

By god, and by thy holy sacrament!
For soothly thou art oon of his assent,
To sleen us yonge folk, thou false theef!'
   'Now, sirs,' quod he, 'if that yow be so leef
To finde Deeth, turne up this croked wey,
For in that grove I lafte him, by my fey,
Under a tree, and ther he wol abyde;
Nat for your boost he wol him no-thing hyde.
See ye that ook? right ther ye shul him finde.
God save yow, that boghte agayn mankinde,
And yow amende!'—thus seyde this olde man.
And everich of thise ryotoures ran,
Til he cam to that tree, and ther they founde
Of florins fyne of golde y-coyned rounde
Wel ny an eighte busshels, as hem thoughte.
No lenger thanne after Deeth they soughte,
But ech of hem so glad was of that sighte,
For that the florins been so faire and brighte,
That doun they sette hem by this precious hord.
The worste of hem he spake the firste word.
   'Brethren,' quod he, 'tak kepe what I seye;
My wit is greet, though that I bourde and pleye.
This tresor hath fortune un-to us yiven,
In mirthe and jolitee our lyf to liven,
And lightly as it comth, so wol we spende.
Ey! goddes precious dignitee! who wende
To-day, that we sholde han so fair a grace?
But mighte this gold be caried fro this place
Hoom to myn hous, or elles un-to youres—
For wel ye woot that al this gold is oures—
Than were we in heigh felicitee.
But trewely, by daye it may nat be;
Men wolde seyn that we were theves stronge,
And for our owene tresor doon us honge.
This tresor moste y-caried be by nighte
As wysly and as slyly as it mighte.
Wherfore I rede that cut among us alle
Be drawe, and lat see wher the cut wol falle;
And he that hath the cut with herte blythe
Shal renne to the toune, and that ful swythe,

bourde, *jest*   doon us honge, *have us hanged*
                        swythe, *early*

30

And bringe us breed and wyn ful prively.
And two of us shul kepen subtilly
This tresor wel; and, if he wol nat tarie,
Whan it is night, we wol this tresor carie
By oon assent, wher-as us thinketh best.'
That oon of hem the cut broughte in his fest,
And bad hem drawe, and loke wher it wol falle;
And it fil on the yongeste of hem alle;
And forth toward the toun he wente anon.
And al-so sone as that he was gon,
That oon of hem spak thus un-to that other,
'Thou knowest wel thou art my sworne brother,
Thy profit wol I telle thee anon.
Thou woost wel that our felawe is agon;
And heer is gold, and that ful greet plentee,
That shal departed been among us three.
But natheles, if I can shape it so
That it departed were among us two,
Hadde I nat doon a freendes torn to thee?'
    That other answerde, 'I noot how that may be;
He woot how that the gold is with us tweye,
What shal be doon, what shal we to him seye?'
    'Shal it be conseil?' seyde the firste shrewe,
'And I shal tellen thee, in wordes fewe,
What we shal doon, and bringe it wel aboute.'
    'I graunte,' quod that other, 'out of doute,
That, by my trouthe, I wol thee nat biwreye.'
    'Now,' quod the firste, 'thou woost wel we be tweye,
And two of us shul strenger be than oon.
Look whan that he is set, and right anoon
Arys, as though thou woldest with him pleye;
And I shal ryve him thurgh the sydes tweye
Whyl that thou strogelest with him as in game,
And with thy dagger look thou do the same;
And than shal al this gold departed be,
My dere freend, bitwixen me and thee;
Than may we bothe our lustes al fulfille,
And pleye at dees right at our owene wille.'
And thus accorded been thise shrewes tweye
To sleen the thridde, as ye han herd me seye.
    This yongest, which that wente un-to the toun,

woost, *knowest*   shrewe, *scoundrel*

3 I

Ful ofte in herte he rolleth up and doun
The beautee of thise florins newe and brighte.
'O lord!' quod he, 'if so were that I mighte
Have al this tresor to my-self allone,
Ther is no man that liveth under the trone
Of god, that sholde live so mery as I!'
And atte laste the feend, our enemy,
Putte in his thought that he shold poyson beye,
With which he mighte sleen his felawes tweye;
For-why the feend fond him in swich lyvinge,
That he had leve him to sorwe bringe,
For this was outrely his fulle entente
To sleen hem bothe, and never to repente.
And forth he gooth, no lenger wolde he tarie,
Into the toun, un-to a pothecarie,
And preyed him, that he him wolde selle
Som poyson, that he mighte his rattes quelle;
And eek ther was a polcat in his hawe,
That, as he seyde, his capouns hadde y-slawe,
And fayn he wolde wreke him, if he mighte,
On vermin, that destroyed him by nighte.

    The pothecarie answerde, 'and thou shalt have
A thing that, al-so god my soule save,
In al this world ther nis no creature,
That ete or dronke hath of this confiture
Noght but the mountance of a corn of whete,
That he ne shal his lyf anon forlete;
Ye, sterve he shal, and that in lasse whyle
Than thou wolt goon a paas nat but a myle;
This poyson is so strong and violent.'

    This cursed man hath in his hond y-hent
This poyson in a box, and sith he ran
In-to the nexte streete, un-to a man,
And borwed him large botels three;
And in the two his poyson poured he;
The thridde he kepte clene for his drinke.
For al the night he shoop him for to swinke
In caryinge of the gold out of that place.
And whan this ryotour, with sory grace,

beye, *buy*   outrely, *completely*   quelle, *kill*
hawe, *yard*   confiture, *mixture*   forlete, *lose*
                   swinke, *work*

Had filled with wyn his grete botels three,
To his felawes agayn repaireth he.
    What nedeth it to sermone of it more?
For right as they had cast his deeth bifore,
Right so they han him slayn, and that anon.
And whan that this was doon, thus spak that oon,
'Now lat us sitte and drinke, and make us merie,
And afterward we wol his body berie.'
And with that word it happed him, par cas,
To take the botel ther the poyson was,
And drank, and yaf his felawe drinke also,
For which anon they storven bothe two.
    But, certes, I suppose that Avicen
Wroot never in no canon, ne in no fen,
Mo wonder signes of empoisoning
Than hadde thise wrecches two, er hir ending.
Thus ended been thise homicydes two,
And eek the false empoysoner also.

storven. *died*

ROBERT HENRYSON

1430-1506

The Taill of the Uponlandis Mous and the Burges Mous

Esope, mine author makis mention
Of twa myis, and they were sisteris dear,
Of wham the eldest dwelt in ane boroughis toun
The other wynnit upon land weill neir,
Solitar, while under bush, while under brier,
Whilis in the corn, and other mennis skaith,
As outlawis dois and livis on thair waith.

This rural mouse, into the wynter tyde,
Had hunger, cauld, and tholit great distress.
The other mouse, that in the borough can byde,
Was guild brother and made ane free burgess;
Toll free als, but custom mair or less,
And freedom had to ga whair ever she list,
Amang the cheese in ark, and meal in kist.

Ane tyme when sho was full and unfutesair,
Sho tuke in mynde her sister upon land,
And langit for to hear of her weilfare,
To see what life sho had under the wand:
Barefute, alone, with pykestaff in her hand,
As poor pilgrim sho passit out of toun,
To seek her sister baith owre dale and doun.

Furth mony wilsum wayis can sho walk,
Through moss and moor, through bankis, bush and brier,
Sho ran cryand, whill sho come to ane balk:
'Cum furth to me, my awin sister dear,
Cry "peip" anis!' With that the mouse can hear
And knew her voice as kinnisman will do,
By very kind; and furth sho come her to.

wynnit, *dwelt*	skaith, *damage*	waith, *plunder*
wand, *willow*	wilsum, *devious*	balk ,*ridge*

34

The hartly joy, God! gif ye had seen,
Beis kith when that thir sisters met;
And great kindness was shawin them between,
For whilis they leuch, and whilis for joy they gret,
While kissit sweit, whilis in armis plet;
And thus they fare, while soberit was their mood,
Syne fute for fute unto the chalmer yude.

As I heard say, it was ane sober wane
Of fog and fern full febillie was made,
Ane sillie shiel under ane steidfast stane,
Of whilk the entres was not high nor braid;
And in the samyn they went but mair abaid,
Without fire or candle birnand bricht,
For commonly sic pikeris luves nocht licht.

When they were lugeit thus, thir sillie mice,
The youngest sister into her buttery yeid,
And brocht furth nuttis and candill instead of spyce,
Gif this was gude fare, I do it on them beside.
The burgess mouse prompit furth in pride,
And said, 'Sister, is this your daily food?'
'Why not,' said sho, 'is not this meat richt gude?'

'Nay by my saule, I think it bot ane scorn.'
'Madame,' quod sho, 'ye be the mair to blame;
My mother said, sister, when we were born
That I and ye baith lay within ane wame:
I keep the rate and custom of my dame,
And of my living into poverty,
For landis have we none in propertie.'

'My fair sister,' quod sho, 'Have me excusit,
This rude diet and I can not accord;
To tender meat my stomach is aye usit,
For whiles I fare als weill as ony lord;
Thir widderit peas and nuttis, or they be bord,
Will brek my teeth and mak my wame full sklender,
Whilk was before usit to meatis tender.'

kith, *made known*   yude, *went*   wane, *dwelling*
    fog, *moss*   sillie shiel, *frail shelter*
I do it on them beside, *I leave it to them to say*   prompit furth, *burst out*

'Weill, weill, sister,' quod the rural mouse,
'Gif it please you, sic thing as ye see here,
Baith meat and drink, herberie and house,
Sall be your awin, will ye remane all year;
Ye sall it have with blyth and merry cheer,
And that suld mak the maissis that are rude,
Amang friendis tender and wonder gude.'

'What pleasure is in feastis delicate
The whilk are gevin with ane glowmand brow?
Ane gentle heart is better recreate
With blyth courage, than seith to him ane cow:
Ane modicum is mair for till allow
So that gude will be carver at the dais,
Than thrawin will and mony spycit mais.'

For all her merry exhortation,
This burgess mouse had little will to sing,
Bot heavily sho kest her browis doun
For all the daynteis that sho culd her bring.
Yit at the last sho said, half in hething,
'Sister, this victual and your royal feast
May weill suffice unto ane rural beast.

'Let be this hole, and cum unto my place;
I sall to you shaw by experience
My Gude Friday is better nor your Pace;
My dish lickingis is wirth your haill expense.
I have houses enow of great defence;
Of cat nor fall-trap I have na dreid.'
'I grant,' quod sho, and on togidder they yeid.

In skugry aye throw rankest grass and corne,
And under bushis privilie culd they creep,
The eldest was the guide and went beforne,
The younger to her wayis took gude keep.
On nycht they ran, and on the day can sleip,
Till in the morning, or the laverock sang,
They fand the toun, and in blythly couth gang.

maissis, *messes*   hething, *derision*   Pace, *Easter*
    skugry, *secrecy*   couth, *did*

36

Not fer fra thence unto ane worthy wane
This burgess brocht them soon where they suld be;
Without godspeed their herberie was tane,
Into ane spence with victual greit plentie;
Baith cheese and butter upon thair shelfis hie,
And flesh and fish eneuch, baith fresh and salt,
And sackis full of meal and eke of malt.

Efter when they disposit were to dyne,
Withoutin grace they wesche and went to meat,
With all coursis that cookis culd devine,
Mutton and beef strucken in tailyeis great;
Ane lordis fare thus culd they counterfeit,
Except ane thing, they drank the water clear
Instead of wine, bot yet they made gude cheer.

With blythe upcast and merry countenance,
The eldest sister speirit at her guest
Gif that she be reason fand difference
Betwix that chalmer and her sorry nest.
'Yea, dame,' quod sho, 'how lang will this lest?'
'Forever mair, I wat, and langer too.'
'Gif it be sae, ye are at ease,' quod sho.

Til eke thair cheer ane subcharge furth she brocht,
Ane plate of grotis, and ane dish full of meal;
Thraif cakis als I trow she sparit nocht,
Abundantly about her for to deal,
And mane full fyne sho brocht instead of geill,
And ane white candle out of ane coffer stall,
In stead of spice to gust thair mouth withal.

Thus made they merry till they micht na mair,
And 'Hail, Yuill hail,' cryit upon hie.
Yit efter joy ofttimes cumis care,
And trouble efter great prosperitie.
Thus as they sat in all thair jolitie,
The spensar come with keyis in his hand,
Openit the door, and them at dinner fand.

spence, *larder* tailyeis, *slices* subcharge, *extra course*
   Thraif, *unleavened* mane, *white bread*

They tarryit not to wash, as I suppose,
Bot on to ga wha that micht foremost win.
The burgess had ane hole, and in sho goes,
Her sister had na hole to hide her in:
To see that selie mouse it was great sin,
So desolate and will of ane gude rede,
For very dreid sho fell in swoon neir deid.

Bot as God wald, it fell ane happie case;
The spenser had na leisure for to byde,
Nouther to seek nor search, to skare nor chase,
Bot on he went and left the door up wide.
The bald burgess his passing weill has spyde;
Out of her hole sho come and cryit on hie,
'How fare ye, sister? Cry peip, wherever ye be!'

This rural mouse lay flatling on the ground,
And for the deith sho was ful sair dredand,
For till her hert straik mony woful stound,
As in ane fever sho trimblit fute and hand;
And when her sister in sic ply her fand,
For very pity sho began to greet,
Syne comfort her with wordis honey-sweet.

'Why lie ye thus? Rise up, my sister dear,
Come to your meat, this peril is overpast.'
The other answerit her with heavie cheir,
'I may not eat, sae sair I am aghast;
I had liever thir fourty dayis fast
With water kale and to gnaw beans and peas
Than all your feast in this dreid and diseis.'

With fair tretie yet sho gart her rise,
And to the burde they went and togidder sat;
And scantlie had they drunkin anis or twice,
When in come Gib hunter, our jolie cat,
And bade godspeed: the burgess up with that,
And till her hole sho went as fire on flint:
Bawdronis the other be the back has hint.

will of ane gude rede, *at a loss*
Bawdronis, *Puss*   hint, *caught*

38

Fra fute to fute he kest her to and fra,
Whilis up, whilis doun, als cant as ony kid;
Whilis wald he lat her rin under the stra,
Whilis wald he wink and play with her bukheid,
Thus to the selie mouse great pain he did,
Till at the last, through fortune and gude hap
Betwix ane burde and the wall sho crap.

And up in haste behind ane parraling
Sho clam sa hie, that Gilbert micht not get her,
Syne be the cluke there craftily can hing
Till he was gane, her cheer was all the better.
Syne doun sho lap when there was nane to let her,
And to the burgess mouse loud can she cry—
'Farewell sister, thy feast here I defy!

'Thy mangerie is mingit all with cair,
Thy goose is gude, thy gansell sour as gall,
The subcharge of thy service is bot sair,
Sae sal thou find hereafterwart, na faill.
I thank yon courtyne and yon perpall wall
Of my defence now fra yon cruel beast.
Almychty God, keep me fra sic ane feast.

'Were I into the kith that I come fra,
For weill nor woe suld I never come agane.'
With that sho took her leave and furth can ga
Whilis through the corn and whilis through the plain.
When sho was furth and free, she was full fain,
And merrilie markit unto the muir:
I cannot tell how efterwort sho fure.

Bot I heard say sho passit to her den
Als warm as wool, suppose it was not great,
Full benelie stuffit, baith but and ben,
Of beanis, nuttis, peis, rye and wheat;
Whenever sho list sho had aneuch to eat,
In quiet and ease, withoutin ony dreid,
Bot to her sisteris feast na mair sho yede.

cant, *lively*   bukheid, *hide and seek*   parraling, *partition*
    cluke, *claw*   mangerie, *feast*   gansell, *sauce*
        perpall, *partition*   kith, *known place*

39

WILLIAM DUNBAR

1465-1530

The Dance of the Sevin Deidly Synnis

Of Februar the fifteen nicht,
Full lang before the dayis licht,
I lay in-till a trance;
And then I saw baith heaven and hell:
Methocht, amangis the fiendis fell,
Mahoun gart cry ane dance
Of shrewis that were never shriven,
Aganis the feast of Fasternis even,
To mak their observance;
He bade gallantis go graith a guise,
And cast up gamountis in the skies,
That last came out of France.

'Lat see,' quod he, 'now wha beginnis';
With that the foul Seven Deidly Sinnis
Begouth to leap at anis.
And first of all in dance was Pride,
With hair collit back and bonnet on side,
Like to mak wastie wanis;
And round about him, as a wheel,
Hang all in rumpillis to the heel
His kethat for the nanis:
Mony proud trumpour with him trippit
Throw scaldand fire, ay as they skippit
They girn'd with hideous granis.
Heilie harlottis on hawtane wise
Come in with mony sundry guise,
Bot yit leuch never Mahoun;

Fasternis even, *Shrove Tuesday*　　　graith a guise, *prepare a masque.*
　gamountis, *capers*　　collit, *cut*　　wastie wanis, *waste dwellings*
　　kethat, *cassock*　　trumpour, *cheat*　　Heilie, *proud*

40

Till priestis come in with bare shaven neckis,
Than all the fiendis leuch, and made geckis,
Black Belly, and Bawsy Brown.

Than Ire come in with sturt and strife;
His hand was ay upon his knife,
He brandeist like a beir:
Boasteris, braggeris, and bargaineris,
Eftir him passit in-to pairis
All bodin in feir of weir;
In jackis and stryppis and bonnettis of steel,
Their leggis were chainyit to the heel,
Frawart was their affeir:
Some upon other with brandis beft,
Some jaggit otheris to the heft,
With knivis that sherp culd shear.

Next in the dance followit Envy
Fill'd full of feid and felony,
Hid malice and despite;
For privy hatrent that traitor trem'lit.
Him followit mony freik dissem'lit,
With feignèd wordis white;
And flatteris in-to menis faces;
And backbiteris in secreit places,
To lie that had delight;
And rounaris of false leasingis;
Alas! that courtis of noble kingis
Of them can never be quite.

Next him in dance come Covatice,
Root of all evil and grund of vice,
That never culd be content;
Caitivis, wretches and okkeraris,
Hud-pikis, hurdaris and gadderaris,
All with that warlo went:

beir, *boar*	bargaineris, *wranglers*	
	bodin in feir of weir, *arrayed in guise of war*	
chainyit, *clad in chain mail*	affeir, *bearing*	feid, *feud*
freik, *man*	rounaris, *whisperers*	leasingis, *lies*
okkeraris, *usurers*	Hud-pikis, *misers*	warlo, *warlock*

Out of their throatis they shot on other
Het molten gold, me thocht a fudder,
As fireflaucht maist fervent;
Ay as they toomit them of shot,
Fiendis fill'd them new up to the throat
With gold of all kin prent.

Syne Sweirness, at the second bidding,
Come like a sow out of a midding,
Full sleepy was his grunyie:
Mony sweir bumbard belly-huddroun,
Mony slute daw and sleepy duddroun,
Him servit ay with sounyie;
He drew them furth in-till a chainyie,
And Belial, with a bridle-reinyie,
Ever lasht them on the lunyie:
In dance they were so slaw of feet,
They gaif them in the fire a heat,
And made them quicker of cunyie.

Than Lechery, that laithly corse,
Come berand like a baggit horse,
And Idleness did him lead;
There was with him ane ugly sort,
And mony stinkand foul tramort,
That had in sin been deid.
When they were entrit in the dance,
They were full strange of countenance,
Like turkas birnand reid;
All led they other by the tersis,
Suppose they fyllt with their ersis,
It micht be na remead.

Then the foul monster Gluttony,
Of wame unsatiable and greedy,

fudder, *great quantity*   fireflaucht, *wildfire*
all kin prent, *all kind(s) of stamp*   Sweirness, *sloth*   grunyie, *snout*
bumbard belly-huddroun, *tun-bellied glutton*   slute, *sluttish*
daw, *sluggard*   duddroun, *sloven*   sounyie, *care*
lunyie, *loins*   cunyie, *apprehension*   berand, *neighing*
baggit horse, *stallion*   tramort, *corpse*   turkas, *pincers*

To dance he did him dress:
Him followit mony foul drunkart,
With can and collep, cop and quart,
In surfeit and excess;
Full mony a waistless wallydrag,
With wamis unwieldable, did furth wag,
In creish that did incress;
Drink! ay they cryit, awith mony a gape,
The fiendis gaif them het leid to laip,
Their lovery was na less.

Na minstrellis playit to them but doubt,
For gleemen there were haldin out,
Be day, and eke by nicht;
Except a minstrel that slew a man,
Swa till his heritage he wan,
And entered be brief of richt.

Than cried Mahoun for a Hieland padyane;
Syne ran a fiend to fetch MacFadzen,
Far northward in a neuk;
Be he the coronach had done shout,
Ersemen so gadderit him about,
In Hell great room they tuk.
Thae termagantis, with tag and tatter,
Full loud in Erse begouth to clatter,
And roup like raven and rook:
The Devil sa deavit was with their yell,
That in the deepest pot of hell
He smoorit them with smoke.

Lament for the Makaris, quhen he was Seik

I that in heill was and gladness,
Am troublit now with great seikness,
And feeblit with infirmity:
    Timor Mortis conturbat me.

collep, *drinking-vessel*   wallydrag, *sloven*   lovery, *portion*
padyane, *pageant*   Be, *by the time that*   Ersemen, **Gaels**
roup, *croak*   deavit, *deafened*   smoorit, *smothered*

Our pleasance here is all vain-glory,
This false warld is bot transitory,
The flesh is brukill, the Fiend is sle;
   Timor Mortis conturbat me.

The state of man dois change and vary,
Now sound, now seik, now blyth, now sary,
Now dansand merry, now like to die;
   Timor Mortis conturbat me.

No state in erd here standis siccar;
As with the wind wavis the wicker,
So wavis this warldis vanitie;
   Timor Mortis conturbat me.

Unto the deid gois all Estatis,
Princes, Prelatis, and Potestatis,
Baith rich and puir of all degree;
   Timor Mortis conturbat me.

He takis the knichtis in-to field,
Enarmit under helm and shield;
Victor he is at all mêlée;
   Timor Mortis conturbat me.

That strang unmerciful tyrand
Takis on the moderis breist soukand
The babe, full of benignitie;
   Timor Mortis conturbat me.

He takis the champion in the stour,
The capitane closit in the tour,
The lady in bour full of beautie;
   Timor Mortis conturbat me.

He sparis no lord for his puissence,
Na clerk for his intelligence;
His awful straik may no man flee;
   Timor Mortis conturbat me.

brukill, *brittle, feeble*   wicker, *willow*   stour, *conflict*
                                  puissance, *power*

Art magicianis, and astrologis,
Rethoris, logicianis, and theologis,
Them helpis no conclusionis sle;
   Timor Mortis conturbat me.

In medicine the most practicianis,
Leechis, surigianis, and phisicianis,
Them-self fra deid may not supple;
   Timor Mortis conturbat me.

I see that makaris amang the lave
Playis here their pageant, syne gois to grave;
Sparit is nocht their facultie;
   Timor Mortis conturbat me.

He has done piteously devour
The noble Chaucer, of makaris flour,
The Monk of Bery, and Gower, all three;
   Timor Mortis conturbat me.

The gude Sir Hew of Eglintoun,
And eke Heriot, and Wyntoun,
He has tane out of this countrie;
   Timor Mortis conturbat me.

That scorpion fell has done infek
Maister John Clerk and James Affleck,
Fra ballad-making and tragedie;
   Timor Mortis conturbat me.

Holland and Barbour he has bereavit;
Alas! that he nocht with us leavit
Sir Mungo Lockhart of the Lea;
   Timor Mortis conturbat me.

Clerk of Tranent eke he has tane,
That made the Aunteris of Gawain;
Sir Gilbert Hay endit has he;
   Timor Mortis conturbat me.

Rethoris, *eloquent writers*   supple, *help*   Aunteris, *adventures*

He has Blind Harry, and Sandy Traill
Slain with his schour of mortal hail,
Whilk Patrick Johnstoun micht nocht flee;
  Timor Mortis conturbat me.

He has reft Merser his endite,
That did in luve so lively write,
So short, so quick, of sentence hie;
  Timor Mortis conturbat me.

He has tane Roull of Aberdeen,
And gentle Roull of Corstorphin;
Two better fellowis did no man see;
  Timor Mortis conturbat me.

In Dunfermline he has done roune
With Maister Robert Henryson;
Sir John the Ross embraced has he;
  Timor Mortis conturbat me.

And he has now tane, last of aw,
Gude gentle Stobo and Quintin Shaw,
Of wham all wichtis has pitie:
  Timor Mortis conturbat me.

Gude Maister Walter Kennedy
In point of deid lies verily,
Great ruth it were that so suld be;
  Timor Mortis conturbat me.

Sen he has all my brether tane
He will nocht lat me live alane,
On force I maun his next prey be;
  Timor Mortis conturbat me.

Sen for the deid remead is none,
Best is that we for deid dispone,
Eftir our deid that live may we;
  Timor Mortis conturbat me.

done roune, *whispered*

The Ballad of Kynd Kittok

My gude dame was a gay wife, bot she was richt gend,
She dwelt furth far into France, upon Falkland Fell;
Thay callit her Kind Kyttok, wha sa her weill kend.
She was like a cauldron cruke clear under kell;
They threpit that she deit of thirst, and made a gude end,
Efter her deid, she dreadit nocht in heaven for to dwell;
And sa to heaven the hieway dreidless she wend,
       Yet she wanderit and yede by to an elriche well.
         She met there, as I ween,
         An ask ridand on a snail,
         And cryit, 'Ourtane fallow, hail!'
         And rade an inch behind the tail,
         Till it was near e'en.

Sa she had hap to be horsit to her herbry,
At an alehouse near heaven it nightit them there;
She deit of thirst in this warld, that gert her be sa dry,
She never eat, bot drank our measure and mair.
She sleepit till the morn at noon, and rais airly;
And to the yetts of heaven fast can the wif fare,
And by Saint Peter, in at the yett she stall privily;
God lukit and saw her lettin in, and lewch his hairt sair.
         And there, yearis seven
         She livit a gude life,
         And was our Ladyis hen-wife:
         And held Saint Peter at strife,
         Ay, while she was in heaven.

She lookit out on a day, and thocht right lang
To see the alehouse beside, intil an evil hour;
And out of heaven the high gait cowth the wife gang
For to get her ane fresh drink, the ale of heaven was sour.
She come again to heavenis yett, when the bell rang,
Saint Peter hit her with a club, till a great clour
Rais in her heid, because the wif yede wrang.
Than to the alehouse again she ran, the pitcheris to pour,

gend, *simple*	cruke, *hook*	kell, *coif*	threpit, *argued*
elriche, *elvish*	ask, *newt*		hap, *luck*
herbry, *lodging*	gert, *made*		yetts, *gates*
	gait, *way*		

47

And for to brew and bake.
Friends I pray you hertfully,
Gif ye be thirsty or dry,
Drink with my guddame, as ye gae by,
Anis for my sake.

Done is a Battle on the Dragon Black

Done is a battle on the dragon black,
Our champion Christ confoundit has his force
The yetts of hell are broken with a crack
The sign triumphal raisit is of the cross,
The devilles trymmillis with hiddous voce,
The souls are borrowit and to the bliss can go,
Christ with his blood our ransomes does indoce;
   Surrexit Dominus de sepulchro.

Dungen is the deadly dragon Lucifer,
The cruel serpent with the mortal stang;
The auld keen tiger, with his teeth on char,
Whilk in a wait has lyen for us so lang,
Thinking to grip us in his clawis strang;
The merciful Lord wald nocht that it were so,
He made him for to failye of that fang;
   Surrexit Dominus de sepulchro.

He for our sake that sufferit to be slain,
And like a lamb in sacrifice was dicht,
Is like a lion risen up again
And as gyane raxit him on hicht
Sprungen is Aurora radious and bricht
On loft is gone the glorious Apollo,
The blissful day departit fro the nicht;
   Surrexit Dominus de sepulchro.

The great victour again is risen on hicht
That for our quarrel to the death was woundit;
The sun that wox all pale now shinis bricht,
And darkness clearit, our faith is now refoundit;

yetts, *gates*	trymmillis, *tremble*	borrowit, *redeemed*
indoce, *endorse*	Dungen, *struck down*	on char, *ajar*
fang, *prey*	dicht, *prepared*	gyane, *giant*	raxit, *stretched*

The knell of mercy fra the heaven is soundit,
The Christian are deliverit of their woe,
The Jewis and their error are confoundit:
  Surrexit Dominus de sepulchro.

The foe is chasit, the battle is done cease,
The prison broken, the jivellouris fleit and flemit;
The weir is gone, confirmit is the peace,
The fetteris lowsit and the dungeon temit,
The ransom made, the prisoneris redeemit;
The field is won, owrecomen is the foe,
Despoilit of the treasure that he yemit;
  Surrexit Dominus de sepulchro.

Sweet Rose of Vertue

Sweet rose of vertue and of gentleness,
Delightsome lily of every lustiness,
  Richest in bounty and in beauty clear,
  And every vertue that is wenit dear,
Except onlie that ye are mercyless.

Into your garth this day I did pursue;
There saw I flouris that freshe were of hew;
  Baith whyte and reid most lusty were to seyne,
  And halesome herbis upon stalkis greene;
Yet leaf nor flower find could I nane of rue.

I doubt that Merch, with his cauld blastis keen,
Has slain this gentil herb, that of I mean;
  Whose piteous death does to my heart sic pain
  That I would make to plant his root againe,—
So comfortand his leavis unto me bene.

jivellouris, *jailors*   fleit and flemit, *terrified and put to flight*
yemit, *guarded*   lustiness, *pleasure*   halesome, *wholesome*

ALEXANDER SCOTT

1525-1584

Return thee, heart, hameward again,
    And bide where thou was wont to be;
Thou art ane fool to suffer pain
    For love of her that loves not thee.
    My heart, lat be sic fantasy;
Love nane but as they mak thee cause;
    And lat her seek ane heart for thee,
For fiend a crumb of thee sho faws.

To what effect sould thou be thrall
    But thank, sen thou has thy free will?
My heart, be not sa bestial,
    But know who does thee good or ill;
    Remain with me and tarry still,
And see wha playis best their pawis,
    And lat fillok ga fling her fill,
For fiend a crumb of thee sho faws.

Though she be fair I will not denyie;
    She is the kind of others ma;
For why there is a fellone menye,
    That seemis good, and are not sae,
    My heart, tak neither pain nor wae,
For Meg, for Marjory, or yet Mause,
    But be thou glad and lat her gae,
For fiend a crumb of thee sho faws.

Because I find she took in ill,
    At her departing thou mak na care;
But all beguiled, go where she will,
    Beshrew the heart that mane maks mair.
    My heart, be merry late and air,
This is the final end and clause,
    And let her follow ane filly fair,
For fiend a crumb of thee sho faws.

faws, *possesses*   fillok, *the filly*

MARK ALEXANDER BOYD

1563-1601

Cupid and Venus

Fra bank to bank, fra wood to wood I rin,
   Ourhailit with my feeble fantasie;
   Like til a leaf that fallis from a tree,
Or til a reed ourblawin with the win.

Twa gods guides me: the ane of them is blin,
   Yea and a bairn brocht up in vanitie;
   The next a wife ingenrit of the sea,
And lichter nor a dauphin with her fin.

Unhappy is the man for evermair
   That tills the sand and sawis in the air;
   But twice unhappier is he, I lairn,
That feidis in his hairt a mad desire,
And follows on a woman throw the fire,
   Led by a blind and teachit by a bairn.

EDMUND SPENSER

1552-1599

Prothalamion

Calm was the day, and through the trembling air
   Sweet-breathing Zephyrus did softly play—
   A gentle spirit, that lightly did delay
Hot Titan's beams, which then did glister fair;
     When I (whom sullen care,
Through discontent of my long fruitless stay
   In princes' court, and expectation vain
Of idle hopes, which still do fly away
   Like empty shadows, did afflict my brain)
     Walk'd forth to ease my pain
Along the shore of silver-streaming Thames;
Whose rutty bank, the which his river hems,
   Was painted all with variable flowers,
And all the meads adorn'd with dainty gems
     Fit to deck maidens' bowers,
     And crown their paramours
Against the bridal day, which is not long:
Sweet Thames, run softly, till I end my song.

There in a meadow by the river's side
   A flock of nymphs I chancèd to espy,
   All lovely daughters of the flood thereby,
With goodly greenish locks all loose untied
     As each had been a bride;
And each one had a little wicker basket
   Made of fine twigs, entrailèd curiously,
In which they gather'd flowers to fill their flasket,
   And with fine fingers cropt full feateously
     The tender stalks on high.
Of every sort which in that meadow grew
They gather'd some; the violet, pallid blue,
   The little daisy that at evening closes,
The virgin lily and the primrose true,

With store of vermeil roses,
    To deck their bridegrooms' posies
Against the bridal day, which was not long:
Sweet Thames, run softly, till I end my song.

With that I saw two Swans of goodly hue
    Come softly swimming down along the Lee;
    Two fairer birds I yet did never see;
The snow which doth the top of Pindus strow
    Did never whiter show,
Nor Jove himself, when he a swan would be
    For love of Leda, whiter did appear;
Yet Leda was (they say) as white as he,
    Yet not so white as these, nor nothing near;
        So purely white they were
That even the gentle stream, the which them bare,
Seem'd foul to them, and bade his billows spare
    To wet their silken feathers, lest they might
Soil their fair plumes with water not so fair,
        And mar their beauties bright
        That shone as Heaven's light
Against their bridal day, which was not long:
Sweet Thames, run softly, till I end my song.

Eftsoons the nymphs, which now had flowers their fill,
    Ran all in haste to see that silver brood
    As they came floating on the crystal flood;
Whom when they saw, they stood amazèd still
    Their wondering eyes to fill;
Them seem'd they never saw a sight so fair
    Of fowls so lovely, that they sure did deem
Them heavenly born, or to be that same pair
    Which through the sky draw Venus' silver team;
        For sure they did not seem
To be begot of any earthly seed,
But rather Angels, or of Angels' breed;
    Yet were they bred of summer's heat, they say,
In sweetest season, when each flower and weed
        The earth did fresh array;
        So fresh they seem'd as day,
Ev'n as their bridal day, which was not long:
Sweet Thames, run softly, till I end my song.

Then forth they all out of their baskets drew
  Great store of flowers, the honour of the field,
  That to the sense did fragrant odours yield,
All which upon those goodly birds they threw
    And all the waves did strew,
That like old Peneus' waters they did seem,
  When down along by pleasant Tempe's shore,
Scatter'd with flowers, through Thessaly they stream,
  That they appear, through lilies' plenteous store,
    Like a bride's chamber-floor.
Two of those nymphs meanwhile two garlands bound
Of freshest flowers which in that mead they found,
  The which presenting all in trim array,
Their snowy foreheads therewithal they crown'd;
    Whilst one did sing this lay
    Prepared against that day,
Against their bridal day, which was not long:
Sweet Thames, run softly, till I end my song.

'Ye gentle birds! the world's fair ornament,
  And Heaven's glory, whom this happy hour
  Doth lead unto your lovers' blissful bower,
Joy may you have, and gentle heart's content
    Of your love's couplement;
And let fair Venus, that is queen of love,
  With her heart-quelling son upon you smile,
Whose smile, they say, hath virtue to remove
  All love's dislike, and friendship's faulty guile
    For ever to assoil.
Let endless peace your steadfast hearts accord,
And blessed plenty wait upon your board;
  And let your bed with pleasures chaste abound,
That fruitful issue may to you afford,
    Which may your foes confound,
    And make your joys redound
Upon your bridal day, which is not long:
Sweet Thames, run softly, till I end my song.'

So ended she; and all the rest around
  To her redoubled that her undersong,
  Which said, their bridal day should not be long.
And gentle Echo from the neighbour ground,
    Their accents did resound.

So forth those joyous birds did pass along
  Adown the Lee that to them murmur'd low,
As he would speak but that he lack'd a tongue;
  Yet did by signs his glad affection show,
    Making his stream run slow.
And all the fowl which in his flood did dwell
'Gan flock about these twain, that did excel
  The rest, so far as Cynthia doth shend
The lesser stars. So they, enrangèd well,
    Did on those two attend,
    And their best service lend
Against their wedding day, which was not long:
Sweet Thames, run softly, till I end my song.

At length they all to merry London came,
  To merry London, my most kindly nurse,
  That to me gave this life's first native source,
Though from another place I take my name,
    An house of ancient fame:
There when they came whereas those bricky towers
  The which on Thames' broad agèd back do ride,
Where now the studious lawyers have their bowers,
  There whilom wont the Templar-knights to bide,
    Till they decay'd through pride;
Next whereunto there stands a stately place,
  Where oft I gainèd gifts and goodly grace
Of that great lord, which therein wont to dwell,
  Whose want too well now feels my friendless case;
    But ah! here fits not well
    Old woes, but joys to tell
Against the bridal day, which is not long:
Sweet Thames, run softly, till I end my song.

Yet therein now doth lodge a noble peer,
  Great England's glory and the world's wide wonder,
Whose dreadful name late through all Spain did
    thunder,
    And Hercules' two pillars standing near
    Did make to quake and fear:
Fair branch of honour, flower of chivalry!
  That fillest England with thy triumphs' fame
Joy have thou of thy noble victory,

And endless happiness of thine own name
 That promiseth the same;
That through thy prowess and victorious arms
 Thy country may be freed from foreign harms,
And great Elisa's glorious name may ring
Through all the world, fill'd with thy wide alarms,
 Which some brave Muse may sing
 To ages following:
Upon the bridal day, which is not long:
Sweet Thames, run softly, till I end my song.

From those high towers this noble lord issùing
 Like radiant Hesper, when his golden hair
 In th' ocean billows he hath bathèd fair,
Descended to the river's open viewing
 With a great train ensuing.
Above the rest were goodly to be seen
 Two gentle knights of lovely face and feature,
Beseeming well the bower of any queen,
 With gifts of wit and ornaments of nature,
 Fit for so goodly stature,
That like the twins of Jove they seem'd in sight,
Which deck the baldric of the Heavens bright;
 They two, forth pacing to the river's side,
Received those two fair brides, their love's delight;
 Which, at th' appointed tide,
 Each one did make his bride
Against their bridal day, which is not long:
Sweet Thames, run softly, till I end my song.

WILLIAM SHAKESPEARE
1564-1616

Come Away, Death

Come away, come away, Death,
And in sad cypress let me be laid;
　Fly away, fly away, breath;
I am slain by a fair cruel maid.
My shroud of white, stuck all with yew,
　　O prepare it!
My part of death, no one so true
　　Did share it.

Not a flower, not a flower sweet
On my black coffin let there be strown;
　Not a friend, not a friend greet
My poor corpse, where my bones shall be thrown:
A thousand thousand sighs to save,
　　Lay me, O, where
Sad true lover never find my grave,
　　To weep there.

Fidele

Fear no more the heat o' the sun
　Nor the furious winter's rages;
Thou thy worldly task hast done,
　Home art gone and ta'en thy wages:
Golden lads and girls all must,
As chimney-sweepers, come to dust.

Fear no more the frown o' the great,
　Thou art past the tyrant's stroke;
Care no more to clothe and eat;
　To thee the reed is as the oak:
The sceptre, learning, physic, must
All follow this, and come to dust.

Fear no more the lightning-flash
    Nor the all-dreaded thunder-stone;
Fear not slander, censure rash;
    Thou hast finish'd joy and moan:
All lovers young, all lovers must
Consign to thee, and come to dust.

It was a lover and his lass

It was a lover and his lass
    With a hey and a ho, and a hey-nonino!
That o'er the green cornfield did pass
In the Spring-time, the only pretty ring time,
When birds do sing hey ding a ding ding:
    Sweet lovers love the Spring.

Between the acres of the rye
These pretty country folks would lie:

This carol they began that hour,
How that a life was but a flower:

And therefore take the present time
    With a hey and a ho, and a hey-nonino!
For love is crownèd with the prime
In Spring-time, the only pretty ring time,
When birds do sing hey ding a ding ding:
    Sweet lovers love the Spring.

Sonnet XVIII

Shall I compare thee to a summer's day?
Thou art more lovely and more temperate:
Rough winds do shake the darling buds of May,
And summer's lease hath all too short a date:
Sometime too hot the eye of heaven shines,
And often is his gold complexion dimm'd:
And every fair from fair sometime declines,
By chance, or nature's changing course, untrimm'd.

But thy eternal summer shall not fade
Nor lose possession of that fair thou owest;
Nor shall Death brag thou wanderest in his shade,
When in eternal lines to time thou growest:—
So long as men can breathe, or eyes can see,
So long lives this, and this gives life to thee.

Sonnet XXIX

When in disgrace with fortune and men's eyes
I all alone beweep my outcast state,
And trouble deaf heaven with my bootless cries,
And look upon myself, and curse my fate;
Wishing me like to one more rich in hope,
Featured like him, like him with friends possest,
Desiring this man's art, and that man's scope,
With what I most enjoy contented least;
Yet in these thoughts myself almost despising,
Haply I think on thee—and then my state,
Like to the lark at break of day arising
From sullen earth, sings hymns at heaven's gate;
For thy sweet love remember'd such wealth brings,
That then I scorn to change my state with kings.

Sonnet XXX

When to the sessions of sweet silent thought
I summon up remembrance of things past,
I sigh the lack of many a thing I sought,
And with old woes new wail my dear time's waste:
Then can I drown an eye, unused to flow,
For precious friends hid in death's dateless night,
And weep afresh love's long since cancell'd woe,
And moan the expense of many a vanish'd sight:
Then can I grieve at grievances foregone,
And heavily from woe to woe tell o'er
The sad account of fore-bemoanéd moan,
Which I new pay as if not paid before.
But if the while I think on thee, dear friend,
All losses are restored and sorrows end.

Sonnet XCIV

They that have power to hurt, and will do none,
That do not do the thing they most do show,
Who, moving others, are themselves as stone,
Unmovèd, cold, and to temptation slow,—
They rightly do inherit Heaven's graces,
And husband Nature's riches from expense;
They are the lords and owners of their faces,
Others, but stewards of their excellence.
The summer's flower is to the summer sweet,
Though to itself it only live and die;
But if that flower with base infection meet,
The basest weed outbraves his dignity;
For sweetest things turn sourest by their deeds;
Lilies that fester smell far worse than weeds.

Sonnet XCVII

How like a winter hath my absence been
From thee, the pleasure of the fleeting year!
What freezings have I felt, what dark days seen,
What old December's bareness everywhere!
And yet this time removed was summer's time:
The teeming autumn, big with rich increase,
Bearing the wanton burden of the prime
Like widow'd wombs after their lords' decease:
Yet this abundant issue seem'd to me
But hope of orphans, and unfather'd fruit;
For summer and his pleasures wait on thee,
And, thou away, the very birds are mute;
Or if they sing, 'tis with so dull a cheer,
That leaves look pale, dreading the winter's near.

Sonnet CVI

When in the chronicle of wasted time
I see descriptions of the fairest wights,
And beauty making beautiful old rhyme
In praise of ladies dead, and lovely knights;

Then in the blazon of sweet beauty's best
Of hand, of foot, of lip, of eye, of brow,
I see their antique pen would have exprest
Ev'n such a beauty as you master now.
So all their praises are but prophecies
Of this our time, all you prefiguring:
And, for they look'd but with divining eyes,
They had not skill enough your worth to sing:
For we, which now behold these present days,
Have eyes to wonder, but lack tongues to praise.

Sonnet CXVI

Let me not to the marriage of true minds
Admit impediments. Love is not love
Which alters when it alteration finds,
Or bends with the remover to remove:
O no! it is an ever-fixèd mark
That looks on tempests, and is never shaken;
It is the star to every wandering bark,
Whose worth's unknown, although his height be taken.
Love's not Time's fool, though rosy lips and cheeks
Within his bending sickle's compass come;
Love alters not with his brief hours and weeks,
But bears it out ev'n to the edge of doom.
If this be error, and upon me proved,
I never writ, nor no man ever loved.

BEN JONSON
1573-1637

Epitaph on Salathiel Pavy,
a Child of Queen Elizabeth's Chapel

Weep with me, all you that read
    This little story;
And know, for whom a tear you shed
    Death's self is sorry.

'Twas a child that so did thrive
    In grace and feature,
As Heaven and Nature seemed to strive
    Which owned the creature.

    Years he numbered scarce thirteen
        When Fates turned cruel,
    Yet three filled zodiacs had he been
        The stage's jewel;

    And did act—what now we moan—
        Old men so duly,
    As, sooth, the Parcae thought him one,
        He played so truly.

    So, by error, to his fate
        They all consented;
    But viewing him since, alas, too late,
        They have repented,

    And have sought—to give new birth—
        In baths to steep him;
    But being so much too good for earth,
        Heaven vows to keep him.

To Master William Shakespeare

To draw no envy (Shakespeare) on thy name,
Am I thus ample to thy book and fame:
While I confess thy writings to be such,
As neither man, nor Muse, can praise too much.
'Tis true, and all men's suffrage. But these ways
Were not the paths I meant unto thy praise:
For silliest ignorance on these may light,
Which, when it sounds at best, but echo's right;
Or blind affection, which doth ne'er advance
The truth, but gropes, and urgeth all by chance;
Or crafty malice, might pretend this praise,
And think to ruin, where it seem'd to raise.
But thou art proof against them, and indeed,
Above th' ill fortune of them, or the need.
I therefore will begin. Soul of the age!
The applause! delight! the wonder of our Stage!
My Shakespeare, rise; I will not lodge thee by
Chaucer, or Spenser, or bid Beaumont lie
A little further, to make thee a room:
Thou art a monument, without a tomb,
And art alive still, while thy book doth live,
And we have wits to read, and praise to give.
That I not mix thee so, my brain excuses;
I mean with great, but disproportion'd Muses:
For, if I thought my judgement were of years,
I should commit thee surely with thy peers,
And tell, how far thou didst our Lyly out-shine,
Or sporting Kyd, or Marlowe's mighty line.
And though thou hadst small Latin, and less Greek,
From thence to honour thee, I would not seek
For names; but call forth thund'ring Æschylus,
Euripides, and Sophocles to us,
Pacuvius, Accius, him of Cordova dead,
To life again, to hear thy buskin tread,
And shake a stage: or, when thy socks were on,
Leave thee alone, for the comparison
Of all that insolent Greece or haughty Rome
Sent forth, or since did from their ashes come.
Triumph, my Britain, thou hast one to show
To whom all scenes of Europe homage owe.

He was not of an age, but for all time!
And all the Muses still were in their prime,
When like Apollo he came forth to warm
Our ears, or like a Mercury to charm!
Nature herself was proud of his designs,
And joy'd to wear the dressing of his lines,
Which were so richly spun, and woven so fit,
As, since, she will vouchsafe no other wit.
The merry Greek, tart Aristophanes,
Neat Terence, witty Plautus, now not please;
But antiquated, and deserted lie
As they were not of Nature's family.
Yet must I not give Nature all: thy art,
My gentle Shakespeare, must enjoy a part.
For though the Poet's matter, Nature be,
His art doth give the fashion; and, that he,
Who casts to write a living line, must sweat,
(Such as thine are) and strike the second heat
Upon the Muses anvil: turn the same,
(And himself with it) that he thinks to frame;
Or for the laurel he may gain a scorn,
For a good poet's made, as well as born;
And such wert thou. Look how the father's face
Lives in his issue, even so, the race
Of Shakespeare's mind, and manners brightly shines
In his well-turned, and true-filed lines;
In each of which, he seems to shake a lance,
As brandish't at the eyes of ignorance.
Sweet swan of Avon! what a sight it were
To see thee in our waters yet appear,
And make those flights upon the banks of Thames
That so did take Eliza, and our James!
But stay, I see thee in the hemisphere
Advanc'd, and made a constellation there!
Shine forth, thou Star of Poets, and with rage,
Or influence, chide, or cheer the drooping Stage;
Which, since thy flight from hence, hath mourn'd like
    night,
And despairs day, but for thy volume's light.

JOHN DONNE
1573-1631

Song

Go and catch a falling star,
  Get with child a mandrake root,
Tell me where all past years are,
  Or who cleft the Devil's foot;
Teach me to hear mermaids singing,
Or to keep off envy's stinging,
     And find
     What wind
Serves to advance an honest mind.

If thou be'st born to strange sights,
  Things invisible to see,
Ride ten thousand days and nights
  Till Age snow white hairs on thee;
Thou, when thou return'st, wilt tell me
All strange wonders that befell thee,
     And swear
     No where
Lives a woman true and fair.

If thou find'st one, let me know;
  Such a pilgrimage were sweet.
Yet do not; I would not go,
  Though at next door we might meet.
Though she were true when you met her,
And last till you write your letter,
     Yet she
     Will be
False, ere I come, to two or three.

As virtuous men pass mildly away,
   And whisper to their souls, to go,
Whilst some of their sad friends do say,
   The breath goes now, and some say, no:

So let us melt, and make no noise,
   No tear-floods, nor sigh-tempests move,
'T were profanation of our joys
   To tell the laity our love.

Moving of th' earth brings harms and fears,
   Men reckon what it did and meant,
But trepidation of the spheres,
   Though greater far, is innocent.

Dull sublunary lovers love
   (Whose soul is sense) cannot admit
Absence, because it doth remove
   Those things which elemented it.

But we by a love, so much refin'd,
   That our selves know not what it is,
Inter-assurèd of the mind,
   Care less, eyes, lips, and hands to miss.

Our two souls therefore, which are one,
   Though I must go, endure not yet
A breach, but an expansion,
   Like gold to airy thinness beat.

If they be two, they are two so
   As stiff twin compasses are two,
Thy soul the fixt foot, makes no show
   To move, but doth, if th' other do.

And though it in the centre sit,
   Yet when the other far doth roam,
It leans, and hearkens after it,
   And grows erect, as that comes home.

Such wilt thou be to me, who must
   Like th' other foot, obliquely run;
Thy firmness makes my circle just,
   And makes me end, where I begun.

Love's Deity

I long to talk with some old lover's ghost,
  Who died before the god of Love was born:
I cannot think that he, who then loved most,
  Sunk so low, as to love one which did scorn.
But since this god produc'd a destiny,
And that vice-nature, custom, lets it be;
  I must love her that loves not me.

Sure, they which made him god, meant not so much,
  Nor he, in his young godhead practised it;
But when an even flame two hearts did touch,
  His office was indulgently to fit
Actives to passives. Correspondency
Only his subject was; It cannot be
  Love, till I love her, that loves me.

But every modern god will now extend
  His vast prerogative as far as Jove.
To rage, to lust, to write to, to commend,
  All is the purlieu of the God of Love.
Oh were we wakened by this tyranny
To ungod this child again, it could not be
  I should love her, who loves not me.

Rebel and atheist too, why murmur I,
  As though I felt the worst that love could do?
Love might make me leave loving, or might try
  A deeper plague, to make her love me too,
Which, since she loves before, I'm loth to see;
Falsehood is worse than hate; and that must be,
  If she whom I love, should love me.

Holy Sonnet XIV

Batter my heart, three personed God; for, you
As yet but knock, breath, shine, and seek to mend;
That I may rise and stand, o'erthrow me, and bend
Your force, to break, blow, burn, and make me new.

I, like an usurpt town, to another due,
Labour to admit you, but Oh, to no end;
Reason your viceroy in me, me should defend,
But is captived, and proves weak or untrue.
Yet dearly I love you, and would be lovèd fain,
But am betrothed unto your enemy:
Divorce me, untie, or break that knot again,
Take me to you, imprison me, for I
Except you enthral me, never shall be free,
Nor ever chaste, except you ravish me.

A Hymn to God the Father

Wilt thou forgive that sin where I begun,
  Which was my sin, though it were done before?
Wilt thou forgive that sin, through which I run,
  And do run still: though still I do deplore?
    When thou hast done, thou hast not done,
      For I have more.

Wilt thou forgive that sin which I have won
  Others to sin? and made my sin their door?
Wilt thou forgive that sin which I did shun
  A year or two, but wallowed in a score?
    When thou hast done, thou hast not done,
      For I have more.

I have a sin of fear, that when I have spun
  My last thread, I shall perish on the shore;
But swear by Thyself, that at my death Thy Son
  Shall shine as He shines now, and heretofore;
    And, having done that, Thou hast done,
      I fear no more.

ROBERT HERRICK
1591-1674

To the Virgins, to make much of Time

Gather ye rosebuds while ye may,
    Old Time is still a-flying:
And this same flower that smiles to-day
    To-morrow will be dying.

The glorious lamp of heaven, the sun,
    The higher he's a-getting,
The sooner will his race be run,
    And nearer he's to setting.

That age is best which is the first,
    When youth and blood are warmer;
But being spent, the worse, and worst
    Times still succeed the former.

Then be not coy, but use your time,
    And while ye may, go marry:
For having lost but once your prime,
    You may for ever tarry.

Upon Julia's Clothes

Whenas in silks my Julia goes,
Then, then, methinks, how sweetly flows
The liquefaction of her clothes.

Next, when I cast mine eye and see
That brave vibration each way free;
O how that glittering taketh me!

To Daffodils

Fair daffodils, we weep to see
  You haste away so soon;
As yet the early-rising sun
  Has not attain'd his noon.
    Stay, stay
  Until the hasting day
    Has run
  But to the evensong;
And, having pray'd together, we
  Will go with you along.
We have short time to stay, as you,
  We have as short a spring;
As quick a growth to meet decay
  As you, or any thing.
    We die
  As your hours do, and dry
    Away
  Like to the summer's rain;
Or as the pearls of morning dew,
  Ne'er to be found again.

A Sweet Disorder

A sweet disorder in the dress
Kindles in clothes a wantonness:
A lawn about the shoulders thrown
Into a fine distraction:
An erring lace, which here and there
Enthrals the crimson stomacher:
A cuff neglectful, and thereby
Ribbands to flow confusedly:
A winning wave, deserving note,
In the tempestuous petticoat:
A careless shoe-string, in whose tie
I see a wild civility:
Do more bewitch me than when art
Is too precise in every part.

To Blossoms

Fair pledges of a fruitful tree,
  Why do ye fall so fast?
  Your date is not so past
But you may stay yet here a while,
  To blush and gently smile;
    And go at last.

What! were ye born to be
  An hour or half's delight
  And so to bid good-night?
'Twas pity Nature brought you forth
  Merely to show your worth,
    And lose you quite.

But you are lovely leaves, where we
  May read how soon things have
  Their end, though ne'er so brave:
And after they have shown their pride
  Like you a while, they glide
    Into the grave.

To Anthea
who may command him anything

Bid me to live, and I will live
  Thy Protestant to be,
Or bid me love, and I will give
  A loving heart to thee.

A heart as soft, a heart as kind,
  A heart as sound and free
As in the whole world thou canst find,
  That heart I'll give to thee.

Bid that heart stay, and it will stay
  To honour thy decree:
Or bid it languish quite away,
  An't shall do so for thee.

Bid me to weep, and I will weep
   While I have eyes to see:
And, having none, yet will I keep
   A heart to weep for thee.

Bid me despair, and I'll despair
   Under that cypress-tree;
Or bid me die, and I will dare
   E'en death, to die for thee.

Thou art my life, my love, my heart,
   The very eyes of me:
And hast command of every part
   To live and die for thee.

GEORGE HERBERT
1593-1633

Virtue

Sweet day, so cool, so calm, so bright!
The bridal of the earth and sky—
The dew shall weep thy fall to-night;
    For thou must die.

Sweet rose, whose hue angry and brave
Bids the rash gazer wipe his eye,
Thy root is ever in its grave,
    And thou must die.

Sweet spring, full of sweet days and roses,
A box where sweets compacted lie,
My music shows ye have your closes,
    And all must die.

Only a sweet and virtuous soul,
Like season'd timber, never gives;
But though the whole world turn to coal,
    Then chiefly lives.

The Collar

I struck the board, and cried, No more;
    I will abroad.
What! shall I ever sigh and pine?
My lines and life are free; free as the road,
Loose as the wind, as large as store.
    Shall I be still in suit?
  Have I no harvest, but a thorn
  To let me blood, and not restore
What I have lost with cordial fruit?

Sure there was wine
Before my sighs did dry it; there was corn
 Before my tears did drown it.
Is the year only lost to me?
 Have I no bays to crown it?
No flowers, no garlands gay? All blasted?
   All wasted?
 Not so, my heart; but there is fruit,
   And thou hast hands.
 Recover all thy sigh-blown age
On double pleasures; leave thy cold dispute
Of what is fit and not; forsake thy cage,
   Thy rope of sands,
Which petty thoughts have made, and made to thee
 Good cable, to enforce and draw
   And be thy law,
While thou didst wink and wouldst not see.
   Away! take heed,
   I will abroad.
Call in thy death's-head there; tie up thy fears.
   He that forbears
 To suit and serve his need
  Deserves his load.
But as I raved, and grew more fierce and wild
   At every word
Methought I heard one calling, *Child!*
 And I replied, *My Lord.*

JOHN MILTON
1608-1674

On the Morning of Christ's Nativity

This is the month, and this the happy morn
Wherein the Son of Heaven's Eternal King,
Of wedded maid and virgin mother born,
Our great redemption from above did bring;
For so the holy sages once did sing,
   That He our deadly forfeit should release,
And with his Father work us a perpetual peace.

That glorious form, that light unsufferable,
And that far-beaming blaze of majesty,
Wherwith he wont at Heaven's high council-table,
To sit the midst of trinal unity,
He laid aside; and here with us to be,
   Forsook the courts of everlasting day,
And chose with us a darksome house of mortal clay.

Say Heavenly Muse, shall not thy sacred vein
Afford a present to the Infant God?
Hast thou no verse, no hymn, or solemn strain,
To welcome Him to this His new abode,
Now while the heaven by the sun's team untrod,
   Hath took no print of the approaching light,
And all the spangled host keep watch in squadrons bright?

See how from far upon the eastern road
The star-led wizards haste with odours sweet!
O run, prevent them with thy humble ode,
And lay it lowly at His blessed feet;
Have thou the honour first thy Lord to greet,
   And join thy voice unto the Angel Choir,
From out His secret altar touch'd with hallowed fire.

75

The Hymn

It was the winter wild,
While the heaven-born Child
All meanly wrapt in the rude manger lies;
Nature, in awe to Him,
Had doff'd her gaudy trim,
With her great Master so to sympathise:
It was no season then for her
To wanton with the Sun, her lusty paramour.

Only with speeches fair
She woos the gentle air
To hide her guilty front with innocent snow;
And on her naked shame,
Pollute with sinful blame,
The saintly veil of maiden white to throw;
Confounded, that her Maker's eyes
Should look so near upon her foul deformities.

But He, her fears to cease,
Sent down the meek-eyed Peace;
She, crown'd with olive green, came softly sliding
Down through the turning sphere,
His ready harbinger,
With turtle wing the amorous clouds dividing;
And, waving wide her myrtle wand,
She strikes a universal peace through sea and land.

No war, or battle's sound,
Was heard the world around:
The idle spear and shield were high uphung;
The hookèd chariot stood,
Unstain'd with hostile blood;
The trumpet spake not to the armèd throng;
And kings sat still with awful eye,
As if they surely knew their sovran Lord was by.

But peaceful was the night
Wherein the Prince of Light
His reign of peace upon the earth began:

The winds, with wonder whist,
Smoothly the waters kissed,
Whispering new joys to the mild oceàn—
Who now hath quite forgot to rave,
While birds of calm sit brooding on the charmèd wave.

The stars, with deep amaze,
Stand fix'd in steadfast gaze,
Bending one way their precious influence;
And will not take their flight
For all the morning light,
Or Lucifer that often warn'd them thence;
But in their glimmering orbs did glow
Until their Lord Himself bespake, and bid them go.

And though the shady gloom
Had given day her room,
The sun himself withheld his wonted speed,
And hid his head for shame,
As his inferior flame
The new-enlighten'd world no more should need;
He saw a greater Sun appear
Than his bright throne, or burning axletree could bear.

The shepherds on the lawn
Or ere the point of dawn
Sat simply chatting in a rustic row;
Full little thought they than
That the mighty Pan
Was kindly come to live with them below;
Perhaps their loves, or else their sheep
Was all that did their silly thoughts so busy keep.

When such music sweet
Their hearts and ears did greet
As never was by mortal finger strook—
Divinely-warbled voice
Answering the stringèd noise,
As all their souls in blissful rapture took:
The air, such pleasure loth to lose,
With thousand echoes still prolongs each heavenly close.

Nature, that heard such sound
Beneath the hollow round
Of Cynthia's seat, the airy region thrilling,
Now was almost won
To think her part was done,
And that her reign had here its last fulfilling;
She knew such harmony alone
Could hold all Heaven and Earth in happier union.

At last surrounds their sight
A globe of circular light
That with long beams the shamefac'd night array'd;
The helmèd Cherubim
And sworded Seraphim
Are seen in glittering ranks with wings display'd,
Harping in loud and solemn choir
With unexpressive notes, to Heaven's new-born Heir.

Such music (as 'tis said)
Before was never made
But when of old the Sons of Morning sung,
While the Creator great
His constellations set,
And the well-balanc'd world on hinges hung,
And cast the dark foundations deep,
And bid the weltering waves their oozy channel keep.

Ring out, ye crystal spheres!
Once bless our human ears,
If ye have power to touch our senses so;
And let your silver chime
Move in melodious time;
And let the bass of heaven's deep organ blow;
And with your ninefold harmony
Make up full consort to the angelic symphony.

For if such holy song
Enwrap our fancy long,
Time will run back, and fetch the age of gold;
And speckled Vanity
Will sicken soon and die;
And leprous Sin will melt from earthly mould;

78

And Hell itself will pass away,
And leave her dolorous mansions to the peering day.

Yea, Truth and Justice then
Will down return to men,
Orb'd in a rainbow; and, like glories wearing,
Mercy will sit between,
Thron'd in celestial sheen,
With radiant feet the tissued clouds down steering;
And Heaven, as at some festival,
Will open wide the gates of her high palace-hall.

But wisest Fate says No;
This must not yet be so;
The Babe yet lies in smiling infancy
That on the bitter cross
Must redeem our loss,
So both Himself and us to glorify:
Yet first, to those ychain'd in sleep
The wakeful trump of doom must thunder through the deep,

With such a horrid clang
As on Mount Sinai rang,
While the red fire and smouldering clouds outbrake:
The aged Earth, aghast
With terror of that blast,
Shall from the surface to the centre shake,
When, at the world's last session,
The dreadful Judge in middle air shall spread His throne.

And then at last our bliss
Full and perfect is,
But now begins; for from this happy day
The old Dragon under ground,
In straiter limits bound,
Not half so far casts his usurpèd sway;
And, wroth to see his kingdom fail,
Swinges the scaly horror of his folded tail.

The Oracles are dumb;
No voice or hideous hum
Runs through the archèd roof in words deceiving.

Apollo from his shrine
Can no more divine,
With hollow shriek the steep of Delphos leaving:
No nightly trance or breathed spell
Inspires the pale-eyed priest from the prophetic cell.

The lonely mountains o'er
And the resounding shore
A voice of weeping heard, and loud lament;
From haunted spring, and dale
Edg'd with poplar pale,
The parting Genius is with sighing sent;
With flower-inwoven tresses torn
The Nymphs in twilight shade of tangled thickets mourn.

In consecrated earth
And on the holy hearth
The Lars and Lemures moan with midnight plaint;
In urns, and altars round,
A drear and dying sound
Affrights the Flamens at their service quaint;
And the chill marble seems to sweat,
While each peculiar Power forgoes his wonted seat.

Peor and Baalim
Forsake their temples dim,
With that twice-batter'd god of Palestine;
And moonèd Ashtaroth,
Heaven's queen and mother both,
Now sits not girt with tapers' holy shine;
The Lybic Hammon shrinks his horn;
In vain the Tyrian maids their wounded Thammuz mourn.

And sullen Moloch, fled,
Hath left in shadows dread
His burning idol all of blackest hue;
In vain with cymbals' ring
They call the grisly king,
In dismal dance about the furnace blue;
The brutish gods of Nile as fast,
Isis, and Orus, and the dog Anubis, haste.

Nor is Osiris seen
In Memphian grove or green,
Trampling the unshower'd grass with lowings loud;
Nor can he be at rest
Within his sacred chest;
Naught but profoundest Hell can be his shroud;
In vain with timbrell'd anthems dark
The sable-stolèd sorcerers bear his worshipt ark.

He feels from Juda's land
The dreaded Infant's hand;
The rays of Bethlehem blind his dusky eyn;
Nor all the gods beside
Longer dare abide,
Not Typhon huge ending in snaky twine:
Our Babe, to show his Godhead true,
Can in His swaddling bands control the damnèd crew.

So, when the sun in bed,
Curtain'd with cloudy red,
Pillows his chin upon an orient wave,
The flocking shadows pale
Troop to the infernal jail,
Each fetter'd ghost slips to his several grave;
And the yellow-skirted fays
Fly after the night-steeds, leaving their moon-lov'd maze.

But see! the Virgin blest
Hath laid her Babe to rest;
Time is our tedious song should here have ending:
Heaven's youngest-teemèd star
Hath fix't her polish'd car,
Her sleeping Lord with hand-maid lamp attending:
And all about the courtly stable
Bright-harness'd Angels sit in order serviceable.

L'Allegro

Hence, loathèd Melancholy,
Of Cerberus and blackest Midnight born,
In Stygian cave forlorn

'Mongst horrid shapes, and shrieks, and sights unholy!
     Find out some uncouth cell,
Where brooding Darkness spreads his jealous wings
     And the night-raven sings;
There, under ebon shades and low-brow'd rocks,
     As ragged as thy locks,
In dark Cimmerian desert ever dwell.

     But come, thou Goddess fair and free,
     In Heaven yclep'd Euphrosyne,
     And by men, heart-easing Mirth,
     Whom lovely Venus at a birth
     With two sister Graces more
     To ivy-crownèd Bacchus bore:
     Or whether (as some sager sing)
     The frolic wind that breathes the spring,
     Zephyr, with Aurora playing,
     As he met her once a-Maying—
     There on beds of violets blue
     And fresh-blown roses wash'd in dew
     Fill'd her with thee, a daughter fair,
     So buxom, blithe, and debonair.
     Haste thee, Nymph, and bring with thee
     Jest, and youthful jollity,
     Quips, and cranks, and wanton wiles,
     Nods, and becks, and wreathèd smiles,
     Such as hang on Hebe's cheek,
     And love to live in dimple sleek;
     Sport that wrinkled Care derides,
     And Laughter holding both his sides.
     Come, and trip it as you go
     On the light fantastic toe;
     And in thy right hand lead with thee
     The mountain nymph, sweet Liberty;
     And if I give thee honour due,
     Mirth, admit me of thy crew,
     To live with her, and live with thee
     In unreprovèd pleasures free;
     To hear the lark begin his flight
     And singing startle the dull night
     From his watch-tower in the skies,
     Till the dappled dawn doth rise;

Then to come, in spite of sorrow,
And at my window bid good-morrow
Through the sweetbriar, or the vine,
Or the twisted eglantine:
While the cock with lively din
Scatters the rear of darkness thin,
And to the stack, or the barn-door,
Stoutly struts his dames before:
Oft listening how the hounds and horn
Cheerly rouse the slumbering morn,
From the side of some hoar hill,
Through the high wood echoing shrill.
Sometime walking, not unseen,
By hedge-row elms, on hillocks green,
Right against the eastern gate
Where the great Sun begins his state
Robed in flames and amber light,
The clouds in thousand liveries dight;
While the ploughman, near at hand,
Whistles o'er the furrow'd land,
And the milkmaid singeth blithe,
And the mower whets his scythe,
And every shepherd tells his tale
Under the hawthorn in the dale.
    Straight mine eye hath caught new pleasures
Whilst the landscape round it measures:
Russet lawns, and fallows grey,
Where the nibbling flocks do stray;
Mountains, on whose barren breast
The labouring clouds do often rest;
Meadows trim with daisies pied,
Shallow brooks, and rivers wide;
Towers and battlements it sees
Bosom'd high in tufted trees,
Where perhaps some Beauty lies,
The Cynosure of neighbouring eyes.
    Hard by, a cottage chimney smokes
From betwixt two aged oaks,
Where Corydon and Thyrsis, met,
Are at their savoury dinner set
Of herbs, and other country messes
Which the neat-handed Phillis dresses;

And then in haste her bower she leaves,
With Thestylis to bind the sheaves;
Or, if the earlier season lead,
To the tanned haycock in the mead.
Sometimes, with secure delight,
The upland hamlets will invite,
When the merry bells ring round,
And the jocund rebecks sound
To many a youth and many a maid
Dancing in the chequered shade,
And young and old come forth to play
On a sunshine holyday,
Till the livelong daylight fail:
Then to the spicy nut-brown ale,
With stories told of many a feat,
How Faery Mab the junkets eat.
She was pinched and pulled, she said;
And he, by Friar's lantern led,
Tells how the drudging goblin sweat
To earn his cream-bowl duly set,
When in one night, ere glimpse of morn,
His shadowy flail hath threshed the corn
That ten day-labourers could not end:
Then lies him down, the lubber fiend,
And, stretch'd out all the chimney's length,
Basks at the fire his hairy strength,
And crop-full out of doors he flings,
Ere the first cock his matin rings.
Thus done the tales, to bed they creep,
By whispering winds soon lulled asleep.
Towered cities please us then,
And the busy hum of men,
Where throngs of knights and barons bold,
In weeds of peace, high triumphs hold,
With store of ladies, whose bright eyes
Rain influence, and judge the prize
Of wit or arms, while both contend
To win her grace, whom all commend.
There let Hymen oft appear
In saffron robe, with taper clear,
And pomp, and feast, and revelry,
With mask, and antique pageantry;

Such sights as youthful poets dream
On summer eves by haunted stream.
Then to the well-trod stage anon,
If Jonson's learned sock be on,
Or sweetest Shakespeare, Fancy's child,
Warble his native wood-notes wild.

    And ever against eating cares
Lap me in soft Lydian airs
Married to immortal verse,
Such as the meeting soul may pierce
In notes, with many a winding bout
Of linkèd sweetness long drawn out,
With wanton heed and giddy cunning,
The melting voice through mazes running,
Untwisting all the chains that tie
The hidden soul of harmony;
That Orpheus' self may heave his head
From golden slumber, on a bed
Of heap'd Elysian flowers, and hear
Such strains as would have won the ear
Of Pluto, to have quite set free
His half-regain'd Eurydice.

    These delights if thou canst give,
Mirth, with thee I mean to live.

Il Penseroso

    Hence, vain deluding Joys,
The brood of Folly without father bred!
    How little you bestead
Or fill the fixèd mind with all your toys!
    Dwell in some idle brain,
And fancies fond with gaudy shapes possess
    As thick and numberless
As the gay motes that people the sunbeams,
    Or likest hovering dreams,
The fickle pensioners of Morpheus' train.

    But hail, thou goddess sage and holy,
Hail, divinest Melancholy!

Whose saintly visage is too bright
To hit the sense of human sight,
And therefore to our weaker view
O'erlaid with black, staid Wisdom's hue;
Black, but such as in esteem
Prince Memnon's sister might beseem,
Or that starr'd Ethiop queen that strove
To set her beauty's praise above
The sea-nymphs, and their powers offended:
Yet thou art higher far descended:
Thee bright-hair'd Vesta, long of yore,
To solitary Saturn bore;
His daughter she; in Saturn's reign
Such mixture was not held a stain:
Oft in glimmering bowers and glades
He met her, and in secret shades
Of woody Ida's inmost grove,
Whilst yet there was no fear of Jove.
    Come, pensive nun, devout and pure,
Sober, steadfast, and demure,
All in a robe of darkest grain
Flowing with majestic train,
And sable stole of cypress lawn
Over thy decent shoulders drawn
Come, but keep thy wonted state,
With even step, and musing gait,
And looks commèrcing with the skies,
Thy rapt soul sitting in thine eyes:
There, held in holy passion still,
Forget thyself to marble, till
With a sad leaden downward cast
Thou fix them on the earth as fast:
And join with thee calm Peace, and Quiet,
Spare Fast, that oft with gods doth diet,
And hears the Muses in a ring
Ay round about Jove's altar sing:
And add to these retired Leisure
That in trim gardens takes his pleasure
But first, and chiefest, with thee bring—
Him that yon soars on golden wing
Guiding the fiery-wheelèd throne,
The cherub Contemplatiòn;

And the mute Silence hist along,
'Less Philomel will deign a song
In her sweetest saddest plight,
Smoothing the rugged brow of Night,
While Cynthia checks her dragon yoke
Gently o'er the accustom'd oak.
—Sweet bird, that shunn'st the noise of folly,
Most musical, most melancholy!
Thee, chauntress, oft the woods among
I woo, to hear thy even-song;
And missing thee, I walk unseen
On the dry smooth-shaven green,
To behold the wandering Moon
Riding near her highest noon,
Like one that had been led astray
Through the heaven's wide pathless way,
And oft, as if her head she bow'd,
Stooping through a fleecy cloud.

Oft, on a plat of rising ground
I hear the far-off curfew sound
Over some wide-water'd shore,
Swinging slow with sullen roar:
Or, if the air will not permit,
Some still removèd place will fit,
Where glowing embers through the room
Teach light to counterfeit a gloom;
Far from all resort of mirth,
Save the cricket on the hearth,
Or the bellman's drowsy charm
To bless the doors from nightly harm.

Or let my lamp at midnight hour
Be seen in some high lonely tower,
Where I may oft out-watch the Bear
With thrice-great Hermes, or unsphere
The spirit of Plato, to unfold
What world or what vast regions hold
The immortal mind, that hath forsook
Her mansion in this fleshly nook:
And of those demons that are found
In fire, air, flood, or under ground,
Whose power hath a true consent
With planet, or with element.

Sometime let gorgeous Tragedy
In scepter'd pall come sweeping by,
Presenting Thebes, or Pelops' line,
Or the tale of Troy divine;
Or what (though rare) of later age
Ennobled hath the buskin'd stage.

But, O sad Virgin, that thy power
Might raise Musæus from his bower,
Or bid the soul of Orpheus sing
Such notes as, warbled to the string,
Drew iron tears down Pluto's cheek
And made Hell grant what Love did seek!
Or call up him that left half-told
The story of Cambuscan bold,
Of Camball, and of Algarsife,
And who had Canacè to wife,
That own'd the virtuous ring and glass;
And of the wondrous horse of brass
On which the Tartar king did ride:
And if aught else great bards beside
In sage and solemn tunes have sung,
Of turneys, and of trophies hung,
Of forests, and enchantments drear,
Where more is meant than meets the ear.

Thus, Night, oft see me in thy pale career,
Till civil-suited Morn appear,
Not trick'd and frounced as she was wont
With the Attic Boy to hunt,
But kercheft in a comely cloud
While rocking winds are piping loud,
Or usher'd with a shower still,
When the gust hath blown his fill,
Ending on the rustling leaves
With minute drops from off the eaves.
And when the sun begins to fling
His flaring beams, me, goddess, bring
To archèd walks of twilight groves,
And shadows brown, that Sylvan loves,
Of pine, or monumental oak,
Where the rude axe, with heavèd stroke,
Was never heard the nymphs to daunt
Or fright them from their hallow'd haunt..

There in close covert by some brook
Where no profaner eye may look,
Hide me from day's garish eye,
While the bee with honey'd thigh,
That at her flowery work doth sing,
And the waters murmuring,
With such consort as they keep
Entice the dewy-feather'd Sleep;
And let some strange mysterious dream
Wave at his wings in airy stream
Of lively portraiture display'd,
Softly on my eyelids laid:
And, as I wake, sweet music breathe
Above, about, or underneath,
Sent by some Spirit to mortals good,
Or the unseen Genius of the wood.
    But let my due feet never fail
To walk the studious cloister's pale,
And love the high-embowèd roof,
With antique pillars massy-proof,
And storied windows richly dight
Casting a dim religious light:
There let the pealing organ blow
To the full-voiced choir below
In service high and anthems clear,
As may with sweetness, through mine ear,
Dissolve me into ecstasies,
And bring all Heaven before mine eyes.
    And may at last my weary age
Find out the peaceful hermitage,
The hairy gown and mossy cell
Where I may sit and rightly spell
Of every star that heaven doth show,
And every herb that sips the dew;
Till old experience do attain
To something like prophetic strain.

    These pleasures, Melancholy, give,
And I with thee will choose to live.

Yet once more, O ye laurels, and once more
Ye myrtles brown, with ivy never sere,
I come to pluck your berries harsh and crude,
And with forced fingers rude
Shatter your leaves before the mellowing year.
Bitter constraint, and sad occasion dear,
Compels me to disturb your season due:
For Lycidas is dead, dead ere his prime,
Young Lycidas, and hath not left his peer:
Who would not sing for Lycidas? he knew
Himself to sing, and build the lofty rhyme.
He must not float upon his watery bier
Unwept, and welter to the parching wind,
Without the meed of some melodious tear.
　　Begin, then, Sisters of the sacred well
That from beneath the seat of Jove doth spring;
Begin, and somewhat loudly sweep the string.
Hence with denial vain and coy excuse:
So may some gentle Muse
With lucky words favour my destin'd urn,
And as he passes turn,
And bid fair peace be to my sable shroud.
　　For we were nursed upon the self-same hill,
Fed the same flock, by fountain, shade, and rill;
Together both, ere the high lawns appeared
Under the opening eyelids of the Morn,
We drove a-field, and both together heard
What time the grey-fly winds her sultry horn,
Battening our flocks with the fresh dews of night,
Oft till the star that rose at evening bright
Toward heaven's descent had sloped his westering wheel.
Meanwhile the rural ditties were not mute,
Tempered to the oaten flute
Rough Satyrs danced, and Fauns with cloven heel
From the glad sound would not be absent long;
And old Damœtas loved to hear our song.
　　But, oh! the heavy change, now thou art gone,
Now thou art gone and never must return!
Thee, Shepherd, thee the woods and desert caves

With wild thyme and the gadding vine o'ergrown,
And all their echoes, mourn:
The willows, and the hazel copses green,
Shall now no more be seen
Fanning their joyous leaves to thy soft lays.
As killing as the canker to the rose,
Or taint-worm to the weanling herds that graze
Or frost to flowers, that their gay wardrobe wear,
When first the white-thorn blows;
—Such, Lycidas, thy loss to shepherd's ear.
  Where were ye, Nymphs, when the remorseless deep
Closed o'er the head of your loved Lycidas?
For neither were ye playing on the steep
Where your old bards, the famous Druids, lie,
Nor on the shaggy top of Mona high,
Nor yet where Deva spreads her wizard stream.
Ay me! I fondly dream
—Had ye been there for what could that have done?
What could the Muse herself that Orpheus bore,
The Muse herself, for her enchanting son
Whom universal nature did lament,
When, by the rout that made the hideous roar,
His gory visage down the stream was sent,
Down the swift Hebrus to the Lesbian shore?
  Alas! what boots it with uncessant care
To tend the homely, slighted, shepherd's trade,
And strictly meditate the thankless Muse?
Were it not better done, as others use,
To sport with Amaryllis in the shade,
Or with the tangles of Neæra's hair?
Fame is the spur that the clear spirit doth raise
(That last infirmity of noble mind)
To scorn delights and live laborious days;
But the fair guerdon when we hope to find,
And think to burst out into sudden blaze,
Comes the blind Fury with th' abhorred shears,
And slits the thin-spun life. 'But not the praise,'
Phœbus replied, and touched my trembling ears:
'Fame is no plant that grows on mortal soil,
Nor in the glistering foil
Set off to the world, nor in broad rumour lies,
But lives and spreads aloft by those pure eyes

And perfect witness of all-judging Jove;
As he pronounces lastly on each deed,
Of so much fame in heaven expect thy meed.'

   O fountain Arethuse, and thou honour'd flood,
Smooth-sliding Mincius, crown'd with vocal reeds,
That strain I heard was of a higher mood:
But now my oat proceeds,
And listens to the herald of the sea
That came in Neptune's plea;
He ask'd the waves, and ask'd the felon winds,
What hard mishap hath doom'd this gentle swain?
And question'd every gust of rugged wings
That blows from off each beakèd promontory:
They knew not of his story;
And sage Hippotades their answer brings,
That not a blast was from his dungeon stray'd;
The air was calm, and on the level brine
Sleek Panope with all her sisters play'd.
It was that fatal and perfidious bark
Built in the eclipse, and rigg'd with curses dark,
That sunk so low that sacred head of thine.

   Next Camus, reverend sire, went footing slow,
His mantle hairy, and his bonnet sedge,
Inwrought with figures dim, and on the edge
Like to that sanguine flower inscribed with woe:
'Ah! who hath reft,' quoth he, 'my dearest pledge?'
Last came, and last did go,
The Pilot of the Galilean lake;
Two massy keys he bore of metals twain
(The golden opes, the iron shuts amain);
He shook his mitred locks, and stern bespake:
'How well could I have spared for thee, young swain,
Enow of such as for their bellies' sake
Creep and intrude and climb into the fold!
Of other care they little reckoning make
Than how to scramble at the shearers' feast,
And shove away the worthy bidden guest.
Blind mouths! that scarce themselves know how to hold
A sheep-hook, or have learn'd aught else the least
That to the faithful herdman's art belongs!
What recks it them? What need they? They are sped;
And when they list, their lean and flashy songs

Grate on their scrannel pipes of wretched straw;
The hungry sheep look up, and are not fed,
But, swoln with wind and the rank mist they draw,
Rot inwardly, and foul contagion spread:
Besides what the grim wolf with privy paw
Daily devours apace, and nothing said:
But that two-handed engine at the door
Stands ready to smite once, and smite no more.'
   Return, Alpheus, the dread voice is past
That shrunk thy streams; return, Sicilian Muse,
And call the vales, and bid them hither cast
Their bells and flowerets of a thousand hues.
Ye valleys low, where the mild whispers use
Of shades, and wanton winds, and gushing brooks,
On whose fresh lap the swart star sparely looks;
Throw hither all your quaint enamelled eyes
That on the green turf suck the honeyed showers,
And purple all the ground with vernal flowers.
Bring the rathe primrose that forsaken dies,
The tufted crow-toe and pale jessamine,
The white pink and the pansy freaked with jet,
The glowing violet,
The musk-rose and the well-attired woodbine,
With cowslips wan that hang the pensive head,
And every flower that sad embroidery wears:
Bid Amaranthus all his beauty shed,
And daffadillies fill their cups with tears,
To strew the laureate hearse where Lycid lies.
For, so to interpose a little ease,
Let our frail thoughts dally with false surmise;
Ay me! whilst thee the shores and sounding seas
Wash far away, where'er thy bones are hurled;
Whether beyond the stormy Hebrides,
Where thou perhaps under the whelming tide
Visit'st the bottom of the monstrous world;
Or whether thou, to our moist vows denied,
Sleep'st by the fable of Bellerus old,
Where the great Vision of the guarded mount
Looks toward Namancos and Bayona's hold.
—Look homeward, Angel, now, and melt with ruth:
And, O ye dolphins, waft the hapless youth.
   Weep no more, woeful shepherds, weep no more,

93

For Lycidas, your sorrow, is not dead,
Sunk though he be beneath the watery floor.
So sinks the day-star in the ocean-bed,
And yet anon repairs his drooping head,
And tricks his beams, and with new-spangled ore
Flames in the forehead of the morning sky:
So Lycidas sunk low, but mounted high,
Through the dear might of Him that walked the waves
Where, other groves and other streams along,
With nectar pure his oozy locks he laves,
And hears the unexpressive nuptial song,
In the blest kingdoms meek of joy and love.
There entertain him all the Saints above,
In solemn troops, and sweet societies,
That sing, and singing in their glory move,
And wipe the tears for ever from his eyes.
Now, Lycidas, the shepherds weep no more;
Henceforth thou art the Genius of the shore,
In thy large recompense, and shalt be good
To all that wander in that perilous flood.

Thus sang the uncouth swain to the oaks and rills,
While the still morn went out with sandals grey:
He touched the tender stops of various quills,
With eager thought warbling his Doric lay:
And now the sun had stretched out all the hills,
And now was dropt into the western bay.
At last he rose, and twitched his mantle blue:
To-morrow to fresh woods, and pastures new.

To the Lord General

Cromwell, our chief of men, who through a cloud
Not of war only, but detractions rude,
Guided by faith and matchless fortitude,
To peace and truth thy glorious way hast ploughed,
And on the neck of crownèd Fortune proud
Hast reared God's trophies, and his work pursued,
While Darwen stream, with blood of Scots imbrued,
And Dunbar field, resounds thy praises loud,

And Worcester's laureate wreath: yet much remains
To conquer still; peace hath her victories
No less renowned than war: new foes arise,
Threatening to bind our souls with secular chains.
Help us to save free conscience from the paw
Of hireling wolves whose gospel is their maw.

The Late Massacre in Piedmont

Avenge, O Lord, thy slaughtered saints, whose bones
Lie scattered on the Alpine mountains cold;
Even them who kept thy truth so pure of old,
When all our fathers worshipped stocks and stones,
Forget not: in thy book record their groans
Who were thy sheep, and in their ancient fold
Slain by the bloody Piedmontese that rolled
Mother with infant down the rocks. Their moans
The vales redoubled to the hills, and they
To heaven. Their martyred blood and ashes sow
O'er all the Italian fields, where still doth sway
The triple Tyrant; that from these may grow
A hundredfold, who, having learnt thy way,
Early may fly the Babylonian woe.

To Mr. Lawrence

Lawrence, of virtuous father virtuous son,
Now that the fields are dank, and ways are mire,
Where shall we sometimes meet, and by the fire
Help waste a sullen day, what may be won
From the hard season gaining? Time will run
On smoother, till Favonius reinspire
The frozen earth, and clothe in fresh attire
The lily and rose, that neither sowed nor spun.
What neat repast shall feast us, light and choice,
Of Attic taste, with wine, whence we may rise
To hear the lute well touched, or artful voice
Warble immortal notes and Tuscan air?
He who of those delights can judge, and spare
To interpose them oft, is not unwise.

To Cyriack Skinner

Cyriack, whose grandsire on the royal bench
Of British Themis, with no mean applause,
Pronounced, and in his volumes taught, our laws,
Which others at their bar so often wrench,
To-day deep thoughts resolve with me to drench
In mirth that after no repenting draws;
Let Euclid rest, and Archimedes pause,
And what the Swede intend, and what the French.
To measure life learn thou betimes, and know
Towards solid good what leads the nearest way;
For other things mild Heaven a time ordains,
And disapproves that care, though wise in show,
That with a superfluous burden loads the day,
And, when God sends a cheerful hour, refrains.

On his Blindness

When I consider how my light is spent
Ere half my days in this dark world and wide,
And that one talent which is death to hide
Lodged with me useless, though my soul more bent
To serve therewith my Maker, and present
My true account, lest He, returning, chide;
'Doth God exact day-labour, light denied?'
I fondly ask: but patience, to prevent
That murmur soon replies: 'God doth not need
Either man's work or his own gifts. Who best
Bear his mild yoke, they serve him best. His state
Is kingly: thousands at his bidding speed,
And post o'er land and ocean without rest;
They also serve who only stand and wait.'

JOHN SUCKLING
1609-1642

Why so pale and wan, fond Lover?

Why so pale and wan, fond lover?
    Prithee, why so pale?
Will, if looking well can't move her,
    Looking ill prevail?
    Prithee, why so pale?

Why so dull and mute, young sinner?
    Prithee, why so mute?
Will, when speaking well can't win her,
    Saying nothing do't?
    Prithee, why so mute?

Quit, quit, for shame! this will not move,
    This cannot take her:
If of herself she will not love,
    Nothing can make her:
    The Devil take her!

The Constant Lover

Out upon it, I have loved
    Three whole days together!
And am like to love three more
    If it prove fair weather.

Time shall moult away his wings
    Ere he shall discover
In the whole wide world again
    Such a constant lover.

But the spite on 't is, no praise
   Is due at all to me:
Love with me had made no stays
   Had it any been but she.

Had it any been but she,
   And that very face,
There had been at least ere this
   A dozen dozen in her place.

JAMES GRAHAM, MARQUIS OF MONTROSE
1612-1650

My Dear and Only Love

My dear and only love, I pray
    This noble world of thee
Be governed by no other sway
    But purest monarchy;
For if confusion have a part
    Which virtuous souls abhor,
And hold a synod in thy heart,
    I'll never love thee more.

Like Alexander I will reign,
    And I will reign alone;
My thoughts shall evermore disdain
    A rival on my throne.
He either fears his fate too much,
    Or his deserts are small,
That dares not put it to the touch,
    To gain or lose it all.

But I will reign and govern still,
    And always give the law,
And have each subject at my will,
    And all to stand in awe;
But 'gainst my batteries if I find
    Thou shun'st the prize so sore,
As that thou set'st me up a blind,
    I'll never love thee more.

And in the empire of thine heart,
    Where I should solely be,
An others do pretend a part,
    And dares to vie with me,
Or if committees thou erect,
    And go on such a score,
I'll laugh and sing at thy neglect
    And never love thee more.

But if thou wilt prove faithful then
   And faithful of thy word,
I'll make thee glorious by my pen,
   And famous by my sword;
I'll serve thee in such noble ways
   Was never heard before;
I'll deck and crown thee all with bays,
   And love thee more and more.

RICHARD LOVELACE
1618-1658

To Althea from Prison

When Love with unconfinèd wings
  Hovers within my gates,
And my divine Althea brings
  To whisper at the grates;
When I lie tangled in her hair
  And fetter'd to her eye,
The Gods that wanton in the air
  Know no such liberty.

When flowing cups run swiftly round
  With no allaying Thames,
Our careless heads with roses crown'd,
  Our hearts with loyal flames;
When thirsty grief in wine we steep,
  When healths and draughts go free—
Fishes that tipple in the deep
  Know no such liberty.

When, like committed linnets, I
  With shriller throat shall sing
The sweetness, mercy, majesty
  And glories of my King;
When I shall voice aloud, how good
  He is, how great should be;
Enlarged winds that curl the flood,
  Know no such liberty.

Stone walls do not a prison make,
  Nor iron bars a cage;
Minds innocent and quiet take
  That for an hermitage:
If I have freedom in my love,
  And in my soul am free;
Angels alone that soar above,
  Enjoy such liberty.

To Lucasta,
on going to the Wars

Tell me not sweet I am unkind,
　　That from the nunnery
Of thy chaste breast, and quiet mind,
　　To war and arms I fly.

True; a new mistress now I chase,
　　The first foe in the field;
And with a stronger faith embrace
　　A sword, a horse, a shield.

Yet this inconstancy is such,
　　As you too shall adore;
I could not love thee dear so much,
　　Lov'd I not honour more.

ANDREW MARVELL
1621-1678

Song of the Emigrants in Bermuda

Where the remote Bermudas ride
In the ocean's bosom unespied,
From a small boat that row'd along
The listening winds received this song.
    'What should we do but sing His praise
That led us through the watery maze
Where He the huge sea-monsters wracks,
That lift the deep upon their backs,
Unto an isle so long unknown,
And yet far kinder than our own?
He lands us on a grassy stage,
Safe from the storms, and prelate's rage;
He gave us this eternal Spring
Which here enamels everything,
And sends the fowls to us in care
On daily visits through the air.
He hangs in shades the orange bright
Like golden lamps in a green night,
And does in the pomgranates close
Jewels more rich than Ormus shows:
He makes the figs our mouths to meet
And throws the melons at our feet;
But apples plants of such a price,
No tree could ever bear them twice.

With cedars chosen by His hand
From Lebanon He stores the land;
And makes the hollow seas that roar
Proclaim the ambergris on shore.
He cast (of which we rather boast)
The Gospel's pearl upon our coast;
And in these rocks for us did frame
A temple where to sound his name.

Oh! let our voice His praise exalt
Till it arrive at Heaven's vault,
Which thence (perhaps) rebounding may
Echo beyond the Mexique bay!'
—Thus sung they in the English boat
A holy and a cheerful note:
And all the way, to guide their chime,
With falling oars they kept the time.

To His Coy Mistress

Had we but world enough, and time,
This coyness, Lady, were no crime.
We would sit down and think which way
To walk and pass our long love's day.
Thou by the Indian Ganges' side
Shouldst rubies find; I by the tide
Of Humber would complain. I would
Love you ten years before the Flood,
And you should, if you please, refuse
Till the conversion of the Jews.
My vegetable love should grow
Vaster than empires, and more slow;
An hundred years should go to praise
Thine eyes and on thy forehead gaze;
Two hundred to adore each breast,
But thirty thousand to the rest;
An age at least to every part,
And the last age should show your heart.
For, Lady, you deserve this state,
Nor would I love at lower rate.
  But at my back I always hear
Time's wingèd chariot hurrying near;
And yonder all before us lie
Deserts of vast eternity.
Thy beauty shall no more be found,
Nor, in thy marble vault, shall sound
My echoing song; then worms shall try
That long preserved virginity,
And your quaint honour turn to dust,
And into ashes all my lust;

The grave's a fine and private place,
But none, I think, do there embrace.
   Now therefore, while the youthful hue
Sits on thy skin like morning dew,
And while thy willing soul transpires
At every pore with instant fires,
Now let us sport us while we may,
And now like amorous birds of prey,
Rather at once our time devour
Than languish in his slow-chapt power.
Let us roll all our strength and all
Our sweetness up into one ball,
And tear our pleasures with rough strife
Thorough the iron gates of life:
Thus, though we cannot make our sun
Stand still, yet we will make him run.

Thoughts in a Garden

How vainly men themselves amaze
To win the palm, the oak, or bays,
And their uncessant labours see
Crowned from some single herb or tree,
Whose short and narrow-vergèd shade
Does prudently their toils upbraid;
While all the flowers and trees do close
To weave the garlands of repose.

Fair Quiet, have I found thee here,
And Innocence, thy sister dear!
Mistaken long, I sought you then
In busy companies of men:
Your sacred plants, if here below,
Only among the plants will grow:
Society is all but rude
To this delicious solitude.

No white nor red was ever seen
So amorous as this lovely green.

Fond lovers, cruel as their flame,
Cut in these trees their mistress' name:
Little, alas, they know or heed
How far these beauties hers exceed!
Fair trees! wheres'e'er your barks I wound,
No name shall but your own be found.

When we have run our passions' heat,
Love hither makes his best retreat:
The gods that mortal beauty chase,
Still in a tree did end their race:
Apollo hunted Daphne so,
Only that she might laurel grow:
And Pan did after Syrinx speed
Not as a nymph, but for a reed.

What wondrous life is this I lead!
Ripe apples drop about my head;
The luscious clusters of the vine
Upon my mouth do crush their wine;
The nectarine, and curious peach,
Into my hands themselves do reach;
Stumbling on melons, as I pass,
Ensnared with flowers, I fall on grass.

Meanwhile the mind, from pleasure less,
Withdraws into its happiness;
The mind, that ocean where each kind
Does straight its own resemblance find;
Yet it creates, transcending these,
Far other worlds, and other seas,
Annihilating all that's made
To a green thought in a green shade.

Here at the fountain's sliding foot,
Or at some fruit-tree's mossy root,
Casting the body's vest aside,
My soul into the boughs does glide:
There, like a bird, it sits and sings,
Then whets and claps its silver wings:
And, till prepared for longer flight,
Waves in its plumes the various light.

Such was that happy Garden-state
While man there walked without a mate:
After a place so pure and sweet,
What other help could yet be meet!
But 'twas beyond a mortal's share
To wander solitary there:
Two paradises 'twere in one,
To live in Paradise alone.

How well the skilful gardener drew
Of flowers and herbs this dial new!
Where, from above, the milder sun
Does through a fragrant zodiac run:
And, as it works, th' industrious bee
Computes its time as well as we.
How could such sweet and wholesome hours
Be reckoned, but with herbs and flowers!

HENRY VAUGHAN
1622-1695

Peace

My soul, there is a country
   Far beyond the stars,
Where stands a wingèd sentry
   All skilful in the wars:
There, above noise and danger,
   Sweet Peace sits crown'd with smiles,
And One born in a manger
   Commands the beauteous files.
He is thy gracious Friend,
   And—O my soul, awake!—
Did in pure love descend
   To die here for thy sake.
If thou canst get but thither,
   There grows the flower of Peace,
The Rose that cannot wither,
   Thy fortress, and thy ease.
Leave then thy foolish ranges;
   For none can thee secure
But One who never changes—
   Thy God, thy life, thy cure.

The Retreat

Happy those early days, when I
Shined in my Angel-infancy!
Before I understood this place
Appointed for my second race,
Or taught my soul to fancy aught
But a white, celestial thought;
When yet I had not walk'd above
A mile or two from my first Love,

And looking back, at that short space
Could see a glimpse of His bright face:
When on some gilded cloud or flower
My gazing soul would dwell an hour,
And in those weaker glories spy
Some shadows of eternity;
Before I taught my tongue to wound
My conscience with a sinful sound,
Or had the black art to dispense
A several sin to every sense,
But felt through all this fleshly dress
Bright shoots of everlastingness.

O how I long to travel back,
And tread again that ancient track!
That I might once more reach that plain
Where first I left my glorious train;
From whence th' enlighten'd spirit sees
That shady City of palm trees!
But ah! my soul with too much stay
Is drunk, and staggers in the way:—
Some men a forward motion love,
But I by backward steps would move;
And when this dust falls to the urn,
In that state I came, return.

Friends Departed

They are all gone into the world of light!
    And I alone sit lingering here;
Their very memory is fair and bright,
    And my sad thoughts doth clear:—

It glows and glitters in my cloudy breast,
    Like stars upon some gloomy grove,
Or those faint beams in which this hill is drest,
    After the sun's remove.

I see them walking in an air of glory,
    Whose light doth trample on my days:
My days, which are at best but dull and hoary,
    Mere glimmering and decays.

O holy Hope! and high Humility,
    High as the heavens above!
These are your walks, and you have shew'd them me,
    To kindle my cold love.

Dear beauteous Death! the jewel of the just,
    Shining no where, but in the dark;
What mysteries do lie beyond thy dust,
    Could man outlook that mark!

He that hath found some fledged bird's nest, may know
    At first sight, if the bird be flown;
But what fair well or grove he sings in now,
    That is to him unknown.

And yet, as Angels in some brighter dreams
    Call to the soul, when man doth sleep;
So some strange thoughts transcend our wonted themes,
    And into glory peep.

BALLADS

A Lyke-Wake Dirge

This ae night, this ae night,
  —*Every night and all,*
Fire and sleete and candle-light,
  And Christ receive thy saul.

When thou from hence away are past,
  —*Every night and all,*
To Whinny-muir thou com'st at last:
  And Christ receive thy saul.

If ever thou gavest hosen and shoon,
  —*Every night and all,*
Sit thee down and put them on:
  And Christ receive thy saul.

If hosen and shoon thou ne'er gav'st nane,
  —*Every night and all,*
The whins shall prick thee to the bare bane;
  And Christ receive thy saul.

From Whinny-muir when thou may'st pass,
  —*Every night and all,*
To Brig o' Dread thou com'st at last;
  And Christ receive thy saul.

From Brig o' Dread when thou may'st pass,
  —*Every night and all,*
To Purgatory fire thou com'st at last;
  And Christ receive thy saul.

If ever thou gavest meat or drink,
  —*Every night and all,*
The fire shall never make thee shrink;
  And Christ receive thy saul.

If meat or drink thou ne'er gav'st nane,
—*Every night and all,*
The fire will burn thee to the bare bane;
And Christ receive thy saul.

This ae night, this ae night,
—*Every night and all,*
Fire and fleet and candle-light,
And Christ receive thy saul.

Sir Patrick Spens

The king sits in Dunfermline town
Drinking the blude-red wine;
'O whar will I get a skeely skipper
To sail this new ship o' mine?'

O up and spak an eldern knight,
Sat at the king's right knee;
'Sir Patrick Spens is the best sailor
That ever sail'd the sea.'

Our king has written a braid letter,
And seal'd it with his hand,
And sent it to Sir Patrick Spens,
Was walking on the strand.

'To Noroway, to Noroway,
To Noroway o'er the faem;
The king's daughter o' Noroway,
'Tis thou must bring her hame.'

The first word that Sir Patrick read
So loud, loud laugh'd he;
The neist word that Sir Patrick read
The tear blinded his e'e.

'O wha is this has done this deed
And tauld the king o' me,
To send us out, at this time o' year,
To sail upon the sea?

'Be it wind, be it weet, be it hail, be it sleet,
    Our ship must sail the faem;
The king's daughter o' Noroway,
    'Tis we must fetch her hame.'

They hoysed their sails on Monenday morn
    Wi' a' the speed they may;
They hae landed in Noroway
    Upon a Wodensday.

'Mak ready, mak ready, my merry men a'!
    Our gude ship sails the morn.'
'Now ever alack, my master dear,
    I fear a deadly storm.

'I saw the new moon late yestreen
    Wi' the auld moon in her arm;
And if we gang to sea, master,
    I fear we'll come to harm.'

They hadna sail'd a league, a league,
    A league but barely three,
When the lift grew dark, and the wind blew loud,
    And gurly grew the sea.

The ankers brak, and the topmast lap,
    It was sic a deadly storm:
And the waves cam owre the broken ship
    Till a' her sides were torn.

'Go fetch a web o' the silken claith,
    Another o' the twine,
And wap them into our ship's side,
    And let nae the sea come in.'

They fetch'd a web o' the silken claith,
    Another o' the twine,
And they wapp'd them round that gude ship's side,
    But still the sea came in.

O laith, laith were our gude Scots lords
    To wet their cork-heel'd shoon;
But lang or a' the play was play'd
    They wat their hats aboon.

And mony was the feather bed
   That flatter'd on the faem;
And mony was the gude lord's son
   That never mair cam hame.

O lang, lang may the ladies sit,
   Wi' their fans into their hand,
Before they see Sir Patrick Spens
   Come sailing to the strand!

And lang, lang may the maidens sit
   Wi' their gowd kames in their hair,
A-waiting for their ain dear loves!
   For them they'll see nae mair.

Half-owre, half-owre to Aberdour,
   'Tis fifty fathoms deep;
And there lies gude Sir Patrick Spens,
   Wi' the Scots lords at his feet!

The Battle of Otterbourne

It fell about the Lammas tide,
   When the muir-men win their hay,
The doughty earl of Douglas rode
   Into England, to catch a prey.

He chose the Gordons and the Græmes,
   With them the Lindesays, light and gay;
But the Jardines wald not with him ride,
   And they rue it to this day.

And he has burn'd the dales of Tyne,
   And part of Bambrough shire;
And three good towers on Roxburgh fells,
   He left them all on fire.

And he march'd up to Newcastle,
   And rode it round about;
'O wha's the lord of this castle,
   Or wha's the lady o't?'

But up spake proud Lord Percy, then,
   And O but he spake hie!
'I am the lord of this castle,
   My wife's the lady gay.'

'If thou'rt the lord of this castle,
   Sae weel it pleases me!
For, ere I cross the border fells,
   The tane of us shall die.'

He took a long spear in his hand,
   Shod with the metal free,
And for to meet the Douglas there
   He rode right furiouslie.

But O how pale his lady look'd
   Frae aff the castle wa',
When down, before the Scottish spear,
   She saw proud Percy fa'.

'Had we twa been upon the green,
   And never an eye to see,
I wad hae had you, flesh and fell;
   But your sword sall gae wi' me.'

'But gae ye up to Otterbourne,
   And wait there dayis three;
And, if I come not ere three days' end,
   A fause knight ca' ye me.'

'The Otterbourne's a bonnie burn;
   'Tis pleasant there to be;
But there is nought at Otterbourne
   To feed my men and me.

'The deer rins wild on hill and dale,
   The birds fly wild from tree to tree;
But there is neither bread nor kale
   To fend my men and me.

'Yet I will stay at Otterbourne,
   Where you shall welcome be;
And, if ye come not at three days' end,
   A fause lord I'll ca' thee.'

'Thither will I come,' proud Percy said,
  'By the might of Our Ladye!'—
'There will I bide thee,' said the Douglas,
  'My trowth I plight to thee.'

They lighted high on Otterbourne,
  Upon the bent sae brown;
They lighted high on Otterbourne,
  And threw their pallions down.

And he that had a bonnie boy,
  Sent out his horse to grass;
And he that had not a bonnie boy,
  His ain servant he was.

But up then spake a little page,
  Before the peep of dawn—
'O waken ye, waken ye, my good lord,
  For Percy's hard at hand.'

'Ye lie, ye lie, ye liar loud!
  Sae loud I hear ye lie:
For Percy had not men yestreen,
  To dight my men and me.

'But I hae dream'd a dreary dream,
  Beyond the Isle of Sky;
I saw a dead man win a fight,
  And I think that man was I.'

He belted on his good braid sword,
  And to the field he ran;
But he forgot the helmet good,
  That should have kept his brain.

When Percy wi' the Douglas met,
  I wat he was fu' fain!
They swakked their swords, till sair they swat,
  And the blood ran down like rain.

But Percy with his good broad sword,
  That could so sharply wound,
Has wounded Douglas on the brow,
  Till he fell to the ground.

Then he call'd on his little foot-page,
    And said—'Run speedilie,
And fetch my ain dear sister's son,
    Sir Hugh Montgomery.'

'My nephew good,' the Douglas said,
    'What recks the death of ane!
Last night I dream'd a dreary dream,
    And I ken the day's thy ain.

'My wound is deep; I fain would sleep;
    Take thou the vanguard of the three,
And hide me by the braken bush,
    That grows on yonder lily lee.

'O bury me by the braken bush,
    Beneath the blooming briar,
Let never living mortal ken
    That ere a kindly Scot lies here.'

He lifted up that noble lord,
    Wi' the saut tear in his e'e;
He hid him in the braken bush,
    That his merrie men might not see.

The moon was clear, the day drew near,
    The spears in flinders flew,
But many a gallant Englishman
    Ere day the Scotsmen slew.

The Gordons good in English blood
    They steep'd their hose and shoon;
The Lindsays flew like fire about,
    Till all the fray was done.

The Percy and Montgomery met,
    That either of other were fain;
They swappèd swords, and they twa swat,
    And aye the blude ran down between.

'Yield thee, O yield thee, Percy!' he said,
    'Or else I vow I'll lay thee low!'
'Whom to shall I yield,' said Earl Percy,
    'Now that I see it must be so?'

'Thou shalt not yield to lord nor loun,
    Nor yet shalt thou yield to me;
But yield thee to the braken bush,
    That grows upon yon lily lee!'

'I will not yield to a braken bush,
    Nor yet will I yield to a briar;
But I would yield to Earl Douglas,
    Or Sir Hugh the Montgomery, if he were here.'

As soon as he knew it was Montgomery,
    He struck his sword's point in the gronde;
And the Montgomery was a courteous knight,
    And quickly took him by the honde.

This deed was done at Otterbourne,
    About the breaking of the day;
Earl Douglas was buried at the braken bush,
    And the Percy led captive away.

The Bonny Earl of Murray

Ye Highlands and ye Lawlands,
    O where hae ye been?
They hae slain the Earl of Murray,
    And hae laid him on the green.

Now wae be to thee, Huntly!
    And wherefore did ye sae!
I bade you bring him wi' you,
    But forbade you him to slay.

He was a braw gallant,
    And he rid at the ring;
And the bonny Earl of Murray,
    O he might hae been a king!

He was a braw gallant,
    And he play'd at the ba';
And the bonny Earl of Murray
    Was the flower amang them a'!

He was a braw gallant,
    And he play'd at the gluve;
And the bonny Earl of Murray,
    O he was the Queen's luve!

O lang will his Lady
    Look owre the Castle Doune,
Ere she see the Earl of Murray
    Come sounding through the toun!

Edward, Edward

Why does your brand sae drap wi' bluid,
                Edward, Edward,
Why does your brand sae drap wi' bluid,
    And why sae sad gang ye O!'
'O I hae killed my hawk sae guid,
                Mither, mither,
O I hae killed my hawk sae guid,
    And I had nae mair but he O.'

'Your hawkis bluid was never sae red,
                Edward, Edward,
Your hawkis bluid was never sae red,
    My dear son I tell thee O.'
'O I hae killed my red-roan steed,
                Mither, mither,
O I hae killed my red-roan steed,
    That erst was sae fair and free O.'

'Your steed was auld, and ye hae gat mair,
                Edward, Edward,
Your steed was auld, and ye hae gat mair,
    Some other dule ye drie O.'
'O I hae killed my father dear,
                Mither, mither,
O I hae killed my father dear,
    Alas, and wae is me O!'

'And whatten penance wul ye drie for that,
                Edward, Edward?
And whatten penance wul ye drie for that?
    My dear son, now tell me O.'

'I'll set my feet in yonder boat,
                    Mither, mither,
I'll set my feet in yonder boat,
        And I'll fare over the sea O.'

'And what wul ye do wi' your towers and your ha',
                    Edward, Edward?
And what wul ye do wi' your towers and your ha',
        That were sae fair to see O?'
'I'll let them stand till they doun fa',
                    Mither, mither,
I'll let them stand till they doun fa',
        For here never mair maun I be O.'

'And what wul ye leave to your bairns and your wife,
                    Edward, Edward?
And what wul ye leave to your bairns and your wife,
        When ye gang over the sea O?'
'The warldis room, let them beg through life,
                    Mither, mither,
The warldis room, let them beg through life,
        For them never mair wul I see O.'

'And what wul ye leave to your ain mither dear,
                    Edward, Edward?
And what wul ye leave to your ain mither dear?
        My dear son, now tell me O.'
'The curse of hell frae me sall ye bear,
                    Mither, mither,
The curse of hell frae me sall ye bear,
        Sic counsels ye gave to me O.'

Lord Randal

'O where hae ye been, Lord Randal, my son?
O where hae ye been, my handsome young man?'
'I hae been to the wild wood; mother, make my bed soon,
For I'm weary wi' hunting, and fain wald lie down.'

'Where gat ye your dinner, Lord Randal, my son?
Where gat ye your dinner, my handsome young man?'
'I dined wi' my true-love; mother, make my bed soon,
For I'm weary wi' hunting, and fain wald lie down.'

'What gat ye to your dinner, Lord Randal, my son?
What gat ye to your dinner, my handsome young man?'
'I gat eels boil'd in broo'; mother, make my bed soon,
For I'm weary wi' hunting, and fain wald lie down.'

'What became of your bloodhounds, Lord Randal, my son?
What became of your bloodhounds, my handsome young
        man?'
'O they swell'd and they died; mother, make my bed soon,
For I'm weary wi' hunting, and fain wald lie down.'

'O I fear ye are poison'd, Lord Randal, my son!
O I fear ye are poison'd, my handsome young man!'
'O yes! I am poison'd; mother, make my bed soon,
For I'm sick at the heart, and I fain wald lie down.'

The Twa Corbies

As I was walking all alane,
I heard twa corbies making a mane:
The tane unto the tither did say,
'Whar sall we gang and dine the day?'

'—In behint yon auld fail dyke
I wot there lies a new-slain knight;
And naebody kens that he lies there
But his hawk, his hound, and his lady fair.

'His hound is to the hunting gane,
His hawk to fetch the wild-fowl hame,
His lady's ta'en anither mate,
So we may mak' our dinner sweet.

'Ye'll sit on his white hause-bane,
And I'll pike out his bonny blue e'en:
Wi' ae lock o' his gowden hair
We'll theek our nest when it grows bare.

'Mony a one for him maks mane,
But nane sall ken whar he is gane:
O'er his white banes, when they are bare,
The wind sall blaw for evermair.'

Late at e'en, drinkin' the wine,
   And ere they paid the lawin'
They set a combat them between,
   To fight it in the dawin'.

'O stay at hame, my noble lord!
   O stay at hame, my marrow!
My cruel brother will you betray,
   On the dowie houms o' Yarrow.'

'O fare ye weel, my lady gay!
   O fare ye weel, my Sarah!
For I maun gae, tho' I ne'er return
   Frae the dowie banks o' Yarrow.'

She kiss'd his cheek, she kamed his hair,
   As she had done before, O;
She belted on his noble brand,
   An' he's awa to Yarrow.

O he's gane up yon high, high hill—
   I wat he gaed wi' sorrow—
An' in a den spied nine arm'd men,
   I' the dowie houms o' Yarrow.

'O are ye come to drink the wine,
   As ye hae doon before, O?
Or are ye come to wield the brand,
   On the bonnie banks o' Yarrow?'

'I am no come to drink the wine,
   As I hae done before, O,
But I am come to wield the brand,
   On the dowie houms o' Yarrow.'

Four he hurt, an' five he slew,
   On the dowie houms o' Yarrow,
Till that stubborn knight came him behind,
   An' ran his body thorrow.

'Gae hame, gae hame, good-brother John,
   An' tell your sister Sarah
To come an' lift her noble lord,
   Who's sleepin' sound on Yarrow.'

'Yestreen I dream'd a dolefu' dream;
   I ken'd there wad be sorrow;
I dream'd I pu'd the heather green,
   On the dowie banks o' Yarrow.'

She gaed up yon high, high hill—
   I wat she gaed wi' sorrow—
An' in a den spy'd nine dead men,
   On the dowie houms o' Yarrow.

She kiss'd his cheek, she kamed his hair,
   As oft she did before, O;
She drank the red blood frae him ran,
   On the dowie houms o' Yarrow.

'O haud your tongue, my douchter dear,
   For what needs a' this sorrow?
I'll wed you on a better lord
   Than him you lost on Yarrow.'

'O haud your tongue, my father dear,
   An' dinna grieve your Sarah;
A better lord was never born
   Than him I lost on Yarrow.

'Tak hame your ousen, tak hame your kye,
   For they hae bred our sorrow;
I wiss that they had a' gane mad
   When they cam first to Yarrow.'

The Wife of Usher's Well

There lived a wife at Usher's well,
   And a wealthy wife was she;
She had three stout and stalwart sons,
   And sent them o'er the sea.

They hadna been a week from her,
    A week but barely ane,
When word came to the carline wife
    That her three sons were gane.

They hadna been a week from her,
    A week but barely three,
When word came to the carline wife
    That her sons she'd never see.

'I wish the wind may never cease,
    Nor fashes in the flood,
Till my three sons come hame to me
    In earthly flesh and blood!'

It fell about the Martinmas,
    When nights are lang and mirk,
The carline wife's three sons came hame,
    And their hats were o' the birk.

It neither grew in syke nor ditch,
    Nor yet in ony sheugh;
But at the gates o' Paradise
    That birk grew fair eneugh.

'Blow up the fire, my maidens!
    Bring water from the well!
For a' my house shall feast this night,
    Since my three sons are well.'

And she has made to them a bed,
    She's made it large and wide;
And she's ta'en her mantle her about,
    Sat down at the bedside.

Up then crew the red, red cock,
    And up then crew the gray;
The eldest to the youngest said,
    ' 'Tis time we were away.'

The cock he hadna craw'd but once,
    And clapp'd his wings at a',
When the youngest to the eldest said,
    'Brother, we must awa.

'The cock doth craw, the day doth daw,
   The channerin' worm doth chide;
Gin we be miss'd out o' our place,
   A sair pain we maun bide.

'Fare ye weel, my mother dear!
   Fareweel to barn and byre!
And fare ye weel, the bonny lass
   That kindles my mother's fire!'

Get up and bar the Door

It fell about the Martinmas time,
   And a gay time it was then,
When our goodwife got puddings to make,
   And she's boil'd them in the pan.

The wind sae cauld blew south and north,
   And blew into the floor;
Quoth our goodman to our goodwife,
   'Gae out and bar the door.'—

'My hand is in my hussyfskap,
   Goodman, as ye may see;
An' it shou'dna be barr'd this hundred year,
   It's no be barr'd for me.'

They made a paction 'tween them twa,
   They made it firm and sure,
That the first word whae'er shou'd speak,
   Shou'd rise and bar the door.

Then by there came two gentlemen,
   At twelve o'clock at night,
And they could neither see house nor hall,
   Nor coal nor candle-light.

'Now whether is this a rich man's house,
   Or whether is it a poor?'
But ne'er a word wad ane o' them speak,
   For barring of the door.

And first they ate the white puddings,
    And then they ate the black.
Tho' muckle thought the goodwife to hersel'
    Yet ne'er a word she spake.

Then said the one unto the other,
    'Here, man, tak ye my knife;
Do ye tak aff the auld man's beard,
    And I'll kiss the goodwife.'—

'But there's nae water in the house,
    And what shall we do than?'—
'What ails ye at the pudding-broo,
    That boils into the pan?'

O up then started our goodman,
    An angry man was he:
'Will ye kiss my wife before my een,
    And sca'd me wi' pudding-bree?'

Then up and started our goodwife,
    Gied three skips on the floor:
'Goodman, you've spoken the foremost word!
    Get up and bar the door.'

JOHN DRYDEN
1631-1700

Song for St. Cecilia's Day, 1687

From Harmony, from heavenly Harmony
   This universal frame began:
  When Nature underneath a heap
   Of jarring atoms lay
  And could not heave her head,
The tuneful voice was heard from high,
   Arise, ye more than dead!
Then cold and hot and moist and dry
In order to their stations leap,
   And Music's power obey.
From harmony, from heavenly harmony
   This universal frame began:
   From harmony to harmony
Through all the compass of the notes it ran,
The diapason closing full in Man.

What passion cannot Music raise and quell?
   When Jubal struck the chorded shell
  His listening brethren stood around,
  And, wondering, on their faces fell
  To worship that celestial sound.
Less than a god they thought there could not dwell
   Within the hollow of that shell
   That spoke so sweetly and so well.
What passion cannot Music raise and quell?

   The trumpet's loud clangour
    Excites us to arms,
   With shrill notes of anger
    And mortal alarms.
   The double double double beat
    Of the thundering drum
    Cries 'Hark! the foes come;
Charge, charge, 'tis too late to retreat!'

The soft complaining flute
  In dying notes discovers
  The woes of hopeless lovers
Whose dirge is whisper'd by the warbling lute.

  Sharp violins proclaim
Their jealous pangs and desperation,
Fury, frantic indignation
Depths of pains, and height of passion
  For the fair disdainful dame.

But oh! what art can teach,
What human voice can reach
  The sacred organ's praise?
Notes inspiring holy love,
Notes that wing their heavenly ways
  To mend the choirs above.

Orpheus could lead the savage race,
And trees uprooted left their place
  Sequacious of the lyre:
But bright Cecilia raised the wonder higher:
When to her organ vocal breath was given
An angel heard, and straight appear'd
  Mistaking Earth for Heaven.

Grand Chorus

As from the power of sacred lays
  The spheres began to move,
And sung the great Creator's praise
  To all the blest above;
So when the last and dreadful hour
This crumbling pageant shall devour,
The trumpet shall be heard on high,
The dead shall live, the living die,
And Music shall untune the sky.

Alexander's Feast
or, The Power of Music

'Twas at the royal feast for Persia won
    By Philip's warlike son—
    Aloft in awful state
    The godlike hero sate
    On his imperial throne;
His valiant peers were placed around,
Their brows with roses and with myrtles bound
    (So should desert in arms be crown'd);
    The lovely Thais by his side
    Sate like a blooming eastern bride
    In flower of youth and beauty's pride:—
    Happy, happy, happy pair!
      None but the brave
      None but the brave
    None but the brave deserves the fair!

    Timotheus placed on high
    Amid the tuneful choir
With flying fingers touch'd the lyre:
The trembling notes ascend the sky
    And heavenly joys inspire.
    The song began from Jove
Who left his blissful seats above—
Such is the power of mighty love!
A dragon's fiery form belied the god;
Sublime on radiant spires he rode
When he to fair Olympia prest,
And while he sought her snowy breast,
Then round her slender waist he curl'd,
And stamp'd an image of himself, a sovereign of the world.
  —The listening crowd admire the lofty sound;
A present deity! they shout around:
A present deity! the vaulted roofs rebound:
      With ravish'd ears
      The monarch hears,
      Assumes the god,
      Affects to nod
    And seems to shake the spheres.

The praise of Bacchus then the sweet musician sung,
  Of Bacchus ever fair and ever young:
    The jolly god in triumph comes!
    Sound the trumpets, beat the drums!
      Flush'd with a purple grace
      He shows his honest face:
Now give the hautboys breath; he comes, he comes!
      Bacchus, ever fair and young,
      Drinking joys did first ordain;
      Bacchus' blessings are a treasure,
      Drinking is the soldier's pleasure:
        Rich the treasure,
        Sweet the pleasure,
      Sweet is pleasure after pain.

  Soothed with the sound, the king grew vain;
  Fought all his battles o'er again,
And thrice he routed all his foes, and thrice he slew the slain
    The master saw the madness rise,
    His glowing cheeks, his ardent eyes;
    And while he Heaven and Earth defied
    Changed his hand and check'd his pride.
      He chose a mournful Muse
      Soft pity to infuse:
    He sung Darius great and good,
      By too severe a fate
    Fallen, fallen, fallen, fallen,
      Fallen from his high estate.
    And weltering in his blood;
  Deserted at his utmost need,
  By those his former bounty fed;
  On the bare earth exposed he lies
  With not a friend to close his eyes.
    —With downcast looks the joyless victor sate,
  Revolving in his alter'd soul
    The various turns of Chance below;
  And now and then a sigh he stole,
    And tears began to flow.

    The mighty master smiled to see
    That love was in the next degree;
    'Twas but a kindred-sound to move,
    For pity melts the mind to love.

Softly sweet, in Lydian measures
Soon he soothed his soul to pleasures.
War, he sung, is toil and trouble,
Honour but an empty bubble;
Never ending, still beginning,
    Fighting still, and still destroying;
If the world be worth thy winning,
    Think, O think, it worth enjoying:
Lovely Thais sits beside thee,
Take the good the gods provide thee!
—The many rend the skies with loud applause;
So Love was crown'd, but Music won the cause.
The prince, unable to conceal his pain,
        Gazed on the fair
        Who caused his care,
And sigh'd and look'd, sigh'd and look'd,
Sigh'd and look'd, and sigh'd again:
At length with love and wine at once opprest
The vanquish'd victor sunk upon her breast.

    Now strike the golden lyre again:
A louder yet, and yet a louder strain!
Break his bands of sleep asunder
And rouse him like a rattling peal of thunder.
Hark, hark! the horrid sound
    Has raised up his head:
    As awaked from the dead
And amazed he stares around.
Revenge, revenge, Timotheus cries,
See the Furies arise!
    See the snakes that they rear
    How they hiss in their hair,
And the sparkles that flash from their eyes!
        Behold a ghastly band,
        Each a torch in his hand!
Those are Grecian ghosts, that in battle were slain
    And unburied remain
    Inglorious on the plain:
    Give the vegeance due
    To the valiant crew!
Behold how they toss their torches on high,
How they point to the Persian abodes

And glittering temples of their hostile gods.
—The princes applaud with a furious joy:
And the King seized a flambeau with zeal to destroy;
     Thais led the way
     To light him to his prey,
  And like another Helen, fired another Troy!

     —Thus, long ago,
Ere heaving bellows learn'd to blow,
  While organs yet were mute,
  Timotheus, to his breathing flute
    And sounding lyre,
Could swell the soul to rage, or kindle soft desire.
  At last divine Cecilia came,
  Inventress of the vocal frame;
The sweet enthusiast from her sacred store
  Enlarged the former narrow bounds,
  And added length to solemn sounds,
With Nature's mother-wit, and arts unknown before.
  —Let old Timotheus yield the prize
  Or both divide the crown;
He raised a mortal to the skies;
  She drew an angel down!

ALEXANDER POPE

1688-1744

The Rape of the Lock

CANTO FIRST

What dire offence from amorous causes springs,
What mighty contests rise from trivial things,
I sing—This verse to CARYLL, muse! is due:
This, ev'n Belinda may vouchsafe to view:
Slight is the subject, but not so the praise,
If she inspire, and he approve my lays.

Say what strange motive, goddess! could compel
A well-bred lord t' assault a gentle belle?
Oh, say what stranger cause, yet unexplored,
Could make a gentle belle reject a lord?
In tasks so bold can little men engage,
And in soft bosoms dwell such mighty rage?

Sol through white curtains shot a tim'rous ray,
And oped those eyes that must eclipse the day:
Now lapdogs give themselves the rousing shake,
And sleepless lovers, just at twelve, awake:
Thrice rung the bell, the slipper knock'd the ground,
And the press'd watch return'd a silver sound.
Belinda still her downy pillow prest,
Her guardian sylph prolong'd the balmy rest:
'T was he had summon'd to her silent bed
The morning-dream that hover'd o'er her head;
A youth more glitt'ring than a birth-night beau,
(That ev'n in slumber caused her cheek to glow)
Seem'd to her ear his winning lips to lay,
And thus in whispers said, or seem'd to say:—

Fairest of mortals, thou distinguish'd care
Of thousand bright inhabitants of air!
If e'er one vision touch'd thy infant thought,
Of all the nurse and all the priest have taught;

Of airy elves by moonlight shadows seen,
The silver token, and the circled green,
Or virgins visited by angel-powers
With golden crowns and wreaths of heavenly flowers;
Hear and believe! thy own importance know,
Nor bound thy narrow views to things below.
Some secret truths, from learned pride conceal'd,
To maids alone and children are reveal'd:
What though no credit doubting wits may give?
The fair and innocent shall still believe.
Know, then, unnumber'd spirits round thee fly,
The light militia of the lower sky:
These, though unseen, are ever on the wing,
Hang o'er the box, and hover round the Ring.
Think what an equipage thou hast in air,
And view with scorn two pages and a chair.
As now your own, our beings were of old,
And once enclosed in woman's beauteous mould;
Thence, by a soft transition, we repair
From earthly vehicles to those of air.
Think not, when woman's transient breath is fled,
That all her vanities at once are dead;
Succeeding vanities she still regards,
And though she plays no more, o'erlooks the cards;
Her joy in gilded chariots, when alive,
And love of ombre, after death survive.
For when the fair in all their pride expire,
To their first elements their souls retire:
The sprites of fiery termagants in flame
Mount up, and take a salamander's name.
Soft yielding minds to water glide away,
And sip, with nymphs, their elemental tea.
The graver prude sinks downward to a gnome
In search of mischief still on earth to roam.
The light coquettes in sylphs aloft repair,
And sport and flutter in the fields of air.
Know farther yet: whoever fair and chaste
Rejects mankind, is by some sylph embrac'd:
For spirits, freed from mortal laws, with ease
Assume what sexes and what shapes they please.
What guards the purity of melting maids,
In courtly balls, and midnight masquerades,

Safe from the treach'rous friend, and daring spark,
The glance by day, the whisper in the dark:
When kind occasion prompts their warm desires,
When music softens, and when dancing fires?
'T is but their sylph, the wise celestials know,
Tho' honour is the word with men below.
Some nymphs there are, too conscious of their face,
For life predestin'd to the gnomes' embrace.
Who swell their prospects and exalt their pride,
When offers are disdain'd, and love denied.
Then gay ideas crowd the vacant brain;
While peers and dukes, and all their sweeping train,
And garters, stars, and coronets appear,
And in soft sounds, Your Grace salutes their ear,
'T is these that early taint the female soul,
Instruct the eyes of young coquettes to roll,
Teach infant-cheeks a hidden blush to know,
And little hearts to flutter at a beau.
Oft when the world imagine women stray,
The sylphs thro' mystic mazes guide their way,
Thro' all the giddy circle they pursue,
And old impertinence expel by new.
What tender maid but must a victim fall
To one man's treat, but for another's ball?
When Florio speaks, what virgin could withstand,
If gentle Damon did not squeeze her hand?
With varying vanities, from ev'ry part,
They shift the moving toyshop of their heart;
Where wigs with wigs, with sword-knots sword-knots
      strive,
Beaux banish beaux, and coaches coaches drive.
This erring mortals levity may call,
Oh, blind to truth! the sylphs contrive it all.
   A sylph am I, who thy protection claim,
A watchful sprite, and Ariel is my name.
Late, as I rang'd the crystal wilds of air,
In the clear mirror of thy ruling star
I saw, alas! some dread event impend,
Ere to the main this morning sun descend,
But Heaven reveals not what, or how, or where:
Warn'd by the sylph, oh, pious maid, beware!
This to disclose is all thy guardian can:

Beware of all, but most beware of man!

He said; when Shock, who thought she slept too long,
Leap'd up, and waked his mistress with his tongue.
'T was then, Belinda, if report say true,
Thy eyes first open'd on a billet-doux;
Wounds, charms, and ardours, were no sooner read,
But all the vision vanish'd from thy head.

And now, unveil'd, the toilet stands display'd,
Each silver vase in mystic order laid.
First, robed in white the nymph intent adores,
With head uncover'd, the cosmetic powers.
A heavenly image in the glass appears,
To that she bends, to that her eyes she rears;
Th' inferior priestess, at her altar's side,
Trembling begins the sacred rites of pride.
Unnumber'd treasures ope at once, and here
The various offerings of the world appear;
From each she nicely culls with careful toil,
And decks the goddess with the glittering spoil.
This casket India's glowing gems unlocks,
And all Arabia breathes from yonder box.
The tortoise here and elephant unite,
Transform'd to combs, the speckled and the white.
Here files of pins extend their shining rows,
Puffs, powders, patches, bibles, billets-doux.
Now awful beauty puts on all its arms;
The fair each moment rises in her charms,
Repairs her smiles, awakens every grace,
And calls forth all the wonders of her face;
Sees by degrees a purer blush arise,
And keener lightnings quicken in her eyes.
The busy sylphs surround their darling care,
These set the head, and those divide the hair,
Some fold the sleeve, whilst others plait the gown;
And Betty's praised for labours not her own.

Canto Second

Not with more glories, in the ethereal plain.
The sun first rises o'er the purpled main,
Than, issuing forth, the rival of his beams
Launch'd on the bosom of the silver Thames.

Fair nymphs and well-dress'd youths around her shone,
But every eye was fix'd on her alone.
On her white breast a sparkling cross she wore,
Which Jews might kiss, and infidels adore.
Her lively looks a sprightly mind disclose,
Quick as her eyes, and as unfix'd as those:
Favours to none, to all she smiles extends;
Oft she rejects, but never once offends.
Bright as the sun, her eyes the gazers strike,
And, like the sun, they shine on all alike.
Yet graceful ease, and sweetness void of pride,
Might hide her faults, if belles had faults to hide.
If to her share some female errors fall,
Look on her face and you 'll forget 'em all.

This nymph, to the destruction of mankind,
Nourish'd two locks, which graceful hung behind
In equal curls, and well conspired to deck
With shining ringlets the smooth ivory neck.
Love in these labyrinths his slaves detains,
And mighty hearts are held in slender chains.
With hairy springes we the birds betray,
Slight lines of hair surprise the finny prey,
Fair tresses man's imperial race ensnare,
And beauty draws us with a single hair.

Th' advent'rous Baron the bright locks admir'd;
He saw, he wish'd, and to the prize aspir'd.
Resolv'd to win, he meditates the way,
By force to ravish, or by fraud betray;
For when success a lover's toil attends,
Few ask if fraud or force attain'd his ends.

For this, ere Phœbus rose, he had implor'd
Propitious Heaven, and every power ador'd,
But chiefly Love—to Love an altar built,
Of twelve vast French romances, neatly gilt.
There lay three garters, half a pair of gloves,
And all the trophies of his former loves;
With tender billets-doux he lights the pyre,
And breathes three am'rous sighs to raise the fire.
Then prostrate falls, and begs with ardent eyes
Soon to obtain, and long possess the prize:
The powers gave ear and granted half his prayer,
The rest the winds dispersed in empty air.

But now secure the painted vessel glides,
The sunbeams trembling on the floating tides:
While melting music steals upon the sky,
And soften'd sounds along the waters die;
Smooth flow the waves, the zephyrs gently play,
Belinda smiled, and all the world was gay.
All but the sylph; with careful thoughts opprest,
Th' impending woe sat heavy on his breast.
He summons straight his denizens of air;
The lucid squadrons round the sails repair:
Soft o'er the shrouds aërial whispers breathe,
That seem'd but zephyrs to the train beneath.
Some to the sun their insect-wings unfold,
Waft on the breeze, or sink in clouds of gold;
Transparent forms, too fine for mortal sight,
Their fluid bodies half dissolved in light,
Loose to the wind their airy garments flew,
Thin glitt'ring textures of the filmy dew,
Dipt in the richest tincture of the skies,
Where light disports in ever-mingling dyes;
While ev'ry beam new transient colours flings,
Colours that change whene'er they wave their wings
Amid the circle, on the gilded mast,
Superior by the head, was Ariel plac'd;
His purple pinions opening to the sun,
He raised his azure wand, and thus begun:—

Ye sylphs and sylphids, to your chief give ear,
Fays, fairies, genii, elves, and dæmons, hear!
Ye know the spheres, and various tasks assign'd
By laws eternal to th' aërial kind.
Some in the fields of purest ether play,
And bask and whiten in the blaze of day;
Some guide the course of wandering orbs on high,
Or roll the planets through the boundless sky;
Some, less refin'd, beneath the moon's pale light,
Pursue the stars that shoot athwart the night,
Or suck the mists in grosser air below,
Or dip their pinions in the painted bow,
Or brew fierce tempests on the wintry main,
Or o'er the glebe distil the kindly rain;
Others on earth o'er human race preside,
Watch all their ways, and all their actions guide:

Of these the chief the care of nations own,
And guard with arms divine the British throne.

Our humbler province is to tend the fair,
Not a less pleasing, tho' less glorious care;
To save the powder from too rude a gale,
Nor let th' imprison'd essences exhale;
To draw fresh colours from the vernal flow'rs;
To steal from rainbows ere they drop in show'rs
A brighter wash; to curl their waving hairs,
Assist their blushes, and inspire their airs;
Nay, oft, in dreams, invention we bestow,
To change a flounce, or add a furbelow.

This day, black omens threat the brightest fair
That e'er deserv'd a watchful spirit's care;
Some dire disaster, or by force or slight;
But what, or where, the fates have wrapt in night.
Whether the nymph shall break Diana's law,
Or some frail China jar receive a flaw;
Or stain her honour, or her new brocade;
Forget her pray'rs, or miss a masquerade;
Or lose her heart, or necklace, at a ball;
Or whether Heav'n has doom'd that Shock must fall.
Haste then, ye spirits! to your charge repair:
The fluttering fan be Zephyretta's care;
The drops to thee, Brillante, we consign;
And, Momentilla, let the watch be thine;
Do thou, Crispissa, tend her favourite Lock;
Ariel himself shall be the guard of Shock.

To fifty chosen sylphs, of special note,
We trust th' important charge, the petticoat:
Oft have we known that sevenfold fence to fail,
Though stiff with hoops and arm'd with ribs of whale;
Form a strong line about the silver bound,
And guard the wide circumference around.

Whatever spirit, careless of his charge,
His post neglects, or leaves the fair at large,
Shall feel sharp vengeance soon o'ertake his sins,
Be stopp'd in vials, or transfixed with pins;
Or plung'd in lakes of bitter washes lie,
Or wedg'd whole ages in a bodkin's eye:
Gums and pomatums shall his flight restrain,
While clogg'd he beats his silken wings in vain;

Or alum styptics, with contracting pow'r,
Shrink his thin essence like a rivelled flow'r
Or, as Ixion fix'd, the wretch shall feel
The giddy motion of the whirling mill,
In fumes of burning chocolate shall glow,
And tremble at the sea that froths below!
   He spoke; the spirits from the sails descend:
Some, orb in orb, around the nymph extend;
Some thread the mazy ringlets of her hair;
Some hang upon the pendants of her ear;
With beating hearts the dire event they wait,
Anxious, and trembling for the birth of fate.

CANTO THIRD

   Close by those meads, for ever crown'd with flow'rs,
Where Thames with pride surveys his rising tow'rs,
There stands a structure of majestic frame,
Which from the neighbouring Hampton takes its name.
Here Britain's statesmen oft the fall foredoom
Of foreign tyrants, and of nymphs at home;
Here thou, great ANNA! whom three realms obey,
Dost sometimes counsel take—and sometimes tea.
   Hither the heroes and the nymphs resort,
To taste a while the pleasures of a court;
In various talk th' instructive hours they pass'd,
Who gave the ball, or paid the visit last;
One speaks the glory of the British Queen,
And one describes a charming Indian screen;
A third interprets motions, looks, and eyes;
At every word a reputation dies.
Snuff, or the fan, supply each pause of chat,
With singing, laughing, ogling, and all that.
   Meanwhile, declining from the noon of day,
The sun obliquely shoots his burning ray:
The hungry judges soon the sentence sign,
And wretches hang that jurymen may dine;
The merchant from th' Exchange returns in peace,
And the long labours of the toilet cease.
Belinda now, whom thirst of fame invites,
Burns to encounter two advent'rous knights,
At ombre singly to decide their doom;

And swells her breast with conquests yet to come.
Straight the three bands prepare in arms to join,
Each band the number of the sacred Nine.
Soon as she spreads her hand, th' aërial guard
Descend, and sit on each important card:
First Ariel perch'd upon a Matadore,
Then each according to the rank they bore;
For sylphs, yet mindful of their ancient race,
Are, as when women, wondrous fond of place.

Behold, four kings, in majesty rever'd,
With hoary whiskers and a forky beard;
And four fair queens whose hands sustain a flow'r,
The expressive emblem of their softer pow'r;
Four knaves in garbs succinct, a trusty band,
Caps on their heads, and halberds in their hand;
And party-colour'd troops, a shining train,
Draw forth to combat on the velvet plain.

The skilful nymph reviews her force with care;
Let spades be trumps! she said, and trumps they were.

Now move to war her sable matadores,
In show like leaders of the swarthy Moors.
Spadillio first, unconquerable lord!
Led off two captive trumps, and swept the board.
As many more Manillio forced to yield,
And march'd a victor from the verdant field.
Him Basto follow'd, but his fate more hard
Gain'd but one trump and one plebeian card.
With his broad sabre next, a chief in years,
The hoary majesty of Spades appears,
Puts forth one manly leg, to sight reveal'd,
The rest, his many-colour'd robe conceal'd.
The rebel knave, who dares his prince engage,
Proves the just victim of his royal rage.
Ev'n mighty Pam, that kings and queens o'erthrew,
And mow'd down armies in the fights of Loo,
Sad chance of war! now destitute of aid,
Falls undistinguish'd by the victor Spade!

Thus far both armies to Belinda yield;
Now to the Baron Fate inclines the field.
His warlike amazon her host invades,
Th' imperial consort of the crown of Spades.
The Club's black tyrant first her victim died,

Spite of his haughty mien and barbarous pride:
What boots the regal circle on his head,
His giant limbs, in state unwieldy spread;
That long behind he trails his pompous robe,
And, of all monarchs, only grasps the globe?

The Baron now his Diamonds pours apace;
Th' embroider'd King who shews but half his face,
And his refulgent Queen, with powers combined
Of broken troops an easy conquest find.
Clubs, Diamonds, Hearts, in wild disorder seen,
With throngs promiscuous strew the level green.
Thus when dispersed a routed army runs,
Of Asia's troops, and Afric's sable sons,
With like confusion different nations fly,
Of various habit, and of various dye;
The pierc'd battalions disunited fall,
In heaps on heaps; one fate o'erwhelms them all.

The Knave of Diamonds tries his wily arts,
And wins (oh shameful chance!) the Queen of Hearts.
At this, the blood the virgin's cheek forsook,
A livid paleness spreads o'er all her look;
She sees, and trembles at the approaching ill,
Just in the jaws of ruin, and codille.
And now (as oft in some distemper'd state)
On one nice trick depends the general fate;
An Ace of Hearts steps forth; the King, unseen,
Lurk'd in her hand, and mourn'd his captive Queen:
He springs to vengeance with an eager pace,
And falls like thunder on the prostrate Ace.
The nymph exulting fills with shouts the sky;
The walls, the woods, and long canals reply.

Oh, thoughtless mortals! ever blind to fate,
Too soon dejected, and too soon elate.
Sudden these honours shall be snatch'd away,
And curs'd for ever this victorious day.

For lo! the board with cups and spoons is crown'd,
The berries crackle, and the mill turns round;
On shining altars of Japan they raise
The silver lamp; the fiery spirits blaze:
From silver spouts the grateful liquors glide,
While China's earth receives the smoking tide:
At once they gratify their scent and taste,

And frequent cups prolong the rich repast.
Straight hover round the fair her airy band;
Some, as she sipp'd, the fuming liquor fann'd,
Some o'er her lap their careful plumes display'd,
Trembling, and conscious of the rich brocade.
Coffee (which makes the politician wise,
And see through all things with his half-shut eyes)
Sent up in vapours to the Baron's brain
New stratagems, the radiant Lock to gain.
Ah cease, rash youth! desist ere 'tis too late,
Fear the just gods, and think of Scylla's fate!
Changed to a bird, and sent to flit in air,
She dearly pays for Nisus' injur'd hair!

But when to mischief mortals bend their will,
How soon they find fit instruments of ill!
Just then Clarissa drew, with tempting grace,
A two-edg'd weapon from her shining case:
So ladies in romance assist their knight,
Present the spear and arm him for the fight.
He takes the gift with reverence, and extends
The little engine on his fingers' ends;
This just behind Belinda's neck he spread,
As o'er the fragrant steams she bends her head.
Swift to the Lock a thousand sprites repair,
A thousand wings, by turns, blow back the hair,
And thrice they twitch'd the diamond in her ear;
Thrice she look'd back, and thrice the foe drew near.
Just in that instant anxious Ariel sought
The close recesses of the virgin's thought:
As on the nosegay in her breast reclin'd,
He watch'd th' ideas rising in her mind,
Sudden he view'd, in spite of all her art,
An earthly lover lurking at her heart.
Amaz'd, confus'd, he found his power expir'd,
Resign'd to fate, and with a sigh retir'd.

The peer now spreads the glittering forfex wide,
T' enclose the Lock; now joins it, to divide.
Even then, before the fatal engine clos'd,
A wretched sylph too fondly interpos'd;
Fate urged the shears, and cut the sylph in twain
(But airy substance soon unites again);
The meeting points the sacred hair dissever

From the fair head, for ever, and for ever!
    Then flash'd the living lightning from her eyes,
And screams of horror rend the affrighted skies;
Not louder shrieks to pitying Heaven are cast,
When husbands, or when lapdogs, breathe their last;
Or when rich China vessels, fallen from high,
In glittering dust and painted fragments lie!
    'Let wreaths of triumph now my temples twine,'
(The victor cried,) 'the glorious prize is mine!
While fish in streams, or birds delight in air,
Or in a coach-and-six the British fair,
So long as Atalantis shall be read,
Or the small pillow grace a lady's bed,
While visits shall be paid on solemn days,
When num'rous wax-lights in bright order blaze,
While nymphs take treats, or assignations give,
So long my honour, name, and praise, shall live!
What time would spare, from steel receives its date,
And monuments, like men, submit to fate!
Steel could the labour of the gods destroy,
And strike to dust th' imperial towers of Troy;
Steel could the works of mortal pride confound,
And hew triumphal arches to the ground.
What wonder, then fair nymph! thy hairs should feel
The conquering force of unresisted steel?'

CANTO FOURTH

    But anxious cares the pensive nymph opprest,
And secret passions labour'd in her breast.
Not youthful kings in battle seiz'd alive,
Not scornful virgins who their charms survive,
Not ardent lovers robb'd of all their bliss,
Not ancient ladies when refus'd a kiss,
Not tyrants fierce that unrepenting die,
Not Cynthia when her manteau's pinn'd awry,
E'er felt such rage, resentment, and despair,
As thou, sad virgin! for thy ravish'd hair.
    For, that sad moment, when the sylphs withdrew,
And Ariel weeping from Belinda flew,
Umbriel, a dusky, melancholy sprite,
As ever sullied the fair face of light,

Down to the central earth, his proper scene,
Repair'd to search the gloomy cave of Spleen.
   Swift on his sooty pinions flits the gnome,
And in a vapour reach'd the dismal dome.
No cheerful breeze this sullen region knows,
The dreaded east is all the wind that blows.
Here in a grotto shelter'd close from air,
And screen'd in shades from day's detested glare,
She sighs for ever on her pensive bed,
Pain at her side, and Megrim at her head.
   Two handmaids wait the throne: alike in place,
But differing far in figure and in face.
Here stood Ill-nature, like an ancient maid,
Her wrinkled form in black and white array'd,
With store of prayers, for mornings, nights, and noons,
Her hand is fill'd; her bosom with lampoons.
   There Affectation, with a sickly mien,
Shews in her cheek the roses of eighteen,
Practised to lisp, and hang the head aside,
Faints into airs, and languishes with pride,
On the rich quilt sinks with becoming woe,
Wrapt in a gown, for sickness, and for show.
The fair ones feel such maladies as these,
When each new nightdress gives a new disease.
   A constant vapour o'er the palace flies;
Strange phantoms rising as the mists arise;
Dreadful, as hermits' dreams in haunted shades,
Or bright, as visions of expiring maids.
Now glaring fiends, and snakes on rolling spires,
Pale spectres, gaping tombs, and purple fires:
Now lakes of liquid gold, Elysian scenes,
And crystal domes, and angels in machines.
   Unnumber'd throngs on every side are seen,
Of bodies changed to various forms by Spleen.
Here living tea-pots stand, one arm held out,
One bent; the handle this, and that the spout:
A pipkin there, like Homer's tripod, walks;
Here sighs a jar, and there a goose-pie talks;
Men prove with child, as powerful fancy works,
And maids, turn'd bottles, call aloud for corks.
   Safe pass'd the gnome through this fantastic band,
A branch of healing spleenwort in his hand.

Then thus address'd the pow'r: 'Hail, wayward queen
Who rule the sex to fifty from fifteen:
Parent of vapours and of female wit,
Who give the hysteric, or poetic fit,
On various tempers act by various ways,
Make some take physic, others scribble plays;
Who cause the proud their visits to delay,
And send the godly in a pet to pray.
A nymph there is that all thy power disdains,
And thousands more in equal mirth maintains.
But oh! if e'er thy gnome could spoil a grace,
Or raise a pimple on a beauteous face,
Like citron-waters matrons' cheeks inflame,
Or change complexions at a losing game;
Or caused suspicion when no soul was rude,
Or discompos'd the head-dress of a prude,
Or e'er to costive lapdog gave disease,
Which not the tears of brightest eyes could ease.
Hear me, and touch Belinda with chagrin,
That single act gives half the world the spleen.'
    The goddess, with a discontented air,
Seems to reject him, tho' she grants his prayer.
A wondrous bag with both her hands she binds,
Like that where once Ulysses held the winds;
There she collects the force of female lungs,
Sighs, sobs, and passions, and the war of tongues.
A vial next she fills with fainting fears,
Soft sorrows, melting griefs, and flowing tears.
The gnome rejoicing bears her gifts away,
Spreads his black wings, and slowly mounts to day.
    Sunk in Thalestris' arms the nymph he found,
Her eyes dejected, and her hair unbound.
Full o'er their heads the swelling bag he rent,
And all the Furies issued at the vent.
Belinda burns with more than mortal ire,
And fierce Thalestris fans the rising fire.
'O wretched maid!' she spread her hands, and cried,
(While Hampton's echoes, 'Wretched maid!' replied,)
'Was it for this you took such constant care
The bodkin, comb, and essence to prepare?
For this your locks in paper durance bound?
For this with torturing irons wreath'd around?

For this with fillets strain'd your tender head
And bravely bore the double loads of lead?
Gods! shall the ravisher display your hair,
While the fops envy, and the ladies stare!
Honour forbid! at whose unrivall'd shrine
Ease, pleasure, virtue, all our sex resign.
Methinks already I your tears survey,
Already hear the horrid things they say;
Already see you a degraded toast,
And all your honour in a whisper lost!
How shall I, then, your hapless fame defend?
'T will then be infamy to seem your friend!
And shall this prize, th' inestimable prize,
Exposed through crystal to the gazing eyes,
And heighten'd by the diamond's circling rays,
On that rapacious hand for ever blaze?
Sooner shall grass in Hyde Park Circus grow,
And wits take lodgings in the sound of Bow;
Sooner let earth, air, sea, to chaos fall,
Men, monkeys, lapdogs, parrots, perish all!'
    She said; then raging to Sir Plume repairs,
And bids her beau demand the precious hairs:
(Sir Plume, of amber snuff-box justly vain,
And the nice conduct of a clouded cane,)
With earnest eyes, and round, unthinking face,
He first the snuff-box open'd, then the case,
And thus broke out—'My lord, why, what the devil!
Z——ds! damn the lock! 'fore Gad, you must be civil!
Plague on 't! 'tis past a jest—nay, prithee, pox!
Give her the hair'—he spoke, and rapp'd his box.
    'It grieves me much' (replied the peer again)
'Who speaks so well should ever speak in vain.
But by this lock, this sacred lock, I swear,
(Which never more shall join its parted hair;
Which never more its honours shall renew,
Clipp'd from the lovely head where late it grew,)
That while my nostrils draw the vital air,
This hand, which won it, shall for ever wear.'
He spoke, and speaking, in proud triumph spread
The long-contended honours of her head.
    But Umbriel, hateful gnome! forbears not so;
He breaks the vial whence the sorrows flow.

Then see! the nymph in beauteous grief appears,
Her eyes half-languishing, half-drown'd in tears;
On her heav'd bosom hung her drooping head,
Which with a sigh she rais'd; and thus she said:—
  'For ever curs'd be this detested day,
Which snatch'd my best, my favourite curl away!
Happy! ah, ten times happy had I been,
If Hampton Court these eyes had never seen!
Yet am not I the first mistaken maid,
By love of courts to num'rous ills betray'd.
Oh, had I rather unadmir'd remain'd
In some lone isle, or distant northern land;
Where the gilt chariot never marks the way,
Where none learn ombre, none e'er taste bohea!
There kept my charms conceal'd from mortal eye,
Like roses, that in deserts bloom and die.
What moved my mind with youthful lords to roam?
Oh, had I stay'd, and said my prayers at home!
'T was this the morning omens seem'd to tell,
Thrice from my trembling hand the patch-box fell;
The tottering china shook without a wind,
Nay, Poll sat mute, and Shock was most unkind!
A sylph, too, warn'd me of the threats of Fate,
In mystic visions, now believ'd too late!
See the poor remnants of these slighted hairs!
My hands shall rend what even thy rapine spares:
These in two sable ringlets taught to break,
Once gave new beauties to the snowy neck;
The sister-lock now sits uncouth, alone,
And in its fellow's fate foresees its own;
Uncurl'd it hangs, the fatal shears demands,
And tempts, once more, thy sacrilegious hands.
Oh, hadst thou, cruel! been content to seize
Hairs less in sight, or any hairs but these!'

CANTO FIFTH

  She said: the pitying audience melt in tears;
But Fate and Jove had stopp'd the Baron's ears.
In vain Thalestris with reproach assails,
For who can move when fair Belinda fails?
Not half so fix'd the Trojan could remain,

148

While Anna begg'd and Dido rag'd in vain.
Then grave Clarissa graceful wav'd her fan;
Silence ensu'd, and thus the nymph began:—
  'Say, why are beauties prais'd and honour'd most,
The wise man's passion, and the vain man's toast?
Why deck'd with all that land and sea afford,
Why angels call'd, and angel-like ador'd?
Why round our coaches crowd the white-glov'd beaux,
Why bows the side-box from its inmost rows?
How vain are all these glories, all our pains,
Unless good sense preserve what beauty gains:
That men may say, when we the front-box grace,
"Behold the first in virtue as in face!"
Oh! if to dance all night, and dress all day,
Charm'd the small-pox, or chas'd old age away;
Who would not scorn what housewife's cares produce,
Or who would learn one earthly thing of use?
To patch, nay ogle, might become a saint,
Nor could it sure be such a sin to paint.
But since, alas! frail beauty must decay,
Curl'd or uncurl'd, since locks will turn to gray;
Since, painted or not painted, all shall fade,
And she who scorns a man must die a maid;
What then remains but well our pow'r to use,
And keep good-humour still whate'er we lose?
And trust me, dear! good-humour can prevail,
When airs, and flights, and screams, and scolding fail;
Beauties in vain their pretty eyes may roll;
Charms strike the sight, but merit wins the soul.'
  So spoke the dame, but no applause ensu'd;
Belinda frown'd, Thalestris call'd her prude.
'To arms, to arms!' the fierce virago cries,
And swift as lightning to the combat flies.
All side in parties, and begin the attack;
Fans clap, silks rustle, and tough whalebones crack;
Heroes' and heroines' shouts confusedly rise,
And bass and treble voices strike the skies.
No common weapons in their hands are found,
Like gods they fight, nor dread a mortal wound.
  So when bold Homer makes the gods engage,
And heavenly breasts with human passions rage;
'Gainst Pallas, Mars; Latona, Hermes arms;

And all Olympus rings with loud alarms:
Jove's thunder roars, heaven trembles all around,
Blue Neptune storms, the bellowing deeps resound:
Earth shakes her nodding towers, the ground gives way,
And the pale ghosts start at the flash of day!
    Triumphant Umbriel, on a sconce's height,
Clapp'd his glad wings, and sate to view the fight:
Propp'd on their bodkin spears, the sprites survey
The growing combat, or assist the fray.
    While through the press enrag'd Thalestris flies,
And scatters death around from both her eyes,
A beau and witling perished in the throng,
One died in metaphor and one in song.
'O cruel nymph! a living death I bear!'
Cried Dapperwit, and sunk beside his chair.
A mournful glance Sir Fopling upwards cast,
'Those eyes are made so killing!'—was his last.
Thus on Mæander's flow'ry margin lies
Th' expiring swan, and as he sings he dies.
    When bold Sir Plume had drawn Clarissa down,
Chloe stepp'd in and kill'd him with a frown;
She smil'd to see the doughty hero slain,
But at her smile the beau reviv'd again.
    Now Jove suspends his golden scales in air,
Weighs the men's wits against the lady's hair:
The doubtful beam long nods from side to side;
At length the wits mount up, the hairs subside.
    See! fierce Belinda on the Baron flies,
With more than usual lightning in her eyes:
Nor fear'd the chief th' unequal fight to try,
Who sought no more than on his foe to die.
But this bold lord, with manly strength endu'd,
She with one finger and a thumb subdu'd:
Just where the breath of life his nostrils drew,
A charge of snuff the wily virgin threw;
The gnomes direct, to every atom just,
The pungent grains of titillating dust.
Sudden with starting tears each eye o'erflows,
And the high dome re-echoes to his nose.
    Now meet thy fate! incens'd Belinda cried,
And drew a deadly bodkin from her side.
(The same, his ancient personage to deck,

Her great-great-grandsire wore about his neck,
In three seal-rings; which after, melted down,
Form'd a vast buckle for his widow's gown:
Her infant grandame's whistle next it grew,
The bells she jingled, and the whistle blew;
Then in a bodkin grac'd her mother's hairs,
Which long she wore, and now Belinda wears.)
   'Boast not my fall, (he cried,) insulting foe!
Thou by some other shalt be laid as low.
Nor think, to die dejects my lofty mind;
All that I dread is leaving you behind!
Rather than so, ah! let me still survive,
And burn in Cupid's flames—but burn alive.'
   'Restore the Lock!' she cries; and all around,
'Restore the Lock!' the vaulted roofs rebound.
Not fierce Othello, in so loud a strain,
Roar'd for the handkerchief that caus'd his pain.
But see how oft ambitious aims are cross'd,
And chiefs contend till all the prize is lost!
The Lock, obtain'd with guilt, and kept with pain,
In every place is sought, but sought in vain:
With such a prize no mortal must be blest,
So Heav'n decrees! with Heav'n who can contest?
   Some thought it mounted to the lunar sphere,
Since all things lost on earth are treasur'd there.
There heroes' wits are kept in pond'rous vases,
And beaux' in snuff-boxes and tweezer-cases;
There broken vows and death-bed alms are found,
And lovers' hearts with ends of riband bound,
The courtier's promises, and sick men's prayers,
The smiles of harlots, and the tears of heirs,
Cages for gnats, and chains to yoke a flea,
Dried butterflies, and tomes of casuistry.
   But trust the Muse—she saw it upward rise,
Though mark'd by none but quick, poetic eyes:
(So Rome's great founder to the heav'ns withdrew,
To Proculus alone confess'd in view:)
A sudden star, it shot through liquid air,
And drew behind a radiant trail of hair.
Not Berenice's locks first rose so bright,
The heavens bespangling with dishevell'd light.
The sylphs behold it kindling as it flies,

And pleas'd pursue its progress through the skies.
    This the beau monde shall from the Mall survey,
And hail with music its propitious ray;
This the blest lover shall for Venus take,
And send up vows from Rosamonda's lake;
This Partridge soon shall view in cloudless skies,
When next he looks through Galileo's eyes;
And hence the egregious wizard shall foredoom
The fate of Louis, and the fall of Rome.
    Then cease, bright Nymph! to mourn thy ravish'd hair,
Which adds new glory to the shining sphere!
Not all the tresses that fair head can boast
Shall draw such envy as the Lock you lost.
For after all the murders of your eye,
When, after millions slain, yourself shall die;
When those fair suns shall set, as set they must,
And all those tresses shall be laid in dust,
This Lock the Muse shall consecrate to fame,
And 'midst the stars inscribe Belinda's name.

THOMAS GRAY
1716-1771

Elegy written in a Country Churchyard

The curfew tolls the knell of parting day,
   The lowing herd wind slowly o'er the lea,
The ploughman homeward plods his weary way,
   And leaves the world to darkness, and to me.

Now fades the glimmering landscape on the sight,
   And all the air a solemn stillness holds,
Save where the beetle wheels his droning flight,
   And drowsy tinklings lull the distant folds.

Save that from yonder ivy-mantled tower
   The moping owl does to the moon complain
Of such as, wandering near her secret bower,
   Molest her ancient solitary reign.

Beneath those rugged elms, that yew-tree's shade,
   Where heaves the turf in many a mouldering heap,
Each in his narrow cell for ever laid,
   The rude Forefathers of the hamlet sleep.

The breezy call of incense-breathing morn,
   The swallow twittering from the straw-built shed,
The cock's shrill clarion, or the echoing horn,
   No more shall rouse them from their lowly bed.

For them no more the blazing hearth shall burn,
   Or busy housewife ply her evening care:
No children run to lisp their sire's return,
   Or climb his knees the envied kiss to share.

Oft did the harvest to their sickle yield,
   Their furrow oft the stubborn glebe has broke;
How jocund did they drive their team afield!
   How bow'd the woods beneath their sturdy stroke!

Let not Ambition mock their useful toil,
  Their homely joys, and destiny obscure;
Nor Grandeur hear with a disdainful smile
  The short and simple annals of the Poor.

The boast of heraldry, the pomp of power,
  And all that beauty, all that wealth e'er gave,
Awaits alike th' inevitable hour:—
  The paths of glory lead but to the grave.

Nor you, ye Proud, impute to these the fault
  If Memory o'er their tomb no trophies raise,
Where through the long-drawn aisle and fretted vault
  The pealing anthem swells the note of praise.

Can storied urn or animated bust
  Back to its mansion call the fleeting breath?
Can Honour's voice provoke the silent dust,
  Or Flattery soothe the dull cold ear of Death?

Perhaps in this neglected spot is laid
  Some heart once pregnant with celestial fire;
Hands, that the rod of empire might have sway'd,
  Or waked to ecstasy the living lyre:

But Knowledge to their eyes her ample page,
  Rich with the spoils of time, did ne'er unroll;
Chill Penury repress'd their noble rage,
  And froze the genial current of the soul.

Full many a gem of purest ray serene
  The dark unfathom'd caves of ocean bear:
Full many a flower is born to blush unseen
  And waste its sweetness on the desert air.

Some village Hampden, that with dauntless breast
  The little tyrant of his fields withstood,
Some mute inglorious Milton here may rest,
  Some Cromwell, guiltless of his country's blood.

Th' applause of list'ning senates to command,
  The threats of pain and ruin to despise,
To scatter plenty o'er a smiling land,
  And read their history in a nation's eyes,

Their lot forbad: nor circumscribed alone
   Their growing virtues, but their crimes confined;
Forbad to wade through slaughter to a throne,
   And shut the gates of mercy on mankind,

The struggling pangs of conscious truth to hide,
   To quench the blushes of ingenuous shame,
Or heap the shrine of Luxury and Pride
   With incense kindled at the Muse's flame.

Far from the madding crowd's ignoble strife,
   Their sober wishes never learn'd to stray;
Along the cool sequester'd vale of life
   They kept the noiseless tenor of their way.

Yet e'en these bones from insult to protect
   Some frail memorial still erected nigh,
With uncouth rhymes and shapeless sculpture deck'd,
   Implores the passing tribute of a sigh.

Their name, their years, spelt by th' unletter'd Muse,
   The place of fame and elegy supply:
And many a holy text around she strews,
   That teach the rustic moralist to die.

For who, to dumb forgetfulness a prey,
   This pleasing anxious being e'er resign'd,
Left the warm precincts of the cheerful day,
   Nor cast one longing lingering look behind?

On some fond breast the parting soul relies,
   Some pious drops the closing eye requires;
E'en from the tomb the voice of Nature cries,
   E'en in our ashes live their wonted fires.

For thee, who, mindful of th' unhonour'd dead,
   Dost in these lines their artless tale relate;
If chance, by lonely contemplation led,
   Some kindred spirit shall inquire thy fate,

Haply some hoary-headed swain may say,
   'Oft have we seen him at the peep of dawn
Brushing with hasty steps the dews away
   To meet the sun upon the upland lawn;

'There at the foot of yonder nodding beech
    That wreathes its old fantastic roots so high,
His listless length at noontide would he stretch,
    And pore upon the brook that babbles by.

'Hard by yon wood, now smiling as in scorn,
    Muttering his wayward fancies he would rove;
Now drooping, woeful wan, like one forlorn,
    Or crazed with care, or cross'd in hopeless love.

'One morn I miss'd him on the custom'd hill,
    Along the heath, and near his favourite tree;
Another came; nor yet beside the rill,
    Nor up the lawn, nor at the wood was he;

'The next with dirges due in sad array
    Slow through the church-way path we saw him borne,—
Approach and read (for thou canst read) the lay
    Graved on the stone beneath yon aged thorn.'

THE EPITAPH

Here rests his head upon the lap of Earth
    A Youth, to Fortune and to Fame unknown;
Fair Science frown'd not on his humble birth,
    And Melancholy mark'd him for her own.

Large was his bounty, and his soul sincere;
    Heaven did a recompense as largely send:
He gave to Misery all he had, a tear,
    He gain'd from Heaven, 'twas all he wish'd, a friend.

No further seek his merits to disclose,
    Or draw his frailties from their dread abode,
There they alike in trembling hope repose,
    The bosom of his Father and his God.

The Bard

A PINDARIC ODE

'Ruin seize thee, ruthless King!
  Confusion on thy banners wait!
Tho' fanned by Conquest's crimson wing
  They mock the air with idle state.
  Helm, nor hauberk's twisted mail,
Nor e'en thy virtues, tyrant, shall avail
To save thy secret soul from nightly fears,
From Cambria's curse, from Cambria's tears!'
—Such were the sounds that o'er the crested pride
  Of the first Edward scatter'd wild dismay,
As down the steep of Snowdon's shaggy side
  He wound with toilsome march his long array:—
Stout Glo'ster stood aghast in speechless trance;
'To arms!' cried Mortimer, and couch'd his quivering lance

On a rock, whose haughty brow
Frowns o'er old Conway's foaming flood,
  Robed in the sable garb of woe,
With haggard eyes the Poet stood;
(Loose his beard and hoary hair
Stream'd like a meteor to the troubled air;)
And with a master's hand and prophet's fire
Struck the deep sorrows of his lyre:
'Hark, how each giant oak and desert cave
  Sighs to the torrent's awful voice beneath!
O'er thee, O King! their hundred arms they wave,
  Revenge on thee in hoarser murmurs breathe;
Vocal no more, since Cambria's fatal day,
To high-born Hoel's harp, or soft Llewellyn's lay.

'Cold is Cadwallo's tongue,
  That hush'd the stormy main:
Brave Urien sleeps upon his craggy bed:
  Mountains, ye mourn in vain
  Modred, whose magic song
Made huge Plinlimmon bow his cloud-topt head.
  On dreary Arvon's shore they lie
Smear'd with gore and ghastly pale:
Far, far aloof the affrighted ravens sail;

The famish'd eagle screams, and passes by.
Dear lost companions of my tuneful art,
    Dear as the light that visits these sad eyes,
Dear as the ruddy drops that warm my heart,
    Ye died amidst your dying country's cries—
No more I weep. They do not sleep;
    On yonder cliffs, a grisly band,
I see them sit; they linger yet,
    Avengers of their native land:
With me in dreadful harmony they join,
And weave with bloody hands the tissue of thy line.

'Weave the warp and weave the woof,
    The winding-sheet of Edward's race:
Give ample room and verge enough
The characters of hell to trace.
Mark the year, and mark the night,
When Severn shall re-echo with affright
The shrieks of death, thro' Berkley's roofs that ring,
Shrieks of an agonising King!
She-wolf of France, with unrelenting fangs
That tears't the bowels of thy mangled mate,
    From thee be born, who o'er thy country hangs
The scourge of Heaven! What terrors round him wait!
Amazement in his van, with Flight combined,
And Sorrow's faded form, and Solitude behind.

'Mighty victor, mighty lord,
    Low on his funeral couch he lies!
No pitying heart, no eye, afford
A tear to grace his obsequies.
Is the sable warrior fled?
Thy son is gone. He rests among the dead.
The swarm that in thy noon-tide beam were born?
—Gone to salute the rising morn.
Fair laughs the Morn, and soft the zephyr blows,
    While proudly riding o'er the azure realm
In gallant trim the gilded Vessel goes:
    Youth on the prow, and Pleasure at the helm:
Regardless of the sweeping Whirlwind's sway,
That, hush'd in grim repose, expects his evening prey.

'Fill high the sparkling bowl,
The rich repast prepare;
    Reft of a crown, he yet may share the feast:
Close by the regal chair
    Fell Thirst and Famine scowl
A baleful smile upon their baffled guest.
Heard ye the din of battle bray,
    Lance to lance, and horse to horse?
    Long years of havoc urge their destined course,
And thro' the kindred squadrons mow their way.
    Ye towers of Julius, London's lasting shame,
With many a foul and midnight murder fed,
    Revere his Consort's faith, his Father's fame,
And spare the meek usurper's holy head!
Above, below, the rose of snow,
    Twined with her blushing foe, we spread;
The bristled boar in infant-gore
    Wallows beneath the thorny shade.
Now, brothers, bending o'er the accursèd loom,
Stamp we our vengeance deep, and ratify his doom.

'Edward, lo! to sudden fate
    (Weave we the woof; the thread is spun;)
Half of thy heart we consecrate.
    (The web is wove; the work is done.)
Stay, O stay! nor thus forlorn
Leave me unbless'd, unpitied, here to mourn:
In yon bright track that fires the western skies
They melt, they vanish from my eyes.
But O! what solemn scenes on Snowdon's height
    Descending slow their glittering skirts unroll?
Visions of glory, spare my aching sight,
    Ye unborn ages, crowd not on my soul!
No more our long-lost Arthur we bewail:—
All hail, ye genuine kings! Britannia's issue, hail!

    'Girt with many a baron bold
Sublime their starry fronts they rear;
    And gorgeous dames, and statesmen old
In bearded majesty, appear.
In the midst a form divine!
Her eye proclaims her of the Briton-Line:

Her lion-port, her awe-commanding face,
Attemper'd sweet to virgin-grace.
What strings symphonious tremble in the air,
    What strains of vocal transport round her play?
Hear from the grave, great Taliessin, hear;
    They breathe a soul to animate thy clay.
Bright Rapture calls, and soaring as she sings,
Waves in the eye of Heaven her many-colour'd wings.

'The verse adorn again
    Fierce War, and faithful Love,
And Truth severe, by fairy Fiction drest.
    In buskin'd measures move
Pale Grief, and pleasing Pain,
With Horror, tyrant of the throbbing breast.
A voice as of the cherub-choir
    Gales from blooming Eden bear,
    And distant warblings lessen on my ear,
That lost in long futurity expire.
Fond impious man, think'st thou yon sanguine cloud
    Raised by thy breath, has quench'd the orb of day?
To-morrow he repairs the golden flood
    And warm the nations with redoubled ray.
Enough for me: with joy I see
    The different doom our fates assign:
Be thine Despair and sceptred Care;
    To triumph and to die are mine.'
—He spoke, and headlong from the mountain's height
Deep in the roaring tide he plunged to endless night.

OLIVER GOLDSMITH
1728-1774

The Deserted Village

Sweet AUBURN! loveliest village of the plain,
Where health and plenty cheer'd the labouring swain,
Where smiling spring its earliest visit paid,
And parting summer's lingering blooms delay'd:
Dear lovely bowers of innocence and ease,
Seats of my youth, when every sport could please,
How often have I loiter'd o'er thy green,
Where humble happiness endear'd each scene;
How often have I paus'd on every charm,
The shelter'd cot, the cultivated farm,
The never-failing brook, the busy mill,
The decent church that topp'd the neighbouring hill,
The hawthorn bush, with seats beneath the shade,
For talking age and whisp'ring lovers made;
How often have I bless'd the coming day,
When toil remitting lent its turn to play,
And all the village train, from labour free,
Led up their sports beneath the spreading tree;
While many a pastime circled in the shade,
The young contending as the old survey'd;
And many a gambol frolick'd o'er the ground,
And sleights of art and feats of strength went round;
And still as each repeated pleasure tir'd,
Succeeding sports the mirthful band inspir'd;
The dancing pair that simply sought renown,
By holding out to tire each other down;
The swain mistrustless of his smutted face,
While secret laughter titter'd round the place;
The bashful virgin's side-long looks of love,
The matron's glance that would those looks reprove:
These were thy charms, sweet village; sports like these,
With sweet succession, taught e'en toil to please;

These round thy bowers their cheerful influence shed,
These were thy charms—But all these charms are fled.

Sweet smiling village, loveliest of the lawn,
Thy sports are fled, and all thy charms withdrawn;
Amidst thy bowers the tyrant's hand is seen,
And desolation saddens all thy green:
One only master grasps the whole domain,
And half a tillage stints thy smiling plain:
No more thy glassy brook reflects the day,
But chok'd with sedges, works its weedy way.
Along thy glades, a solitary guest,
The hollow-sounding bittern guards its nest;
Amidst thy desert walks the lapwing flies,
And tires their echoes with unvaried cries.
Sunk are thy bowers in shapeless ruin all,
And the long grass o'ertops the mould'ring wall:
And trembling, shrinking from the spoiler's hand,
Far, far away, thy children leave the land.

Ill fares the land, to hast'ning ills a prey,
Where wealth accumulates, and men decay:
Princes and lords may flourish, or may fade;
A breath can make them, as a breath has made;
But a bold peasantry, their country's pride,
When once destroy'd, can never be supplied.

A time there was, ere England's griefs began,
When every rood of ground maintain'd its man;
For him light labour spread her wholesome store,
Just gave what life requir'd, but gave no more:
His best companions, innocence and health;
And his best riches, ignorance of wealth.

But times are alter'd; trade's unfeeling train
Usurp the land and dispossess the swain;
Along the lawn, where scatter'd hamlets rose,
Unwieldy wealth, and cumbrous pomp repose;
And every want to opulence allied,
And every pang that folly pays to pride.
Those gentle hours that plenty bade to bloom,
Those calm desires that ask'd but little room,

Those healthful sports that grac'd the peaceful scene,
Liv'd in each look, and brighten'd all the green;
These, far departing, seek a kinder shore,
And rural mirth and manners are no more.

Sweet AUBURN! parent of the blissful hour,
Thy glades forlorn confess the tyrant's power.
Here as I take my solitary rounds,
Amidst thy tangling walks, and ruin'd grounds,
And, many a year elaps'd, return to view
Where once the cottage stood, the hawthorn grew,
Remembrance wakes with all her busy train,
Swells at my breast, and turns the past to pain.

In all my wand'rings round this world of care,
In all my griefs—and GOD has given my share—
I still had hopes my latest hours to crown,
Amidst these humble bowers to lay me down;
To husband out life's taper at the close,
And keep the flame from wasting by repose.
I still had hopes, for pride attends us still,
Amidst the swains to show my book-learn'd skill,
Around my fire an evening group to draw,
And tell of all I felt, and all I saw;
And, as a hare, whom hounds and horns pursue,
Pants to the place from whence at first she flew,
I still had hopes, my long vexations pass'd,
Here to return—and die at home at last.

O blest retirement, friend to life's decline,
Retreats from care, that never must be mine,
How happy he who crowns in shades like these,
A youth of labour with an age of ease;
Who quits a world where strong temptations try
And, since 'tis hard to combat, learns to fly!
For him no wretches, born to work and weep,
Explore the mine, or tempt the dangerous deep;
No surly porter stands in guilty state
To spurn imploring famine from the gate,
But on he moves to meet his latter end,
Angels around befriending Virtue's friend;
Bends to the grave with unperceiv'd decay,
While Resignation gently slopes the way;

And, all his prospects bright'ning to the last,
His Heaven commences ere the world be pass'd!

Sweet was the sound, when oft at evening's close
Up yonder hill the village murmur rose;
There, as I pass'd with careless steps and slow,
The mingling notes came soften'd from below;
The swain responsive as the milk-maid sung,
The sober herd that low'd to meet their young;
The noisy geese that gabbled o'er the pool,
The playful children just let loose from school;
The watchdog's voice that bay'd the whisp'ring wind,
And the loud laugh that spoke the vacant mind;
These all in sweet confusion sought the shade,
And fill'd each pause the nightingale had made.
But now the sounds of population fail,
No cheerful murmurs fluctuate in the gale,
No busy steps the grass-grown foot-way tread,
For all the bloomy flush of life is fled.
All but yon widow'd, solitary thing
That feebly bends beside the plashy spring;
She, wretched matron, forc'd, in age, for bread,
To strip the brook with mantling cresses spread,
To pick her wintry faggot from the thorn,
To seek her nightly shed, and weep till morn;
She only left of all the harmless train,
The sad historian of the pensive plain.

Near yonder copse, where once the garden smil'd,
And still where many a garden flower grows wild;
There, where a few torn shrubs the place disclose,
The village preacher's modest mansion rose.
A man he was to all the country dear,
And passing rich with forty pounds a year;
Remote from towns he ran his godly race,
Nor e'er had chang'd, nor wished to change his place;
Unpractis'd he to fawn, or seek for power,
By doctrines fashion'd to the varying hour;
Far other aims his heart had learned to prize,
More skill'd to raise the wretched than to rise.
His house was known to all the vagrant train;
He chid their wand'rings, but reliev'd their pain;

The long-remember'd beggar was his guest,
Whose beard descending swept his aged breast;
The ruin'd spendthrift, now no longer proud,
Claim'd kindred there, and had his claims allow'd;
The broken soldier, kindly bade to stay,
Sat by his fire, and talk'd the night away;
Wept o'er his wounds, or tales of sorrow done,
Shoulder'd his crutch, and show'd how fields were won,
Pleas'd with his guests, the good man learn'd to glow.
And quite forgot their vices in their woe;
Careless their merits, or their faults to scan,
His pity gave ere charity began.

Thus to relieve the wretched was his pride,
And e'en his failings lean'd to Virtue's side;
But in his duty prompt at every call,
He watch'd and wept, he pray'd and felt, for all.
And, as a bird each fond endearment tries
To tempt its new-fledg'd offspring to the skies,
He tried each art, reprov'd each dull delay,
Allur'd to brighter worlds, and led the way.

Beside the bed where parting life was laid,
And sorrow, guilt, and pain, by turns dismay'd,
The reverend champion stood. At his control,
Despair and anguish fled the struggling soul;
Comfort came down the trembling wretch to raise,
And his last falt'ring accents whisper'd praise.

At church, with meek and unaffected grace,
His looks adorn'd the venerable place;
Truth from his lips prevail'd with double sway,
And fools, who came to scoff, remain'd to pray.
The service pass'd, around the pious man,
With steady zeal, each honest rustic ran;
Even children follow'd with endearing wile,
And pluck'd his gown, to share the good man's smile.
His ready smile a parent's warmth express'd,
Their welfare pleas'd him, and their cares distress'd;
To them his heart, his love, his griefs were given,
But all his serious thoughts had rest in Heaven.
As some tall cliff, that lifts its awful form,
Swells from the vale, and midway leaves the storm,

Though round its breast the rolling clouds are spread,
Eternal sunshine settles on its head.

Beside yon straggling fence that skirts the way,
With blossom'd furze unprofitably gay,
There, in his noisy mansion, skill'd to rule,
The village master taught his little school;
A man severe he was, and stern to view;
I knew him well, and every truant knew;
Well had the boding tremblers learn'd to trace
The day's disasters in his morning face;
Full well they laugh'd, with counterfeited glee,
At all his jokes, for many a joke had he;
Full well the busy whisper, circling round,
Convey'd the dismal tidings when he frown'd;
Yet he was kind; or if severe in aught,
The love he bore to learning was in fault;
The village all declar'd how much he knew;
'Twas certain he could write, and cypher too;
Lands he could measure, terms and tides presage,
And e'en the story ran that he could gauge.
In arguing too, the parson own'd his skill,
For e'en though vanquish'd, he could argue still;
While words of learned length and thund'ring sound
Amazed the gazing rustics rang'd around,
And still they gaz'd, and still the wonder grew,
That one small head could carry all he knew.

But past is all his fame. The very spot
Where many a time he triumph'd, is forgot.
Near yonder thorn, that lifts its head on high,
Where once the sign-post caught the passing eye,
Low lies that house where nut-brown draughts inspir'd,
Where grey-beard mirth and smiling toil retir'd,
Where village statesmen talk'd with looks profound,
And news much older than their ale went round.
Imagination fondly stoops to trace
The parlour splendours of that festive place;
The white-wash'd wall, the nicely sanded floor,
The varnish'd clock that click'd behind the door;
The chest contriv'd a double debt to pay,
A bed by night, a chest of drawers by day;

The pictures plac'd for ornament and use,
The twelve good rules, the royal game of goose;
The hearth, except when winter chill'd the day,
With aspen boughs, and flowers, and fennel gay;
While broken tea-cups, wisely kept for show,
Rang'd o'er the chimney, glisten'd in a row.

Vain, transitory splendours! Could not all
Reprieve the tottering mansion from its fall?
Obscure it sinks, nor shall it more impart
An hour's importance to the poor man's heart;
Thither no more the peasant shall repair
To sweet oblivion of his daily care;
No more the farmer's news, the barber's tale,
No more the wood-man's ballad shall prevail;
No more the smith his dusky brow shall clear,
Relax his pond'rous strength, and lean to hear;
The host himself no longer shall be found
Careful to see the mantling bliss go round;
Nor the coy maid, half willing to be press'd,
Shall kiss the cup to pass it to the rest.

Yes! let the rich deride, the proud disdain,
These simple blessings of the lowly train;
To me more dear, congenial to my heart,
One native charm, than all the gloss of art;
Spontaneous joys, where Nature has its play,
The soul adopts, and owns their first-born sway;
Lightly they frolic o'er the vacant mind,
Unenvied, unmolested, unconfin'd:
But the long pomp, the midnight masquerade,
With all the freaks of wanton wealth array'd,
In these, ere triflers half their wish obtain,
The toiling pleasure sickens into pain;
And, e'en while fashion's brightest arts decoy,
The heart distrusting asks, if this be joy.

Ye friends to truth, ye statesmen, who survey
The rich man's joys increase, the poor's decay,
'Tis yours to judge, how wide the limits stand
Between a splendid and a happy land.
Proud swells the tide with loads of freighted ore,
And shouting Folly hails them from her shore;

Hoards e'en beyond the miser's wish abound,
And rich men flock from all the world around.
Yet count our gains. This wealth is but a name
That leaves our useful products still the same.
Not so the loss. The man of wealth and pride
Takes up a space that many poor supplied;
Space for his lake, his park's extended bounds,
Space for his horses, equipage, and hounds;
The robe that wraps his limbs in silken sloth
Has robb'd the neighbouring fields of half their growth;
His seat, where solitary sports are seen,
Indignant spurns the cottage from the green;
Around the world each needful product flies,
For all the luxuries the world supplies:
While thus the land adorn'd for pleasure, all
In barren splendour feebly waits the fall.

As some fair female unadorn'd and plain,
Secure to please while youth confirms her reign,
Slights every borrow'd charm that dress supplies,
Nor shares with art the triumph of her eyes:
But when those charms are pass'd, for charms are frail,
When time advances, and when lovers fail,
She then shines forth, solicitous to bless,
In all the glaring impotence of dress.
Thus fares the land, by luxury betray'd,
In nature's simplest charms at first array'd;
But verging to decline, its splendours rise,
Its vistas strike, its palaces surprise;
While scourg'd by famine from the smiling land,
The mournful peasant leads his humble band;
And while he sinks, without one arm to save,
The country blooms—a garden, and a grave.

Where then, ah! where, shall poverty reside,
To 'scape the pressure of contiguous pride?
If to some common's fenceless limits stray'd,
He drives his flock to pick the scanty blade,
Those fenceless fields the sons of wealth divide,
And e'en the bare-worn common is denied.

If to the city sped—What waits him there?
To see profusion that he must not share;

To see ten thousand baneful arts combin'd
To pamper luxury, and thin mankind;
To see those joys the sons of pleasure know
Extorted from his fellow creature's woe.
Here, while the courtier glitters in brocade,
There the pale artist plies the sickly trade;
Here, while the proud their long-drawn pomps display,
There the black gibbet glooms beside the way.
The dome where Pleasure holds her midnight reign
Here, richly deck'd, admits the gorgeous train:
Tumultuous grandeur crowds the blazing square,
The rattling chariots clash, the torches glare.
Sure scenes like these no troubles e'er annoy!
Sure these denote one universal joy!
Are these thy serious thoughts?—Ah, turn thine eyes
Where the poor houseless shiv'ring female lies.
She once, perhaps, in village plenty bless'd,
Has wept at tales of innocence distress'd;
Her modest looks the cottage might adorn,
Sweet as the primrose peeps beneath the thorn;
Now lost to all, her friends, her virtue fled,
Near her betrayer's door she lays her head,
And, pinch'd with cold, and shrinking from the shower,
With heavy heart deplores that luckless hour,
When idly first, ambitious of the town,
She left her wheel and robes of country brown.

Do thine, sweet AUBURN, thine, the loveliest train,
Do thy fair tribes participate her pain?
E'en now, perhaps, by cold and hunger led,
At proud men's doors they ask a little bread!

Ah, no. To distant climes, a dreary scene,
Where half the convex world intrudes between,
Through torrid tracts with fainting steps they go,
Where wild Altama murmurs to their woe.
Far different there from all that charm'd before,
The various terrors of that horrid shore;
Those blazing suns that dart a downward ray,
And fiercely shed intolerable day;
Those matted woods where birds forget to sing,
But silent bats in drowsy clusters cling;

Those pois'nous fields with rank luxuriance crown'd,
Where the dark scorpion gathers death around;
Where at each step the stranger fears to wake
The rattling terrors of the vengeful snake;
Where crouching tigers wait their hapless prey,
And savage men more murd'rous still than they;
While oft in whirls the mad tornado flies,
Mingling the ravag'd landscape with the skies.
Far different these from every former scene,
The cooling brook, the grassy-vested green,
The breezy covert of the warbling grove,
That only shelter'd thefts of harmless love.

Good heaven! what sorrows gloom'd that parting day,
That call'd them from their native walks away;
When the poor exiles, every pleasure pass'd,
Hung round their bowers, and fondly look'd their last,
And took a long farewell, and wish'd in vain
For seats like these beyond the western main;
And shudd'ring still to face the distant deep,
Return'd and wept, and still return'd to weep.
The good old sire the first prepared to go
To new-found worlds, and wept for others' woe;
But for himself, in conscious virtue brave,
He only wish'd for worlds beyond the grave.
His lovely daughter, lovelier in her tears,
The fond companion of his helpless years,
Silent went next, neglectful of her charms,
And left a lover's for a father's arms.
With louder plaints the mother spoke her woes,
And bless'd the cot where every pleasure rose,
And kiss'd her thoughtless babes with many a tear,
And clasp'd them close, in sorrow doubly dear;
Whilst her fond husband strove to lend relief
In all the silent manliness of grief.

O Luxury! thou curs'd by Heaven's decree,
How ill exchang'd are things like these for thee!
How do thy potions, with insidious joy,
Diffuse their pleasures only to destroy!
Kingdoms, by thee, to sickly greatness grown,
Boast of a florid vigour not their own;

At every draught more large and large they grow,
A bloated mass of rank unwieldy woe;
Till sapp'd their strength, and every part unsound,
Down, down they sink, and spread a ruin round.

E'en now the devastation is begun,
And half the business of destruction done;
E'en now, methinks, as pond'ring here I stand,
I see the rural virtues leave the land:
Down where yon anchoring vessel spreads the sail,
That idly waiting flaps with ev'ry gale,
Downward they move, a melancholy band,
Pass from the shore, and darken all the strand.
Contented toil, and hospitable care,
And kind connubial tenderness, are there;
And piety, with wishes plac'd above,
And steady loyalty, and faithful love.
And thou, sweet Poetry, thou loveliest maid,
Still first to fly where sensual joys invade;
Unfit in these degenerate times of shame
To catch the heart, or strike for honest fame;
Dear charming nymph, neglected and decried,
My shame in crowds, my solitary pride;
Thou source of all my bliss, and all my woe,
That found'st me poor at first, and keep'st me so;
Thou guide by which the nobler arts excel,
Thou nurse of every virtue, fare thee well!
Farewell, and Oh! where'er thy voice be tried,
On Torno's cliffs, or Pambamarca's side,
Whether where equinoctial fervours glow,
Or winter wraps the polar world in snow,
Still let thy voice, prevailing over time,
Redress the rigours of th' inclement clime;
Aid slighted truth; with thy persuasive strain
Teach erring man to spurn the rage of gain;
Teach him, that states of native strength possess'd,
Though very poor, may still be very bless'd;
That trade's proud empire hastes to swift decay,
As ocean sweeps the labour'd mole away;
While self-dependent power can time defy,
As rocks resist the billows and the sky.

LADY GRISEL BAILLIE
1665-1746

There ance was a May

There ance was a May, and she loo'd na men;
She biggit her bonnie bower doun in yon glen;
But now she cries, Dool! and well-a-day!
Come doun the green gait and come here away!

When bonnie young Johnnie cam' ower the sea,
He said he saw naething sae lovely as me;
He hecht me baith rings and mony braw things,—
And werena my heart licht I wad dee.

He had a wee titty that loo'd na me,
Because I was twice as bonnie as she;
She raised such a pother 'twixt him and his mother
That werena my heart licht I wad dee.

The day it was set, and the bridal to be:
The wife took a dwam, and lay doun to dee;
She maned and she graned out o' dolour and pain,
Till he vow'd he never wad see me again.

His kin was for ane of a higher degree,
Said, What had he to do wi' the like of me?
Albeit I was bonnie, I wasna for Johnnie,—
And werena my heart licht I wad dee.

They said I had neither cow nor calf,
Nor dribbles o' drink rins through the draff,
Nor pickles o' meal rins through the mill-e'e;
And werena my heart licht I wad dee.

May, *maiden*	hecht, *offered*	titty, *sister*
dwam, *faint*	draff, *refuse of malt*	mill-e'e, *hole in the millstone*

172

His titty she was baith wylie and slee:
She spied me as I cam' ower the lea;
And then she ran in and made a loud din,—
Believe your ain een an' ye trow na me.

His bonnet stood aye fu' round on his brow,—
His auld ane look'd aye as weel as some's new;
But now he lets 't wear ony gait it will hing,
And casts himself dowie upon the corn-bing.

And now he gaes daund'ring about the dykes,
And a' he dow do is to hund the tykes:
The live-lang nicht he ne'er steeks his e'e;
And werena my heart licht I wad dee.

Were I but young for thee, as I hae been,
We should hae been gallopin' doun on yon green,
And linkin' it on the lily-white lea,—
And wow! gin I were but young for thee!

      bing, *heap*   dow, *can*

ALLAN RAMSAY
1686-1758

To Phyllis

AN ODE

Look up to Pentland's towering tap,
Buried beneath great wreaths of snaw,
O'er ilka cleugh, ilk scar and slap,
As high as ony Roman wa'.

Driving their ba's frae whin or tee,
There's no ae gowfer to be seen,
Nor doucer folk wysing ajee
The bias bowls on Tamson's green.

Then fling on coals, and ripe the ribs,
And beek the house baith but and ben,
That mutchkin stoup it hauds but dribs,
Then let's get in the tappit hen.

Good claret best keeps out the cauld,
And drives away the winter soon,
It makes a man baith gash and bauld,
And heaves his saul beyond the moon.

Leave to the gods your ilka care,
If that they think us worth their while,
They can a rowth of blessings spare,
Which will our fashious fears beguile.

For what they have a mind to do,
That will they do, should we gang wud,
If they command the storms to blaw,
Then upo' sight the hailstanes thud.

cleugh, *cleft in hills*	wysing ajee, *turning aside*	beek, *warm*
mutchkin, *four gill measure*	tappit hen, *quart measure*	gash, *shrewd*
rowth, *plenty*	fashious, *troublesome*	wud, *mad*

But soon as e'er they cry, Be quate,
The blatt'ring winds dare nae mair move,
But cour into their caves, and wait
The high command of supreme Jove.

Let neist day come as it thinks fit,
The present minute's only ours,
On pleasure let's employ our wit,
And laugh at Fortune's feckless power.

Be sure ye dinna quat the grip
Of ilka joy when ye are young,
Before auld Age your vitals nip,
And lay ye twafald o'er a rung.

Sweet youth's a blyth and heartsome time,
Then lads and lasses while it's May
Gae pu' the gowan in its prime,
Before it wither and decay.

Watch the saft minutes of delight
When Jenny speaks beneath her breath,
And kisses, laying a' the wyte
On you if she kepp ony scaith.

Haith ye're ill bred, she'll smiling say,
Ye'll worry me ye greedy rook;
Syne frae your arms she'll rin away,
And hide hersell in some dark nook:

Her laugh will lead you to the place
Where lies the happiness ye want,
And plainly tells ye to your face,
Nineteen nay-says are half a grant.

Now to her heaving bosom cling,
And sweetlie toolie for a kiss,
Frae her fair finger whop a ring,
As taiken of a future bliss.

These benisons, I'm very sure,
Are of the gods indulgent grant;
Then surly carles, whisht, forbear
To plague us with your whining cant.

twafald, *double*   rung, *stick*   wyte, *blame*
    kepp, *catch*   toolie, *struggle*

Song from 'The Gentle Shepherd'

My Peggy is a young thing,
 Just entered in her teens,
Fair as the day, and sweet as May,
Fair as the day, and always gay:
 My Peggy is a young thing,
  And I'm not very auld,
  Yet well I like to meet her at
  The wauking of the fauld.

My Peggy speaks sae sweetly,
 Whene'er we meet alane,
I wish nae mair to lay my care,
I wish nae mair of a' that's rare,
 My Peggy speaks sae sweetly,
  To all the lave I'm cauld;
  But she gars a' my spirits glow,
  At wauking of the fauld.

My Peggy smiles sae kindly
 Whene'er I whisper love,
That I look down on a' the town,
That I look down upon a crown.
 My Peggy smiles sae kindly
  It makes me blyth and bauld;
  And naething gies me sic delight
  As wauking of the fauld.

My Peggy sings sae saftly,
 When on my pipe I play,
By a' the rest it is confesst
By a' the rest that she sings best.
 My Peggy sings sae saftly,
  And in her sangs are tauld,
  With innocence the wale of sense,
  At wauking of the fauld.

wauking, *watching*

The Carle he came o'er the Croft

The carle he came o'er the croft,
  And his beard new shaven,
He looked at me as he'd been daft,
  The carle trows that I wad hae him.
Hoot awa! I winna hae him,
  Na forsooth I winna hae him,
For a' his beard's new shaven,
  Ne'er a bit will I hae him.

A siller brooch he gae me niest,
  To fasten on my curtchea nooked;
O wore't a wee upon my breast,
  But soon, alak! the tongue o't crooked;
And sae may his: I winna hae him;
  Na forsooth I winna hae him;
Ane twice a bairn's a lass's jest;
  Sae ony fool for me may hae him.

The carle has nae faut but ane,
  For he has land and dollars plenty;
But waes me for him! skin and bane
  Is no for a plump lass of twenty.
Hoot awa! I winna hae him,
  Na forsooth I winna hae him;
What signifies his dirty riggs
  And cash, without a man with them?

But should my cankered daddy gar
  Me tak him 'gainst my inclination,
I warn the fumbler to beware,
  That antlers dinna claim their station.
Hoot awa! I winna hae him,
  Na forsooth I winna hae him;
I'm fleed to crack the haly band,
  Sae Lawty says I shouldna hae him.

    curtchea, *kerchief*   nooked, *tucked in*
                fleed, *afraid*

Elegy on Lucky Wood in the Canongate

O Cannigate! poor elritch hole,
What loss, what crosses does thou thole!
London and Death gars thee look drole,
    And hing thy head;
Wow, but thou has e'en a cauld coal
    To blaw indeed.

Hear me ye hills, and every glen,
Ilk craig, ilk cleugh, and hollow den,
And Echo shrill, that a' may ken
    The waefu' thud,
Be rackless Death, wha came unsenn
    To Lucky Wood.

She's dead o'er true, she's dead and gane,
Left us and Willie burd alane,
To bleer and greet, to sob and mane,
    And rugg our hair,
Because we'll ne'er see her again
    For evermair.

She gaed as fait as a new prin,
And kept her housie snod and bien,
Her peuther glanced upo' your een
    Like siller plate;
She was a donsie wife and clean,
    Without debate.

It did ane good to see her stools,
Her boord, fire-side, and facing-tools;
Rax, chandlers, tangs, and fire-shools,
    Basket wi' bread.
Poor facers now may chew pea-hools
    Since Lucky's dead.

She ne'er gae in a lawin fause,
Nor stoups a' froath aboon the hause,

thole, *suffer*	rackless, *careless*	unsenn, *unsent-for*
fait, *neat*	prin, *pin*	bien, *comfortable*
donsie, *tidy*	facing-tools, *drinking vessels*	Rax, *andirons*
chandlers, *candlesticks*	fire-shools, *fire shovels*	
pea-hools, *pea-shells*	lawin, *reckoning*	hause, *neck*

Nor kept dow'd tip within her wa's,
  But reaming swats;
She never ran sour jute because
  It gies the batts.

She had the gate sae weel to please,
With *gratis* beef, dry fish, or cheese;
Which kept our purses aye at ease,
  And health in tift,
And lent her fresh nine-gallon trees
  A hearty lift.

She ga'e us aft hail legs o' lamb,
And didna hain her mutton ham;
Than aye at Yule, whene'er we cam,
  A braw goose pie,
And was na that good belly balm?
  Nane dare deny.

The Writer lads fu' well may mind her,
Furthy was she, her luck designed her
Their common Mither, sure nae kinder
  Ever brake bread;
She hasna left her make behind her,
  But now she's dead.

To the sma' hours we aft sat still,
Nick'd round our toasts and snishing-mill,
Good cakes we wanted ne'er at will,
  The best of bread,
Which aften cost us mony a gill
  To Aitkenhead.

Could our saut tears like Clyde down rin,
And had we cheeks like Corra's Linn,
That a' the warld might hear the din
  Rair frae ilk head;
She was the wale of a' her kin,
  But now she's dead.

dow'd tip, *twopenny ale that has gone flat*
jute, *flat liquor*   batts, *colic*   tift, *good order*   trees, *casks*
  hain, *spare*   Furthy, *forward*   nick'd, *drank heartily*
    snishing-mill, *snuff-box*   wale, *most choice*

O Lucky Wood, 'tis hard to bear
The loss; but Oh! we maun forbear:
Yet sall thy memory be dear
      While blooms a tree,
And after ages bairns will spier
      'Bout thee and me.

EPITAPH

  Beneath this sod
  Lies Lucky Wood,
Whom a' men might put faith in;
   Wha wasna sweer
   While she winned here
To cram our wames for naething.

sweer, *loth*   winned, *dwelt*   wames, *bellies*

JANE ELLIOT
1727-1805

The Flowers of the Forest

I've heard them lilting at our ewe-milking,
Lasses a-lilting before the dawn of day;
But now they are moaning on ilka green loaning—
The Flowers of the Forest are a' wede away.

At bughts, in the morning, nae blythe lads are scorning,
The lasses are lonely, and dowie, and wae;
Nae daffin', nae gabbin', but sighing and sabbing,
Ilk ane lifts her leglin and hies her away.

In har'st, at the shearing, nae youths now are jeering,
Bandsters are lyart, and runkled, and gray;
At fair or at preaching, nae wooing, nae fleeching—
The Flowers of the Forest are a' wede away.

At e'en, in the gloaming, nae younkers are roaming
'Bout stacks wi' the lasses at bogle to play;
But ilk ane sits drearie, lamenting her dearie—
The Flowers of the Forest are weded away.

Dool and wae for the order sent our lads to the Border!
The English, for ance, by guile wan the day;
The Flowers of the Forest, that fought aye the foremost,
The prime of our land, are cauld in the clay.

We'll hear nae mair lilting at our ewe-milking;
Women and bairns are heartless and wae;
Sighing and moaning on ilka green loaning—
The Flowers of the Forest are a' wede away.

bughts, *sheep-folds*   dowie, *downcast*   daffin, *joking*   gabbin, *chattering*
leglin, *milk-pail*   bandsters, *binders*   lyart, *grizzled*   fleeching, *wheedling*
bogle, *hide and seek*   dool, *sorrow*   wae, *woeful*

ROBERT FERGUSSON

1750-1774

The Farmer's Ingle

Whan gloaming grey out o'er the welkin keeks,
    When Batie ca's his owsen to the byre,
Whan Thrasher John, sair dung, his barn-door steeks,
    And lusty lasses at the dighting tire:
What bangs fu' leal the e'enings coming cauld,
    And gars snaw-tappit winter freeze in vain;
Gars dowie mortals look baith blythe and bauld,
    Nor fley'd wi' a' the poortith o' the plain;
    Begin, my Muse, and chant in hamely strain.

Frae the big stack, weel winnow't on the hill,
    Wi' divots theekit frae the weet and drift,
Sods, peats, and heathery tufts the chimley fill,
    And gar their thick'ning smeek salute the lift;
The gudeman, new come hame, is blythe to find,
    Whan he out o'er the halland flings his een,
That ilka turn is handled to his mind,
    That a' his housie looks sae cosh and clean;
    For cleanly house looes he, tho' e'er sae mean.

Weel kens the gudewife that the pleughs require
    A heartsome meltith, and refreshing synd
O' nappy liquor, o'er a bleezing fire:
    Sair wark and poortith douna weel be join'd.
Wi' butter'd bannocks now the girdle reeks,
    I' the far nook the bowie briskly reams;
The readied kail stand by the chimley cheeks,
    And haud the riggin het wi' welcome steams,
    Whilk than the daintiest kitchen nicer seems.

dung, *beaten*	dighting, *winnowing*	bangs, *attacks*
dowie, *downcast*	poortith, *poverty*	lift, *sky*
halland, *partition*	meltith, *meal*	synd, *wash-down*
bowie, *wooden vessel*	riggin, *roof*	kitchen, *savoury*

Frae this lat gentler gabs a lesson lear;
  Wad they to labouring lend an eident hand,
They'd rax fell strang upo' the simplest fare,
  Nor find their stamacks ever at a stand.
Fu' hale and healthy wad they pass the day,
  At night in calmest slumbers dose fu' sound,
Nor doctor need their weary life to spae,
  Nor drogs their noddle and their sense confound,
  Till death slip seely on, and gi'e the hindmost wound.

On sickan food has mony a doughty deed
  By Caledonia's ancestors been done;
By this did mony wight fu' weirlike bleed
  In brulzies frae the dawn to set o' sun:
'Twas this that brac'd their gardies, stiff and strang,
  That bent the deidly yew in ancient days,
Laid Denmark's daring sons on yird alang,
  Gar'd Scottish thristles bang the Roman bays;
  For near our crest their heads they doughtna raise.

The couthy cracks begin whan supper's o'er,
  The cheering bicker gars them glibly gash
O' simmer's showery blinks and winters sour,
  Whase floods did erst their mailin's produce hash:
'Bout kirk and market eke their tales gae on,
  How Jock woo'd Jenny here to be his bride,
And there how Marion, for a bastard son,
  Upo' the cutty-stool was forc'd to ride,
  The waefu' scald o' our Mess John to bide.

The fient a cheep's amang the bairnies noo;
  For a' their anger's wi' their hunger gane:
Ay maun the childer, wi' a fastin' mou,
  Grumble and greet, and make an unco mane,
In rangles round before the ingle's low:
  Frae gudame's mouth auld warld tale they hear,
O' warlocks louping round the wirricow,
  O' ghaists that win in glen and kirk-yaird drear,
  Whilk touzles a' their tap, and gars them shak wi' fear.

gabs, *tastes* eident, *diligent* rax, *grow* seely, *gently* brulzies, *brawls*
  gardies, *arms* yird, *earth* bicker, *wooden vessel* gash, *talk*
  mailin's, *farm's* cutty-stool, *stool of repentance* scald, *scolding*
  Mess John, *clergyman* rangles, *clusters* low, *flame* louping, *leaping*
    wirricow, *goblin* win, *dwell*

For weel she trows that fiends and fairies be
    Sent frae the de'il to fleech us to our ill;
That kye hae tint their milk wi' evil e'e,
    And corn been scowder'd on the glowing kill.
O mock na this, my friends! but rather mourn,
    Ye in life's brawest spring wi' reason clear,
Wi' eild our idle fancies a' return,
    And dim our dolefu' days wi' bairnly fear;
       The mind's aye cradled when the grave is near.

Yet thrift, industrious, bides her latest days,
    Tho' age her sair dow'd front wi' runcles wave,
Yet frae the russet lap the spindle plays,
    Her e'ening stent reels she as weel's the lave.
On some feast-day, the wee things buskit braw
    Shall heeze her heart up wi' a silent joy,
Fu' cadgie that her head was up and saw
    Her ain spun cleething on a darling oy,
       Careless tho' death should make the feast her foy.

In its auld lerroch yet the deas remains,
    Whare the gudeman aft streeks him at his ease,
A warm and canny lean for weary banes
    O' lab'rers doil'd upo' the wintry leas:
Round him will baudrins and the collie come,
    To wag their tail, and cast a thankfu' ee
To him who kindly flings them mony a crum
    O' kebbuck whanged, and dainty fadge to prie;
       This a' the boon they crave, and a' the fee.

Frae him the lads their morning counsel tak,
    What stacks he wants to thrash, what rigs to till;
How big a birn maun lie on Bassie's back,
    For meal and multure to the thirling mill.
Niest the gudewife her hireling damsels bids
    Glowr thro' the byre, and see the hawkies bound,
Take tent case Crummy tak her wonted tids,
    And ca' the leglin's treasure on the ground,
       Whilk spills a kebbuck nice, or yellow pound.

fleech, *flatter*   tint, *lost*   scowder'd, *scorched*   kill, *kiln*   eild, *age*
dow'd, *faded* stent, *allowance* lave, *rest* buskit, *dressed* heeze, *lift up*
   cadgie, *happy*   oy, *grandchild*   foy, *farewell feast*   doil'd *stupefied*
      lerroch, *place*   deas, *dais*   baudrins, *pussy*   kebbuck, *cheese*
whanged, *sliced* fadge, *cake* prie, *taste* birn, *burden* Bassie, *old horse*
   multure, *toll of meal* hawkies, *cows* tids, *tantrums* leglin, *milk-pail*

Then a' the house for sleep begin to grien,
    Their joints to slack frae industry a while;
The leaden god fa's heavy on their een,
    And hafflins steeks them frae their daily toil:
The cruizy too can only blink and bleer,
    The restit ingle's done the maist it dow;
Tacksman and cottar eke to bed maun steer,
    Upo' the cod to clear their drumly pow,
    Till wauken'd by the dawning's ruddy glow.

Peace to the husbandman and a' his tribe,
    Whase care fells a' our wants frae year to year;
Lang may his sock and couter turn the glebe,
    And bauks o' corn bend down wi' laded ear.
May SCOTIA's simmer's aye look gay and green,
    Her yellow hairsts frae scowry blasts decreed;
May a' her tenants sit fu' snug and bien,
    Frae the hard grip of ails and poortith freed,
    And a lang lasting train o' peacefu' hours succeed.

To the Tron-Kirk Bell

Wanwordy, crazy, dinsome thing,
As e'er was fram'd to jow or ring,
What gar'd them sic in steeple hing
    They ken themsel',
But weel wat I they couldna bring
    War sounds frae hell.

What de'il are ye? that I shud ban,
You're neither kin to pat nor pan;
Nor uly pig nor master-cann
    But weel may gie
Mair pleasure to the ear o' man
    Than stroke o' thee.

hafflins, *half*   steeks, *shuts*   cruizy, *open iron lamp with rush wick*
restit, *made up for the night*   dow, *can*   Tacksman, *tenant*   cod, *pillow*
drumly, *muddled by sleep*   pow, *head*   sock and couter, *plough*
bauks, *strips*   scowry, *showery*   bien, *comfortable*   Wanwordy, *worthless*
jow, *clang*   uly pig, *oil jar*   master-cann, *vessel to hold bleach*

Fleece merchants may look bauld, I trow,
Sin a' Auld Reekie's childer now
Maun stap their lugs wi' teats o' woo'
        Thy sound to bang,
And keep it frae gaun through and through
        Wi' jarrin' twang.

Your noisy tongue, there's nae abidin' 't,
Like scaulding wife's, there is nae guidin' 't:
Whan I'm 'bout ony business eident
        It's sair to thole;
To deave me than, ye tak a pride in 't
        Wi' senseless knoll.

O! war I provost o' the town,
I swear by a' the pow'rs aboon,
I'd bring ye wi a reesle down;
        Nor shud you think
(Sae sair I'd crack and clour your crown)
        Again to clink.

For whan I've toom'd the muckle cap,
An' fain wud fa' owre in a nap,
Troth I cud doze as sound 's a tap,
        Were 't na for thee,
That gies the tither weary chap
        To waukin me.

I dreamt ae nicht I saw Auld Nick;
Quo he, 'This bell o' mine's a trick,
A wylie piece o' politic,
        A cunnin' snare,
To trap folk in a cloven stick
        Ere they're aware.

'As lang 's my dautit bell hings there
A' body at the kirk will scare;
Quo they, gif he that preaches there
        Like it can wound,
We douna care a single hair
        For joyfu' sound.'

eident, *diligent* thole, *bear* reesle, *clatter* toom'd, *emptied* dautit, *darling*

If magistrates wi' me wud 'gree,
For ay *tongue-tackit* shud you be,
Nor fleg wi' *antimelody*
        Sic honest folk,
Whase lugs were never made to dree
        Thy doolfu' shock.

But far frae thee the bailies dwell,
Or they wud scunner at your knell,
Gie the *foul thief* his riven bell,
        And than, I trow,
The by-word hauds, 'the de'il himsel'
        Has got his due.'

Braid Claith

Ye wha are fain to hae your name
Wrote in the bonny book o' fame,
Let merit nae pretension claim
        To laurel'd wreath,
But hap ye weel, baith back and wame,
        In gude Braid Claith.

He that some ells o' this may fa,
An' slae-black hat on pow like snaw,
Bids bauld to bear the gree awa'
        Wi' a' this graith,
Whan bienly clad wi' shell fu' braw
        O' gude Braid Claith.

Waesuck for him wha has na feck o't!
For he's a gowk they're sure to geck at,
A chiel that ne'er will be respeckit
        While he draws breath,
Till his four quarters are bedeckit
        Wi' gude Braid Claith.

fleg, *frighten*   dree, *suffer*   hap, *cover*
wame, *belly*   fa, *achieve*   gree, *prize*
graith, *gear*   bienly, *comfortably*   Waesuck, *alas*
    feck, *portion*   geck, *mock*

On Sabbath days the barber spark,
Whan he has done wi' scrapin' wark,
Wi' siller broachie in his sark,
   Gangs trigly, faith!
Or to the Meadow, or the Park,
   In gude Braid Claith.

Weel might ye trow, to see them there,
That they to shave your haffits bare,
Or curl and sleek a pickle hair
   Would be right laith,
Whan pacing wi' a gawsy air
   In gude Braid Claith.

If ony mettl'd stirrah green
For favour frae a lady's e'en,
He maunna care for being seen
   Before he sheath
His body in a scabbard clean
   O' gude Braid Claith.

For, gin he come wi' coat thread-bare,
A feg for him she winna care,
But crook her bonny mou' fu' sair,
   And scald him baith.
Wooers should aye their travel spare
   Without Braid Claith.

Braid Claith lends folk an unco heese,
Makes mony kail-worms butter-flies,
Gies mony a doctor his degrees
   For little skaith:
In short, you may be what you please
   Wi' gude Braid Claith.

For thof ye had as wise a snout on
As *Shakespeare* or Sir *Isaac Newton*,
Your judgement folk would hae a doubt on,
   I'll tak my aith,
Till they could see ye wi' a suit on
   O' gude Braid Claith.

| trigly, *smartly* | haffits, *side whiskers* | gawsy, *confident* |
| stirrah, *buck* | green, *longs* | heese, *lift* | skaith, *trouble* |

LADY ANNE LINDSAY
1750-1825

Auld Robin Gray

When the sheep are in the fauld, and the kye at hame,
And a' the warld to rest are gane,
The waes o' my heart fa' in showers frae my e'e,
While my gudeman lies sound by me.

Young Jamie lo'ed me weel, and sought me for his bride;
But saving a croun he had naething else beside:
To make the croun a pund, young Jamie gaed to sea;
And the croun and the pund were baith for me.

He hadna been awa' a week but only twa,
When my father brak his arm, and the cow was stown awa';
My mother she fell sick,—and my Jamie at the sea—
And auld Robin Gray came a-courtin' me.

My faither couldna wark, and my mither couldna spin:
I toil'd day and nicht, but their bread I couldna win:
Auld Rob maintained them baith, and wi' tears in his e'e
Said, 'Jeanie, for their sakes, will ye no marry me?'

My heart it said nay—I look'd for Jamie back;
But the wind it blew high, and the ship it was a wrack;
His ship it was a wrack—why didna Jamie dee?
Or why do I live to cry, Wae's me?

My faither urged me sair: my mither didna speak;
But she look'd in my face till my heart was like to break.
They gi'ed him my hand,—my heart was at the sea;
Sae auld Robin Gray he was gudeman to me.

I hadna been a wife a week but only four,
When mournfu' as I sat on the stane at the door,
I saw my Jamie's wraith,—for I couldna think it he,
Till he said, 'I'm come hame to marry thee.'

stown, *stolen*

189

O sair did we greet, and muckle did we say:
We took but ae kiss, and I bade him gang away.
I wish that I was dead, but I'm no like to dee,—
And why was I born to say, Wae's me?

I gang like a ghaist, and I carena to spin:
I daurna think on Jamie, for that wad be a sin:
But I'll do my best a gude wife to be,
For auld Robin Gray is kind to me.

ROBERT BURNS

1759-1796

Tam o' Shanter

A TALE

Of Brownyis and of Bogillis full is this buke.
GAWIN DOUGLAS

When chapman billies leave the street,
And drouthy neebors, neebors meet
As market-days are wearing late,
An' folk begin to tak the gate;
While we sit bousing at the nappy,
An' getting fou and unco happy,
We think na on the lang Scots miles,
The mosses, waters, slaps, and styles,
That lie between us and our hame,
Whare sits our sulky sullen dame,
Gathering her brows like gathering storm,
Nursing her wrath to keep it warm.

This truth fand honest Tam o' Shanter,
As he frae Ayr ae night did canter,
(Auld Ayr, wham ne'er a town surpasses,
For honest men and bonny lasses).

O Tam! had'st thou but been sae wise,
As ta'en thy ain wife Kate's advice!
She tauld thee weel thou was a skellum,
A blethering, blustering, drunken blellum;
That frae November till October,
Ae market-day thou was nae sober
That ilka melder, wi' the miller,
Thou sat as lang as thou had siller;

chapman, *packman*   billies, *fellows*   gate, *road*   nappy, *ale*
slaps, *gaps in walls*   skellum, *rogue* blellum, *babbler* melder, *meal-grinding*

That ev'ry naig was ca'd a shoe on,
The smith and thee gat roaring fou on;
That at the Lord's house, even on Sunday,
Thou drank wi' Kirkton Jean till Monday.
She prophesied that, late or soon,
Thou would be found deep drown'd in Doon;
Or catch'd wi' warlocks in the mirk,
By Alloway's auld haunted kirk.

Ah, gentle dames! it gars me greet,
To think how mony counsels sweet,
How mony lengthen'd sage advices,
The husband frae the wife despises!

But to our tale: Ae market-night,
Tam had got planted unco right;
Fast by an ingle, bleezing finely,
Wi' reaming swats, that drank divinely;
And at his elbow, Souter Johnny,
His ancient, trusty, drouthy crony;
Tam lo'ed him like a vera brither;
They had been fou for weeks thegither.
The night drave on wi' sangs and clatter;
And ay the ale was growing better
The landlady and Tam grew gracious,
Wi' favours, secret, sweet, and precious:
The Souter tauld his queerest stories;
The landlord's laugh was ready chorus:
The storm without might rair and rustle,
Tam did na mind the storm a whistle.

Care, mad to see a man sae happy,
E'en drown'd himsel amang the nappy:
As bees flee hame wi' lades o' treasure,
The minutes wing'd their way wi' pleasure:
Kings may be blest, but Tam was glorious,
O'er a' the ills o' life victorious!

But pleasures are like poppies spread,
You seize the flow'r, its bloom is shed;

reaming swats, *foaming ale*   Souter, *cobbler*

Or like the snow falls in the river,
A moment white—then melts for ever;
Or like the borealis race,
That flit ere you can point their place;
Or like the rainbow's lovely form
Evanishing amid the storm.—
Nae man can tether time or tide;
The hour approaches Tam maun ride;
That hour, o' night's black arch the key-stane,
That dreary hour he mounts his beast in;
And sic a night he taks the road in,
As ne'er poor sinner was abroad in.

The wind blew as 'twad blawn its last;
The rattling showers rose on the blast;
The speedy gleams the darkness swallow'd;
Loud, deep, and lang, the thunder bellow'd:
That night, a child might understand,
The Deil had business on his hand.

Weel mounted on his gray mare, Meg,
A better never lifted leg,
Tam skelpit on thro' dub and mire,
Despising wind, and rain, and fire;
Whiles holding fast his gude blue bonnet;
Whiles crooning o'er some auld Scots sonnet;
Whiles glowring round wi' prudent cares,
Lest bogles catch him unawares:
Kirk-Alloway was drawing nigh,
Whare ghaists and houlets nightly cry.—

By this time he was cross the ford,
Whare, in the snaw, the chapman smoor'd;
And past the birks and meikle stane,
Whare drunken Charlie brak's neck-bane;
And thro' the whins, and by the cairn,
Whare hunters fand the murder'd bairn;
And near the thorn, aboon the well,
Whare Mungo's mither hang'd hersel.—
Before him Doon pours all his floods;
The doubling storm roars thro' the woods;

houlets, *owls*   smoor'd, *smothered*   birks, *birch trees*

The lightnings flash from pole to pole;
Near and more near the thunders roll:
When, glimmering thro' the groaning trees,
Kirk-Alloway seem'd in a bleeze;
Thro' ilka bore the beams were glancing;
And loud resounded mirth and dancing.—

Inspiring bold John Barleycorn!
What dangers thou canst make us scorn!
Wi' tippeny, we fear nae evil;
Wi' usquabae, we'll face the devil!—
The swats sae ream'd in Tammie's noddle,
Fair play, he car'd na deils a boddle.
But Maggie stood right sair astonish'd,
Till, by the heel and hand admonish'd,
She ventur'd forward on the light;
And, vow! Tam saw an unco sight!
Warlocks and witches in a dance;
Nae cotillion, brent new frae France,
But hornpipes, jigs, strathspeys, and reels,
Put life and mettle in their heels.
A winnock-bunker in the east,
There sat auld Nick, in shape o' beast;
A towzie tyke, black, grim, and large,
To gie them music was his charge:
He screw'd the pipes and gart them skirl,
Till roof and rafters a' did dirl.—
Coffins stood round, like open presses,
That shaw'd the dead in their last dresses;
And by some devilish cantraip slight
Each in its cauld hand held a light.—
By which heroic Tam was able
To note upon the haly table,
A murderer's banes in gibbet airns;
Twa span-lang, wee, unchristen'd bairns;
A thief, new-cutted frae a rape,
Wi' his last gasp his gab did gape;
Five tomahawks, wi' blude red-rusted;
Five scymitars, wi' murder crusted;

tippeny, *ale*   usquabae, *whisky*   boddle, *farthing*   brent, *brand*
winnock-bunker, *window seat*   towzie tyke, *unkempt dog*

A garter, which a babe had strangled;
A knife, a father's throat had mangled,
Whom his ain son o' life bereft,
The grey hairs yet stack to the heft;
Wi' mair o' horrible and awefu',
Which even to name wad be unlawfu'.

As Tammie glowr'd, amaz'd, and curious,
The mirth and fun grew fast and furious:
The piper loud and louder blew;
The dancers quick and quicker flew;
They reel'd, they set, they cross'd, they cleekit,
Till ilka carlin swat and reekit,
And coost her duddies to the wark,
And linket at it in her sark!

Now, Tam, O Tam! had thae been queans,
A' plump and strapping in their teens,
Their sarks, instead o' creeshie flannen,
Been snaw-white seventeen hunder linen!
Thir breeks o' mine, my only pair,
That ance were plush, o' gude blue hair,
I wad hae gi'en them off my hurdies,
For ae blink o' the bonnie burdies!

But wither'd beldams, auld and droll,
Rigwoodie hags wad spean a foal,
Lowping and flinging on a crummock,
I wonder didna turn thy stomach.

But Tam kend what was what fu' brawlie,
There was ae winsome wench and walie,
That night enlisted in the core,
(Lang after kend on Carrick shore;
For mony a beast to dead she shot,
And perish'd mony a bonnie boat,
And shook baith meikle corn and bear,
And kept the country-side in fear).

coost, *cast off*	duddies, *rags*	sark, *shirt*
queans, *girls*	creeshie, *greasy*	hurdies, *buttocks*
burdies, *lasses*	rigwoodie, *gallows worthy*	crummock, *staff*
walie, *choice*	bear, *barley*	

Her cutty sark, o' Paisley harn,
That while a lassie she had worn,
In longitude tho' sorely scanty,
It was her best, and she was vauntie.—
Ah! little kend thy reverend grannie,
That sark she coft for her wee Nannie,
Wi' twa pund Scots ('twas a' her riches),
Wad ever grac'd a dance of witches!

But here my Muse her wing maun cour;
Sic flights are far beyond her pow'r;
To sing how Nannie lap and flang,
(A souple jade she was, and strang),
And how Tam stood, like ane bewitch'd,
And thought his very een enrich'd;
Even Satan glowr'd, and fidg'd fu' fain,
And hotch'd and blew wi' might and main:
Till first ae caper, syne anither,
Tam tint his reason a' thegither,
And roars out, 'Weel done, Cutty-sark!'
And in an instant all was dark:
And scarcely had he Maggie rallied,
When out the hellish legion sallied.

As bees bizz out wi' angry fyke,
When plundering herds assail their byke;
As open pussie's mortal foes,
When, pop! she starts before their nose;
As eager runs the market-crowd,
When 'Catch the thief!' resounds aloud;
So Maggie runs, the witches follow,
Wi' mony an eldritch skreech and hollow.

Ah, Tam! Ah, Tam! thou'll get thy fairin!
In hell they'll roast thee like a herrin!
In vain thy Kate awaits thy comin!
Kate soon will be a woefu' woman!

cutty, *short*	Paisley harn, *coarse cloth*	vauntie, *proud*
coft, *bought*	cour, *cower*	fu' fain, *eagerly*
tint, *lost*	fyke, *fuss*	herds, *shepherds*
byke, *hive*	pussie's, *the hare's*	eldritch, *unearthly*

Now, do thy speedy utmost, Meg,
And win the key-stane of the brig;
There at them thou thy tail may toss,
A running stream they dare na cross.
But ere the key-stane she could make,
The fient a tail she had to shake!
For Nannie, far before the rest,
Hard upon noble Maggie prest,
And flew at Tam wi' furious ettle;
But little wist she Maggie's mettle—
Ae spring brought off her master hale,
But left behind her ain grey tail:
The carlin claught her by the rump,
And left poor Maggie scarce a stump.

Now, wha this tale o' truth shall read,
Ilk man and mother's son, take heed:
Whene'er to drink you are inclin'd,
Or cutty-sarks run in your mind,
Think, ye may buy the joys o'er dear,
Remember Tam o' Shanter's mare.

The Twa Dogs

A TALE

'Twas in that place o' Scotland's isle,
That bears the name o' Auld King Coil,
Upon a bonnie day in June,
When wearing thro' the afternoon,
Twa dogs, that were na thrang at hame,
Foregather'd ance upon a time.

The first I'll name, they ca'd him Cæsar,
Was keepit for his Honour's pleasure;
His hair, his size, his mouth, his lugs,
Shew'd he was nane o' Scotland's dogs,
But whalpit some place far abroad,
Whare sailors gang to fish for cod.

ettle, *intention*   claught, *clutched*   thrang, *busy*

His locked, letter'd, braw brass collar
Shew'd him the gentleman and scholar;
But tho' he was o' high degree,
The fient a pride, na pride had he,
But wad hae spent an hour caressin,
Ev'n wi' a tinkler-gypsey's messin:
At kirk or market, mill or smiddie,
Nae tawted tyke, tho' e'er sae duddie,
But he wad stan't, as glad to see him,
And stroan't on stanes an' hillocks wi' him.

The tither was a ploughman's collie,
A rhyming, ranting, raving billie,
Wha for his friend and comrade had him,
And in his freaks had Luath ca'd him,
After some dog in Highland sang,
Was made lang syne, Lord knows how lang.

He was a gash an' faithful tyke,
As ever lap a sheugh or dyke.
His honest, sonsie, baws'nt face
Ay gat him friends in ilka place;
His breast was white, his touzie back
Weel clad wi' coat o' glossy black;
His gawcie tail, wi' upward curl,
Hung owre his hurdies wi' a swirl.

Nae doubt but they were fain o' ither,
An' unco pack an' thick thegither;
Wi' social nose whyles snuff'd an' snowkit,
Whyles mice an' moudieworts they howkit;
Whyles scour'd awa in lang excursion,
An' worry'd ither in diversion;
Till tir'd at last wi' mony a farce,
They sat them down upon their arse,
And there began a lang digression
About the *lords o' the creation.*

messin, *mongrel*   tawted, *matted*   duddie, *ragged*
      wad stan't, *would have stood*   stroan't, *watered*
gash, *wise*   sheugh, *ditch*   sonsie, *jolly*
      baws'nt, *white-striped*   gawcie, *handsome*
fain o' ither, *fond of each other*   pack an' thick, *intimate*
snowkit, *scented*   moudieworts, *moles*   howkit, *dug up*

I've aften wonder'd, honest Luath,
What sort o' life poor dogs like you have;
An' when the gentry's life I saw,
What way poor bodies liv'd ava.

Our Laird gets in his racked rents,
His coals, his kain, and a' his stents:
He rises when he likes himsel;
His flunkies answer at the bell;
He ca's his coach; he ca's his horse;
He draws a bonnie, silken purse
As lang's my tail, whare thro the steeks,
The yellow letter'd Geordie keeks.

Frae morn to e'en it's nought but toiling,
At baking, roasting, drying, boiling;
An' tho' the gentry first are stechin,
Yet ev'n the ha' folk fill their pechan
Wi' sauce, ragouts, and siclike trashtrie,
That's little short o' downright wastrie.
Our Whipper-in, wee, blastit wonner,
Poor, worthless elf, it eats a dinner,
Better than ony tenant man
His Honour has in a' the lan':
An' what poor cot-folk pit their painch in,
I own it's past my comprehension.

LUATH

Trowth, Cæsar, whyles they're fash't enough;
A cotter howkin in a sheugh,
Wi' dirty stanes biggin a dyke,
Baring a quarry, and siclike,
Himsel, a wife, he thus sustains,
A smytrie o' wee duddie weans,
An' nought but his han' darg to keep
Them right an' tight in thack an' rape.

kain, *rents in kind*   stents, *taxes*   steeks, *stitches*   Geordie, *guinea*
stechin, *stuffing*   ha' folk, *servants*   pechan, *stomachs*   painch, *paunch*
fash't, *troubled*   biggin, *building*   smytrie, *swarm*   duddie, *ragged*
han' darg, *hand's labour*   thack an' rape, *thatch and rope*

An' when they meet wi' sair disasters,
Like loss o' health or want o' masters,
Ye maist wad think, a wee touch langer,
An' they maun starve o' cauld and hunger:
But how it comes, I never kend yet,
They're maistly wonderfu' contented;
An' buirdly chiels, an' clever hizzies,
Are bred in sic a way as this is.

CÆSAR

But then to see how ye're negleckit,
How huff'd, and cuff'd, and disrespeckit!
Lord, man, our gentry care as little
For delvers, ditchers, an' sic cattle;
They gang as saucy by poor folk,
As I wad by a stinking brock.

I've notic'd, on our Laird's court-day,
An' mony a time my heart's been wae,
Poor tenant bodies, scant o' cash,
How they maun thole a factor's snash;
He'll stamp an' threaten, curse an' swear,
He'll apprehend them, poind their gear:
While they maun stan', wi' aspect humble,
An' hear it a', an' fear an' tremble!

I see how folk live that hae riches;
But surely poor folk maun be wretches!

LUATH

They're nae sae wretched's ane wad think;
Tho' constantly on poortith's brink,
They're sae accustom'd wi' the sight,
The view o't gies them little fright.

Then chance an' fortune are sae guided,
They're ay in less or mair provided;
An' tho' fatigu'd wi' close employment,
A blink o' rest's a sweet enjoyment.

| buirdly chiels, *stout lads* | hizzies, *young women* | brock, *badger* |
| snash, *abuse* | poind, *seize* | poortith, *poverty* |

The dearest comfort o' their lives,
Their grushie weans an' faithfu' wives;
The prattling things are just their pride,
That sweetens a' their fire-side.

An' whyles twalpennie worth o' nappy
Can make the bodies unco happy;
They lay aside their private cares,
To mind the Kirk and State affairs;
They'll talk o' patronage and priests,
Wi' kindling fury in their breasts,
Or tell what new taxation's comin,
An' ferlie at the folk in Lon'on.

As bleak-fac'd Hallowmass returns,
They get the jovial, ranting Kirns,
When rural life, o' ev'ry station,
Unite in common recreation;
Love blinks, Wit slaps, an' social Mirth
Forgets there's Care upo' the earth.

That merry day the year begins,
They bar the door on frosty win's;
The nappy reeks wi' mantling ream,
An' sheds a heart-inspiring steam;
The luntin pipe, an' sneeshin mill,
Are handed round wi' right guid will;
The cantie, auld folks, crackin crouse,
The young anes ranting thro' the house—
My heart has been sae fain to see them,
That I for joy hae barkit wi' them.

Still it's owre true that ye hae said,
Sic game is now owre aften play'd;
There's monie a creditable stock
O' decent, honest fawsont folk,
Are riven out baith root and branch,
Some rascal's pridefu' greed to quench,

grushie, *thriving*   nappy, *ale*   ferlie, *marvel*
Kirns, *Harvest-homes*   luntin, *smoking*   sneeshin mill, *snuff box*
cantie, *cheerful*   crackin crouse, *talking merrily*
                         fawsont, *seemly*

201

Wha thinks to knit himself the faster
In favour wi' some gentle Master,
Wha aiblins thrang a parliamentin
For Britain's guid his saul indentin——

CÆSAR

Haith, lad, ye little ken about it;
For Britain's guid! guid faith! I doubt it.
Say rather, gaun as Premiers lead him,
An' saying *aye* or *no*'s they bid him:
At operas an' plays parading,
Mortgaging, gambling, masquerading:
Or maybe, in a frolic daft,
To Hague or Calais taks a waft,
To mak a tour, an' tak a whirl,
To learn *bon ton* an' see the worl'.

There, at Vienna or Versailles,
He rives his father's auld entails;
Or by Madrid he taks the rout,
To thrum guitars an' fecht wi' nowt;
Or down Italian vista startles,
Whore hunting amang groves o' myrtles:
Then bouses drumly German water,
To mak himsel look fair and fatter,
An' clear the consequential sorrows,
Love-gifts of Carnival Signoras.

For Britain's guid! for her destruction!
Wi' dissipation, feud an' faction.

LUATH

Hech man! dear sirs! is that the gate
They waste say mony a braw estate!
Are we sae foughten an' harass'd
For gear to gang that gate at last!

O would they stay aback frae courts,
An' please themsels wi' countra sports,

aiblins, *perhaps*   thrang, *busy*   rives, *wastes*   nowt, *cattle*
drumly, *muddy*   gate, *way*   foughten, *troubled*   gear, *wealth*

It wad for ev'ry ane be better,
The Laird, the Tenant, an' the Cotter!
For thae frank, rantin, ramblin billies,
Fient haet o' them's ill hearted fellows;
Except for breakin o' their timmer,
Or speakin lightly o' their limmer,
Or shootin o' a hare or moorcock,
The ne'er-a-bit they're ill to poor folk.

But will ye tell me, master Cæsar,
Sure great folk's life's a life o' pleasure?
Nae cauld nor hunger e'er can steer them,
The vera thought o't need na fear them.

CÆSAR

Lord, man, were ye but whyles whare I am,
The gentles ye wad ne'er envy 'em.

It's true, they need na starve or sweat,
Thro' winter's cauld, or Simmer's heat;
They've nae sair wark to craze their banes,
An' fill auld age wi' grips an' granes;
But human bodies are sic fools,
For a' their colleges and schools,
That when nae real ills perplex them,
They mak enow themsels to vex them;
An' ay the less they hae to sturt them,
In like proportion, less will hurt them.
A country fellow at the pleugh,
His acres till'd, he's right eneugh;
A country girl at her wheel,
Her dizzen's done, she's unco weel:
But Gentlemen, an' Ladies warst,
Wi' eve'ndown want o' wark are curst.
They loiter, lounging, lank an' lazy;
Tho' deil haet ails them, yet uneasy;
Their days, insipid, dull an' tasteless,
Their nights, unquiet, lang, and restless,
An' ev'n their sports, their balls an' races,
Their galloping thro' public places,

Fient haet, *Devil a one*   timmer, *timber*   limmer, *mistress*
sturt, *annoy*   dizzen, *dozen*   deil haet, *devil a thing*

There's sic parade, sic pomp an' art,
The joy can scarcely reach the heart.
The Men cast out in party matches,
Then sowther a' in deep debauches,
Ae night, they're mad wi' drink an' whoring,
Niest day their life is past enduring.
The Ladies arm-in-arm in clusters,
As great an' gracious a' as sisters;
But hear their absent thoughts o' ither,
They're a' run deils an' jads thegither.
Whyles, owre the wee bit cup an' platie,
They sip the scandal potion pretty;
Or lee-lang nights, wi' crabbit leuks,
Pore owre the devil's pictur'd beuks;
Stake on a chance a farmer's stackyard,
An' cheat like ony unhang'd blackguard.

There's some exception, man an' woman;
But this is Gentry's life in common.

By this, the sun was out o' sight,
An' darker gloamin brought the night:
The bum-clock humm'd wi' lazy drone,
The kye stood rowtin i' the loan;
When up they gat an' shook their lugs,
Rejoic'd they were na *men*, but *dogs*;
An' each took aff his several way,
Resolv'd to meet some ither day.

Holy Willie's Prayer

Argument

Holy Willie was a rather oldish batchelor Elder in the parish of Mauchline [Ayrshire], & much & justly famed for that polemical chattering which ends in tippling Orthodoxy, & for that Spiritualized Bawdry which refines to Liquorish Devotion.—In a Sessional process with a gentleman in Mauchline, a Mr. Gavin Hamilton, Holy Willie, & his priest, father

sowther, *solder*   run, *downright*   lee-lang, *live-long*
          bum-clock, *beetle*   rowtin, *lowing*

Auld, after full hearing in the Presbytery of Ayr, came off but second best; owing partly to the oratorical powers of Mr. Robt. Aiken, Mr. Hamilton's Counsel; but chiefly to Mr. Hamilton's being one of the most irreproachable & truly respectable characters in the country.—On losing his Process, the Muse overheard him at his devotions as follows—

O thou that in the heavens does dwell!
Wha, as it pleases best thysel,
Sends ane to heaven and ten to hell,
  A' for thy glory!
And no for ony gude or ill
  They've done afore thee.

I bless and praise thy matchless might,
When thousands thou hast left in night,
That I am here before thy sight,
  For gifts and grace,
A burning and a shining light
  To a' this place.

What was I, or my generation,
That I should get such exaltation?
I, wha deserv'd most just damnation,
  For broken laws
Sax thousand years ere my creation,
  Thro' Adam's cause.

When from my mother's womb I fell,
Thou might hae plunged me deep in hell,
To gnash my gooms, and weep, and wail,
  In burning lakes,
Where damned devils roar and yell
  Chain'd to their stakes.

Yet I am here, a chosen sample,
To shew thy grace is great and ample:
I'm here, a pillar o' thy temple
  Strong as a rock,
A guide, a ruler and example
  To a' thy flock.

But yet—O Lord—confess I must—
At times I'm fash'd wi' fleshly lust;
And sometimes too, in warldly trust
      Vile Self gets in;
But thou remembers we are dust,
      Defil'd wi' sin.

Maybe thou lets this fleshly thorn
Buffet thy servant e'en and morn,
Lest he o'er proud and high should turn,
      That he's sae gifted;
If sae, thy hand maun e'en be borne
      Until thou lift it.

Lord bless thy Chosen in this place,
For here thou has a chosen race:
But God, confound their stubborn face,
      And blast their name,
Wha bring thy rulers to disgrace
      And open shame.

Lord mind Gaun Hamilton's deserts!
He drinks, and swears, and plays at cartes,
Yet has sae mony taking arts
      Wi' Great and Sma',
Frae God's ain priest the people's hearts
      He steals awa.

And when we chasten'd him therefore,
Thou kens how he bred sic a splore,
And set the warld in a roar
      O' laughin at us:
Curse thou his basket and his store,
      Kail and potatoes.

Lord hear my earnest cry and prayer
Against that Presbytery of Ayr!
Thy strong right hand, Lord, make it bare
      Upon their heads!
Lord visit them, and dinna spare,
      For their misdeeds!

fash'd, *troubled*   cartes, *cards*   splore, *disturbance*

O Lord my God, that glib-tongu'd Aiken!
My very heart and flesh are quaking
To think how I sat, sweating, shaking,
　　　　　And piss'd wi' dread,
While Auld wi' hingin lip gaed sneaking
　　　　　And hid his head!

Lord, in thy day o' vengeance try him!
Lord, visit him that did employ him!
And pass not in thy mercy by them;
　　　　　Nor hear their prayer;
But for thy people's sake destroy them,
　　　　　And dinna spare!

But Lord; remember me and mine
Wi' mercies temporal and divine!
That I for grace and gear may shine,
　　　　　Excell'd by nane!
And a' the glory shall be thine!
　　　　　Amen! Amen!

To William Simpson, *Ochiltree*

I gat your letter, winsome Willie;
Wi' grateful heart I thank you brawlie;
Tho' I maun say't, I wad be silly,
　　　　　An' unco vain,
Should I believe, my coaxin billie,
　　　　　Your flatterin strain.

But I'se believe ye kindly meant it,
I sud be laith to think ye hinted
Ironic satire, sidelins sklented
　　　　　On my poor Musie;
Tho' in sic phraisin' terms ye've penn'd it,
　　　　　I scarce excuse ye.

My senses wad be in a creel,
Should I but dare a hope to speel,

gear, *wealth*　　　　　sidelins sklented, *side ways squinted*
　　creel, *whirl*　　　　　speel, *climb*

207

Wi' Allan, or wi' Gilbertfield,
   The braes o' fame;
Or Ferguson, the writer-chiel,
   A deathless name.

(O Ferguson! thy glorious parts
Ill suited law's dry, musty arts!
My curse upon your whunstane hearts,
   Ye Enbrugh Gentry!
The tythe o' what ye waste at cartes
   Wad stow'd his pantry!)

Yet when a tale comes i' my head,
Or lasses gie my heart a screed,
As whiles they're like to be my dead,
   (O sad disease!)
I kittle up my rustic reed;
   It gies me ease.

Auld Coila, now, may fidge fu' fain,
She's gotten Poets o' her ain,
Chiels wha their chanters winna hain,
   But tune their lays,
Till echoes a' resound again
   Her weel-sung praise.

Nae Poet thought her worth his while,
To set her name in measur'd style;
She lay like some unkend-of isle
   Beside New Holland,
Or whare wild-meeting oceans boil
   Besouth Magellan.

Ramsay an' famous Ferguson
Gied Forth an' Tay a lift aboon;
Yarrow an' Tweed, to monie a tune,
   Owre Scotland rings,
While Irwin, Lugar, Ayr, an' Doon,
   Naebody sings.

writer-chiel, *lawyer fellow* stow'd, *stored* screed, *tear*
 kittle, *tickle* fidge fu' fain, *tingle eagerly* hain, *spare*

Th' Illissus, Tiber, Thames, an' Seine,
Glide sweet in monie a tunefu' line;
But, Willie, set your fit to mine,
   An' cock your crest,
We'll gar our streams an' burnies shine
   Up wi' the best.

We'll sing auld Coila's plains an' fells,
Her moors red-brown wi' heather bells,
Her banks an' braes, her dens an' dells,
   Whare glorious Wallace
Aft bure the gree, as story tells,
   Frae Suthron billies.

At Wallace' name, what Scottish blood
But boils up in a spring-tide flood!
Oft have our fearless fathers strode
   By Wallace' side,
Still pressing onward, red-wat shod,
   Or glorious dy'd!

O sweet are Coila's haughs an' woods,
When lintwhites chant amang the buds,
And jinkin hares, in amorous whids,
   Their loves enjoy,
While thro' the braes the cushat croods
   With wailfu' cry!

Ev'n winter bleak has charms to me
When winds rave thro' the naked tree;
Or frosts on hills of Ochiltree
   Are hoary gray;
Or blinding drifts wild-furious flee,
   Dark'ning the day!

O Nature! a' thy shews an' forms
To feeling, pensive hearts hae charms!
Whether the Summer kindly warms,
   Wi' life an' light,
Or Winter howls, in gusty storms,
   The lang, dark night!

| bure, *bore away* | gree, *prize* | haughs, *low lying land* |
| whids, *gambols* | cushat, *wood pigeon* | croods, *croons* |

The Muse, nae Poet ever fand her,
Till by himsel he learn'd to wander,
Adown some trotting burn's meander,
          An' no think lang;
O sweet, to stray an' pensive ponder
          A heart-felt sang!

The warly race may drudge an' drive,
Hog-shouther, jundie, stretch an' strive,
Let me fair Nature's face descrive,
          And I, wi' pleasure,
Shall let the busy, grumbling hive
          Bum owre their treasure.

Fareweel, 'my rhyme-composing brither!'
We've been owre lang unkenn'd to ither:
Now let us lay our heads thegither,
          In love fraternal:
May Envy wallop in a tether,
          Black fiend, infernal!

While Highlandmen hate tolls an' taxes;
While moorlan herds like guid, fat braxies;
While Terra Firma, on her axis,
          Diurnal turns,
Count on a friend, in faith an' practice,
          In Robert Burns.

Address to the Deil

O Prince! O Chief of many throned Pow'rs,
That led th' embattl'd Seraphim to war.
                                        MILTON

O Thou! whatever title suit thee,
Auld Hornie, Satan, Nick, or Clootie,
Wha in yon cavern grim an' sootie,
          Clos'd under hatches,
Spairges about the brunstane cootie,
          To scaud poor wretches.

warly, *worldly*	Hog-shouther, *push*	jundie, *jostle*
braxies, *dead sheep*	Spairges, *splashes*	cootie, *bowl*

Hear me, auld Hangie, for a wee,
An' let poor, damned bodies be;
I'm sure sma' pleasure it can gie,
        Ev'n to a deil,
To skelp an' scaud poor dogs like me,
        An' hear us squeal!

Great is thy pow'r, an' great thy fame;
Far kend an' noted is thy name;
An' tho' yon lowin heugh's thy hame,
        Thou travels far;
An' faith! thou's neither lag nor lame,
        Nor blate nor scaur.

Whyles, ranging like a roarin lion,
For prey, a' holes an' corners tryin;
Whyles, on the strong-wing'd Tempest flyin,
        Tirlin the kirks;
Whyles, in the human bosom pryin,
        Unseen thou lurks.

I've heard my reverend Graunie say,
In lanely glens ye like to stray;
Or where auld, ruin'd castles, gray,
        Nod to the moon,
Ye fright the nightly wand'rer's way,
        Wi' eldritch croon.

When twilight did my Graunie summon,
To say her pray'rs, douce, honest woman!
Aft yont the dyke she's heard you bummin
        Wi' eerie drone;
Or, rustlin, thro' the boortries comin,
        Wi' heavy groan.

Ae dreary, windy, winter night,
The stars shot down wi' sklentin light,
Wi' you, mysel, I gat a fright,
        Ayont the loch;
Ye, like a rash-buss, stood in sight,
        Wi' waving sough.

scaud, *scald*   lowin heugh, *flaming pit*   lag, *backward*
blate, *bashful*   scaur, *scared*   Tirlin, *unroofing*   eldritch, *unearthly*
douce, *decent*   boortries, *elder trees*   sough, *moan*

211

The cudgel in my nieve did shake,
Each bristl'd hair stood like a stake,
When wi' an eldritch, stoor quaick, quaick,
      Amang the springs,
Awa ye squatter'd like a drake,
      On whistling wings.

Let warlocks grim, an' wither'd hags,
Tell how wi' you on ragweed nags,
They skim the muirs an' dizzy crags,
      Wi' wicked speed;
And in kirk-yards renew their leagues,
      Owre howkit dead.

Thence, countra wives, wi' toil an' pain,
May plunge an' plunge the kirn in vain;
For, Oh! the yellow treasure's taen
      By witching skill;
An' dawtit, twal-pint hawkie's gaen
      As yell's the bill.

Thence, mystic knots mak great abuse,
On young Guidmen, fond, keen, an' crouse;
When the best wark-lume i' the house,
      By cantraip wit,
Is instant made no worth a louse,
      Just at the bit.

When thowes dissolve the snawy hoord,
An' float the jinglin icy-boord,
Then, Water-kelpies haunt the foord,
      By your direction,
An' nighted Trav'llers are allur'd
      To their destruction.

An' aft your moss-traversing Spunkies
Decoy the wight that late an' drunk is:

nieve, *fist*	stoor, *harsh*	kirn, *churn*
dawtit, *petted*	yell's, *dry as*	bill, *bull*
Guidmen, *husbands*	crouse, *brisk*	wark-lume, *tool* thowes, *thaws*
hoord, *hoard*	boord, *surface*	Spunkies, *Will o' the wisps*

The bleezin, curst, mischievous monkies
        Delude his eyes,
Till in some miry slough he sunk is,
        Ne'er mair to rise.

When Masons' mystic word an' grip,
In storms an' tempests raise you up,
Some cock or cat your rage maun stop,
        Or, strange to tell!
The youngest Brother ye wad whip
        Aff straught to hell.

Lang syne in Eden's bonnie yard,
When youthfu' lovers first were pair'd,
An' all the Soul of Love they shar'd,
        The raptur'd hour,
Sweet on the fragrant, flowr'y swaird,
        In shady bow'r:

Then you, ye auld, snick-drawing dog!
Ye cam to Paradise incog.
An' played on man a cursed brogue,
        (Black be your fa'!)
An' gied the infant warld a shog,
        'Maist ruin'd a'.

D'ye mind that day, when in a bizz,
Wi' reekit duds, an' reestit gizz,
Ye did present your smoutie phiz,
        'Mang better folk,
An' sklented on the man of Uzz
        Your spitefu' joke?

An' how ye gat him i' your thrall,
An' brak him out o' house an' hal',
While scabs an' botches did him gall,
        Wi' bitter claw,
An' lows'd his ill-tongu'd, wicked Scawl,
        Was warst ava?

yard, *garden*   snick-drawing, *stealthy*   brogue, *trick*
shog, *shake*   reekit duds, *smoky clothes*   reestit gizz, *scorched wig*
   sklented, *cast*   lows'd, *loosed*   Scawl, *scolding wife*

But a' your doings to rehearse,
Your wily snares an' fechtin fierce,
Sin' that day Michael did you pierce,
      Down to this time,
Wad ding a Lallan tongue, or Erse,
      In prose or rhyme.

An' now, auld Cloots, I ken ye're thinkin,
A certain Bardie's rantin, drinkin,
Some luckless hour will send him linkin
      To your black pit;
But, faith! he'll turn a corner jinkin,
      An' cheat you yet.

But fare you weel, auld Nickie-ben!
O wad ye tak a thought an' men'!
Ye aiblins might—I dinna ken—
      Still hae a stake—
I'm wae to think upo' yon den,
      Ev'n for your sake!

I love my Jean

Of a' the airts the wind can blaw,
  I dearly like the west,
For there the bonnie Lassie lives,
  The Lassie I lo'e best:
There's wild-woods grow, and rivers row,
  And mony a hill between;
But day and night my fancy's flight
  Is ever wi' my Jean.

I see her in the dewy flowers,
  I see her sweet and fair;
I hear her in the tunefu' birds,
  I hear her charm the air:
There's not a bonnie flower, that springs
  By fountain, shaw, or green,
There's not a bonnie bird that sings,
  But minds me o' my Jean.

ding, *defeat*   Lallan, *lowland*   linkin, *hurrying*   aiblins, *perhaps*
airts, *directions*   row, *roll*   shaw, *wood*

Ae fond Kiss

Ae fond kiss, and then we sever;
Ae fareweel and then for ever!
Deep in heart-wrung tears I'll pledge thee,
Warring sighs and groans I'll wage thee.
Who shall say that fortune grieves him
While the star of hope she leaves him?
Me, nae cheerfu' twinkle lights me;
Dark despair around benights me.

I'll ne'er blame my partial fancy,
Naething could resist my Nancy:
But to see her, was to love her;
Love but her, and love for ever.
Had we never lov'd sae kindly,
Had we never lov'd sae blindly,
Never met—or never parted,
We had ne'er been broken-hearted.

Fare thee weel, thou first and fairest!
Fare thee weel, thou best and dearest!
Thine be ilka joy and treasure,
Peace, enjoyment, love and pleasure!
Ae fond kiss, and then we sever;
Ae fareweel, Alas! for ever!
Deep in heart-wrung tears I'll pledge thee,
Warring sighs and groans I'll wage thee.

A red, red Rose

O my Luve's like a red, red, rose
    That's newly sprung in June.
O my Luve's like the melodie
    That's sweetly play'd in tune.

As fair art thou, my bonnie lass,
    So deep in luve am I;
And I will love thee still, my Dear,
    Till a' the seas gang dry.

Till a' the seas gang dry, my Dear,
    And the rocks melt wi' the sun:
I will love thee still, my Dear,
    While the sands o' life shall run:

And fare thee weel, my only Luve!
    And fare thee weel, a while!
And I will come again, my Luve,
    Tho' it were ten thousand mile!

John Anderson my Jo

John Anderson my jo, John,
    When we were first acquent;
Your locks were like the raven,
    Your bonnie brow was brent;
But now your brow is beld, John,
    Your locks are like the snaw;
But blessings on your frosty pow,
    John Anderson my Jo.

John Anderson my jo, John,
    We clamb the hill the gither;
And mony a canty day John,
    We've had wi' ane anither:
Now we maun totter down, John,
    And hand in hand we'll go;
And sleep the gither at the foot,
    John Anderson my Jo.

Last May a braw Wooer

Last May a braw wooer cam' down the lang glen,
    And sair wi' his love he did deave me;
I said, there was naething I hated like men,
    The deuce gae wi' him to believe me, believe me,
    The deuce gae wi' him to believe me.

jo, *dear*	brent, *smooth*	beld, *bald*
pow, *head*	canty, *cheerful*	deave, *deafen*

216

He spak o' the darts in my bonnie black e'en,
    And vow'd for my love he was dying;
I said he might die when he liked for Jean;
    The Lord forgi'e me for lying, for lying,
    The Lord forgi'e me for lying!

A weel stocked mailin, himsel' for the laird,
    And marriage aff hand were his proffers:
I never loot on that I kend it, or car'd,
    But thought I might hae waur offers, waur offers,
    But thought I might hae waur offers.

But what wad ye think? in a fortnight or less,
    The de'il tak' his taste to gae near her!
He up the lang loan to my black cousin Bess,
    Guess ye how the jad! I could bear her, could bear her,
    Guess ye how the jad! I could bear her.

But a' the niest week as I petted wi' care,
    I gaed to the tryste o' Dalgarnock;
And wha but my fine fickle lover was there,
    I glowr'd as I'd seen a warlock, a warlock,
    I glowr'd as I'd seen a warlock.

But owre my left shouther I ga'e him a blink,
    Lest neebours might say I was saucy:
My wooer he caper'd as he'd been in drink,
    And vow'd I was his dear lassie, dear lassie,
    And vow'd I was his dear lassie.

I speir'd for my cousin fu' couthy and sweet,
    If she had recover'd her hearing;
And how her new shoon fit her auld, shachl't feet;
    But heavens! how he fell a-swearing, a-swearing,
    But heavens! how he fell a-swearing.

He begged, for gude-sake I wad be his wife,
    Or else I wad kill him with sorrow:
So e'en to preserve the poor body in life,
    I think I maun wed him—to-morrow, to-morrow,
    I think I maun wed him to-morrow.

mailin, *farm*	loan, *lane*	tryste, *fair*
speir'd, *asked*	couthy, *kind*	shachl't, *misshapen*

O Whistle, and I'll come to you, my Lad

O whistle, and I'll come to you, my lad,
O whistle, and I'll come to you, my lad;
Tho' father and mother and a' should gae mad,
O whistle, and I'll come to you, my lad.

But warily tent, when ye come to court me,
And come na unless the back-yett be a-jee;
Syne up the back-style, and let naebody see,
And come, as ye were na coming to me,
And come, as ye were na coming to me.

At kirk, or at market, whene'er ye meet me,
Gang by me as tho' that ye car'd nae a flie;
But steal me a blink o' your bonnie black e'e,
Yet look as ye were na looking at me,
Yet look as ye were na looking at me.

Ay vow and protest that ye carena for me,
And *whyles* ye may lightly my beauty a wee;
But court nae anither, tho' joking ye be,
For fear that she wyle your fancy frae me,
For fear that she wyle your fancy frae me.

Duncan Gray

Duncan Gray cam here to woo,
Ha, ha, the wooing o't,
On blythe yule night when we were fou,
Ha, ha, the wooing o't,
Maggie coost her head fu' high,
Look'd asklent and unco skeigh,
Gart poor Duncan stand abiegh;
Ha, ha, the wooing o't.

Duncan fleech'd, and Duncan pray'd;
Ha, ha, the wooing o't,
Meg was deaf as Ailsa Craig,
Ha, ha, the wooing o't,

tent, *watch*	yett, *gate*	Syne, *then*
lightly, *disparage*	yule night, *Christmas eve*	asklent, *askance*
skeigh, *skittish*	abiegh, *aside*	fleech'd, *wheedled*

Duncan sigh'd baith out and in,
Grat his een baith bleer't and blin',
Spak o' lowpin o'er a linn;
   Ha, ha, the wooing o't.

Time and chance are but a tide,
   Ha, ha, the wooing o't.
Slighted love is sair to bide,
   Ha, ha, the wooing o't,
Shall I, like a fool, quoth he,
For a haughty hizzie die?
She may gae to—France for me!
   Ha, ha, the wooing o't.

How it comes let doctors tell,
   Ha, ha, the wooing o't,
Meg grew sick—as he grew heal,
   Ha, ha, the wooing o't,
Something in her bosom wrings,
For relief a sigh she brings;
And O, her e'en, they spak sic things!
   Ha, ha, the wooing o't.

Duncan was a lad o' grace,
   Ha, ha, the wooing o't,
Maggie's was a piteous case,
   Ha, ha, the wooing o't,
Duncan could na be her death,
Swelling pity smoor'd his wrath;
Now they're crouse and canty baith.
   Ha, ha, the wooing o't.

Willie brew'd a Peck o' Maut

O Willie brew'd a peck o' maut,
   And Rob and Allan cam to see;
Three blyther hearts, that lee lang night,
   Ye wad na found in Christendie.

| linn, *waterfall* | smoor'd, *smothered* | crouse, *brisk* |
| canty, *cheerful* | maut, *malt* | lee lang, *live-long* |

We are na fou, we're nae that fou,
    But just a drappie in our e'e;
The cock may craw, the day may daw,
    And ay we'll taste the barley bree.

Here are we met, three merry boys,
    Three merry boys I trow are we;
And mony a night we've merry been,
    And mony mae we hope to be!

It is the moon, I ken her horn,
    That's blinkin in the lift sae hie;
She shines sae bright to wyle us hame,
    But by my sooth she'll wait a wee!

Wha first shall rise to gang awa,
    A cuckold, coward loun is he!
Wha first beside his chair shall fa',
    He is the king amang us three!

bree, *brew*

LADY NAIRNE

1766-1845

The Laird o' Cockpen

The Laird o' Cockpen he's proud an' he's great,
His mind is ta'en up wi' the things o' the State;
He wanted a wife his braw house to keep,
But favour wi' wooin' was fashious to seek.

Doon by the dyke-side a lady did dwell,
At his table-head he thocht she'd look well;
M'Cleish's ae dochter, o' Clavers-ha' Lee,
A penniless lass wi' a lang pedigree.

His wig was weel pouther'd, as gude as when new;
His waistcoat was white, his coat it was blue;
He put on a ring, a sword, an' cocked hat,
An' wha could refuse the Laird wi' a' that?

He took the grey mare, he rade cannilie,
An' rapped at the yett o' Clavers-ha' Lee;
'Gae tell Mistress Jean to come speedily ben,—
She's wanted to speak wi' the Laird o' Cockpen.'

Mistress Jean she was makin' the elder-flow'r wine;
'An' what brings the Laird at sic a like time?'
She put aff her apron, an' on her silk goon,
Her mutch wi' red ribbons, an' gaed awa doon.

An' when she cam' ben he bowèd fu' low,
An' what was his errand he soon let her know;
Amazed was the Laird when the lady said 'Na!'
An' wi' a laigh curtsie she turned awa'!

fashious, *troublesome*   pouther'd, *powdered*   yett, **door**
          mutch, *cap*   laigh, *low*

Dumbfounder'd was he, but nae sigh did he gi'e,
He mounted his mare an' he rade cannilie;
An' often he thocht, as he gaed through the glen,
'She's daft to refuse the Laird o' Cockpen!'

Caller Herrin'

Wha'll buy my caller herrin'?
 They're bonnie fish and halesome farin';
Wha'll buy my caller herrin',
 New drawn frae the Forth?

When ye were sleepin' on your pillows,
 Dream'd ye aught o' our puir fellows,
Darkling as they fac'd the billows,
 A' to fill the woven willows?
  Buy my caller herrin',
  New drawn frae the Forth.

Wha'll buy my caller herrin'?
 They're no brought here without brave darin';
Buy my caller herrin',
 Haul'd through wind and rain.
  Wha'll buy my caller herrin'? etc.

Wha'll buy my caller herrin'?
 Oh, ye may ca' them vulgar farin'—
Wives and mithers, maist despairin',
 Ca' them lives o' men.
  Wha'll buy my caller herrin'? etc.

When the creel o' herrin' passes,
 Ladies, clad in silks and laces,
Gather in their braw pelisses,
 Cast their heads and screw their faces.
  Wha'll buy my caller herrin'? etc.

Caller herrin's no got lightlie:—
 Ye can trip the spring fu' tightlie;
Spite o' tauntin', flauntin', flingin',
 Gow has set you a' a-singing
  Wha'll buy my caller herrin'? etc.

caller, *fresh*

222

Neebour wives, now tent my tellin';
　　When the bonnie fish ye're sellin',
At ae word be in your dealin'—
　　Truth will stand when a' thing's failin',
　　　Wha'll buy my caller herrin'?
　　　　They're bonnie fish and halesome **farin'**;
　　　Wha'll buy my caller herrin',
　　　　New drawn frae the Forth?

　　　　tent, *attend to*

WILLIAM BLAKE

1757-1827

The Tyger

Tyger! Tyger! burning bright
In the forests of the night,
What immortal hand or eye
Could frame thy fearful symmetry?

In what distant deeps or skies
Burnt the fire of thine eyes?
On what wings dare he aspire?
What the hand dare seize the fire?

And what shoulder, and what art
Could twist the sinews of thy heart?
And, when thy heart began to beat,
What dread hand forged thy dread feet?

What the hammer? what the chain?
In what furnace was thy brain?
What the anvil? what dread grasp
Dare its deadly terrors clasp?

When the stars threw down their spears,
And water'd heaven with their tears,
Did He smile His work to see?
Did He who made the Lamb make thee?

Tyger! Tyger! burning bright
In the forests of the night,
What immortal hand or eye
Dare frame thy fearful symmetry?

And did those Feet in Ancient Times

And did those feet in ancient times
   Walk upon England's mountains green?
And was the holy Lamb of God
   On England's pleasant pastures seen?

And did the Countenance Divine
   Shine forth upon our clouded hills?
And was Jerusalem builded here
   Among these dark Satanic Mills?

Bring me my bow of burning gold!
   Bring me my arrows of desire!
Bring me my spear! O clouds, unfold!
   Bring me my chariot of fire!

I will not cease from mental fight,
   Nor shall my sword sleep in my hand,
Till we have built Jerusalem
   In England's green and pleasant land.

Introduction to 'Songs of Innocence'

Piping down the valleys wild,
   Piping songs of pleasant glee,
On a cloud I saw a child,
   And he laughing said to me:

'Pipe a song about a Lamb!'
   So I piped with merry cheer.
'Piper, pipe that song again!'
   So I piped: he wept to hear.

'Drop thy pipe, thy happy pipe;
   Sing thy songs of happy cheer':
So I sang the same again,
   While he wept with joy to hear.

'Piper, sit thee down and write
   In a book, that all may read.'
So he vanished from my sight;
   And I plucked a hollow reed,

And I made a rural pen,
    And I stained the water clear,
And I wrote my happy songs
    Every child may joy to hear.

The Lamb

    Little Lamb, who made thee?
    Dost thou know who made thee?
Gave thee life, and bid thee feed,
By the stream and o'er the mead;
Gave thee clothing of delight,
Softest clothing, woolly, bright;
Gave thee such a tender voice,
Making all the vales rejoice?
    Little Lamb, who made thee?
    Dost thou know who made thee?

    Little Lamb, I'll tell thee,
    Little Lamb, I'll tell thee:
He is callèd by thy name,
For He calls Himself a Lamb.
He is meek, and He is mild,
He became a little child.
I a child, and thou a lamb,
We are callèd by His name.
    Little Lamb, God bless thee!
    Little Lamb, God bless thee!

A Poison Tree

I was angry with my friend:
I told my wrath, my wrath did end.
I was angry with my foe:
I told it not, my wrath did grow.

And I water'd it in fears,
Night and morning with my tears;
And I sunnèd it with smiles,
And with soft deceitful wiles.

And it grew both day and night,
Till it bore an apple bright;
And my foe beheld it shine,
And he knew that it was mine,

And into my garden stole
When the night had veil'd the pole:
In the morning glad I see
My foe outstretch'd beneath the tree.

London

I wander thro' each charter'd street,
Near where the charter'd Thames does flow,
And mark in every face I meet
Marks of weakness, marks of woe.

In every cry of every man,
In every Infant's cry of fear,
In every voice, in every ban,
The mind-forg'd manacles I hear.

How the chimney-sweeper's cry
Every black'ning church appals;
And the hapless soldier's sigh
Runs in blood down palace walls.

But most thro' midnight streets I hear
How the youthful harlot's curse
Blasts the new-born infant's tear
And blights with plagues the marriage hearse.

WILLIAM WORDSWORTH

1770-1850

*Lines composed near Tintern Abbey, on re-visiting
the banks of the Wye during a tour*

July 13, 1798

Five years have past; five summers, with the length
Of five long winters! and again I hear
These waters, rolling from their mountain-springs
With a soft inland murmur.—Once again
Do I behold these steep and lofty cliffs,
That on a wild secluded scene impress
Thoughts of more deep seclusion; and connect
The landscape with the quiet of the sky.
The day is come when I again repose
Here, under this dark sycamore, and view
These plots of cottage-ground, these orchard-tufts,
Which at this season, with their unripe fruits,
Are clad in one green hue, and lose themselves
'Mid groves and copses. Once again I see
These hedge-rows, hardly hedge-rows, little lines
Of sportive wood run wild: these pastoral farms,
Green to the very door; and wreaths of smoke
Sent up, in silence, from among the trees!
With some uncertain notice, as might seem
Of vagrant dwellers in the houseless woods,
Or of some Hermit's cave, where by his fire
The Hermit sits alone.

                These beauteous forms,
Through a long absence, have not been to me
As is a landscape to a blind man's eye:
But oft, in lonely rooms, and 'mid the din
Of towns and cities, I have owed to them,
In hours of weariness, sensations sweet,
Felt in the blood, and felt along the heart;
And passing even into my purer mind,

With tranquil restoration:—feelings too
Of unremembered pleasure: such, perhaps,
As have no slight or trivial influence
On that best portion of a good man's life,
His little, nameless, unremembered, acts
Of kindness and of love. Nor less, I trust,
To them I may have owed another gift,
Of aspect more sublime; that blessed mood,
In which the burthen of the mystery,
In which the heavy and the weary weight
Of all this unintelligible world,
Is lightened:—that serene and blessed mood,
In which the affections gently lead us on,—
Until, the breath of this corporeal frame
And even the motion of our human blood
Almost suspended, we are laid asleep
In body, and become a living soul:
While with an eye made quiet by the power
Of harmony, and the deep power of joy,
We see into the life of things.
                              If this
Be but a vain belief, yet, oh! how oft—
In darkness and amid the many shapes
Of joyless daylight; when the fretful stir
Unprofitable, and the fever of the world,
Have hung upon the beatings of my heart—
How oft, in spirit, have I turned to thee,
O sylvan Wye! thou wanderer thro' the woods,
How often has my spirit turned to thee!

   And now, with gleams of half-extinguished thought,
With many recognitions dim and faint,
And somewhat of a sad perplexity,
The picture of the mind revives again:
While here I stand, not only with the sense
Of present pleasure, but with pleasing thoughts
That in this moment there is life and food
For future years. And so I dare to hope,
Though changed, no doubt, from what I was when first
I came among these hills; when like a roe
I bounded o'er the mountains, by the sides
Of the deep rivers, and the lonely streams,

Wherever nature led: more like a man
Flying from something that he dreads than one
Who sought the thing he loved. For nature then
(The coarser pleasures of my boyish days,
And their glad animal movements all gone by)
To me was all in all. I cannot paint
What then I was. The sounding cataract
Haunted me like a passion: the tall rock,
The mountain, and the deep and gloomy wood,
Their colours and their forms, were then to me
An appetite; a feeling and a love,
That had no need of a remoter charm,
By thought supplied, nor any interest
Unborrowed from the eye.—That time is past,
And all its aching joys are now no more,
And all its dizzy raptures. Not for this
Faint I, nor mourn nor murmur; other gifts
Have followed; for such loss, I would believe,
Abundant recompense. For I have learned
To look on nature, not as in the hour
Of thoughtless youth; but hearing oftentimes
The still, sad music of humanity,
Nor harsh nor grating, though of ample power
To chasten and subdue. And I have felt
A presence that disturbs me with the joy
Of elevated thoughts; a sense sublime
Of something far more deeply interfused,
Whose dwelling is the light of setting suns,
And the round ocean and the living air,
And the blue sky, and in the mind of man:
A motion and a spirit, that impels
All thinking things, all objects of all thought,
And rolls through all things. Therefore am I still
A lover of the meadows and the woods,
And mountains; and of all that we behold
From this green earth; of all the mighty world
Of eye, and ear,—both what they half create,
And what perceive; well pleased to recognise
In nature and the language of the sense
The anchor of my purest thoughts, the nurse,
The guide, the guardian of my heart, and soul
Of all my moral being.

Nor perchance,
If I were not thus taught, should I the more
Suffer my genial spirits to decay:
For thou art with me here upon the banks
Of this fair river; thou my dearest Friend,
My dear, dear Friend; and in thy voice I catch
The language of my former heart, and read
My former pleasures in the shooting lights
Of thy wild eyes. Oh! yet a little while
May I behold in thee what I was once,
My dear, dear Sister! and this prayer I make,
Knowing that Nature never did betray
The heart that loved her; 'tis her privilege,
Through all the years of this our life, to lead
From joy to joy: for she can so inform
The mind that is within us, so impress
With quietness and beauty, and so feed
With lofty thoughts, that neither evil tongues,
Rash judgements, nor the sneers of selfish men,
Nor greetings where no kindness is, nor all
The dreary intercourse of daily life,
Shall e'er prevail against us, or disturb
Our cheerful faith, that all which we behold
Is full of blessings. Therefore let the moon
Shine on thee in thy solitary walk;
And let the misty mountain-winds be free
To blow against thee: and, in after years,
When these wild ecstasies shall be matured
Into a sober pleasure; when thy mind
Shall be a mansion for all lovely forms,
Thy memory be as a dwelling-place
For all sweet sounds and harmonies; oh! then,
If solitude, or fear, or pain, or grief,
Should be thy portion, with what healing thoughts
Of tender joy wilt thou remember me,
And these my exhortations! Nor, perchance—
If I should be where I no more can hear
Thy voice, nor catch from thy wild eyes these gleams
Of past existence—wilt thou then forget
That on the banks of this delightful stream
We stood together; and that I, so long
A worshipper of Nature, hither came

Unwearied in that service: rather say
With warmer love—oh! with far deeper zeal
Of holier love. Nor wilt thou then forget
That after many wanderings, many years
Of absence, these steep woods and lofty cliffs,
And this green pastoral landscape, were to me
More dear, both for themselves and for thy sake!

Sonnet on the Sonnet

Scorn not the Sonnet; Critic, you have frowned,
Mindless of its just honours; with this key
Shakespeare unlocked his heart; the melody
Of this small lute gave ease to Petrarch's wound;
A thousand times this pipe did Tasso sound;
With it Camöens soothed an exile's grief;
The Sonnet glittered a gay myrtle leaf
Amid the cypress with which Dante crowned
His visionary brow: a glow-worm lamp,
It cheered mild Spenser, called from Faery-land
To struggle through dark ways; and when a damp
Fell round the path of Milton, in his hand
The Thing became a trumpet, whence he blew
Soul animating strains—alas, too few.

Upon Westminster Bridge

Earth has not anything to show more fair:
Dull would he be of soul who could pass by
A sight so touching in its majesty:
This City now doth like a garment wear
The beauty of the morning: silent, bare,
Ships, towers, domes, theatres, and temples lie
Open unto the fields, and to the sky,
All bright and glittering in the smokeless air.
Never did sun more beautifully steep
In his first splendour valley, rock, or hill;
Ne'er saw I, never felt, a calm so deep!
The river glideth at his own sweet will:
Dear God! the very houses seem asleep;
And all that mighty heart is lying still!

To Sleep

A flock of sheep that leisurely pass by,
One after one; the sound of rain, and bees
Murmuring; the fall of rivers, winds and seas,
Smooth fields, white sheets of water, and pure sky;
I have thought of all by turns, and yet do lie
Sleepless! and soon the small birds' melodies
Must hear, first uttered from my orchard trees;
And the first cuckoo's melancholy cry.
Even thus last night, and two nights more, I lay
And could not win thee, Sleep! by any stealth:
So do not let me wear to-night away:
Without Thee what is all the morning's wealth?
Come, blessed barrier between day and day,
Dear mother of fresh thoughts and joyous health!

London, 1802

Milton! thou shouldst be living at this hour:
England hath need of thee; she is a fen
Of stagnant waters: altar, sword, and pen,
Fireside, the heroic wealth of hall and bower
Have forfeited their ancient English dower
Of inward happiness. We are selfish men:
O! raise us up, return to us again;
And give us manners, virtue, freedom, power.
Thy soul was like a star, and dwelt apart;
Thou hadst a voice whose sound was like the sea,
Pure as the naked heavens, majestic, free;
So didst thou travel on life's common way
In cheerful godliness; and yet thy heart
The lowliest duties on herself did lay.

September, 1803

When I have borne in memory what has tamed
Great nations; how ennobling thoughts depart
When men change swords for ledgers, and desert
The student's bower for gold—some fears unnamed
I had, my Country!—am I to be blamed?

Now, when I think of thee, and what thou art,
Verily, in the bottom of my heart
Of those unfilial fears I am ashamed.
For dearly must we prize thee; we who find
In thee a bulwark for the cause of men;
And I by my affection was beguiled:
What wonder if a Poet now and then,
Among the many movements of his mind,
Felt for thee as a lover or a child!

To the Skylark

Ethereal minstrel! pilgrim of the sky!
Dost thou despise the earth where cares abound?
Or, while the wings aspire, are heart and eye
Both with thy nest upon the dewy ground?
Thy nest which thou canst drop into at will,
Those quivering wings composed, that music still!

Leave to the nightingale her shady wood;
A privacy of glorious light is thine;
Whence thou dost pour upon the world a flood
Of harmony, with instinct more divine;
Type of the wise, who soar, but never roam;
True to the kindred points of Heaven and Home!

To the Cuckoo

O blithe new-comer! I have heard,
   I hear thee and rejoice:
O Cuckoo! shall I call thee Bird,
   Or but a wandering Voice?

While I am lying on the grass
   Thy twofold shout I hear;
From hill to hill it seems to pass,
   At once far off and near.

Though babbling only to the vale
   Of sunshine and of flowers,
Thou bringest unto me a tale
   Of visionary hours.

Thrice welcome, darling of the Spring!
    Even yet thou art to me
No bird, but an invisible thing,
    A voice, a mystery;

The same whom in my schoolboy days
    I listen'd to; that Cry
Which made me look a thousand ways
    In bush, and tree, and sky.

To seek thee did I often rove
    Through woods and on the green;
And thou wert still a hope, a love;
    Still longed for, never seen.

And I can listen to thee yet;
    Can lie upon the plain
And listen, till I do beget
    That golden time again.

O blessèd Bird! the earth we pace
    Again appears to be
An unsubstantial, fairy place,
    That is fit home for Thee.

The Small Celandine

There is a Flower, the lesser Celandine,
That shrinks like many more from cold and rain,
And the first moment that the sun may shine,
Bright as the sun himself, 'tis out again!

When hailstones have been falling, swarm on swarm,
Or blasts the green field and the trees distrest,
Oft have I seen it muffled up from harm
In close self-shelter, like a thing at rest.

But lately, one rough day, this Flower I past,
And recognised it, though an alter'd form,
Now standing forth an offering to the blast,
And buffeted at will by rain and storm.

I stopp'd and said, with inly-mutter'd voice,
'It doth not love the shower, nor seek the cold;
This neither is its courage nor its choice,
But its necessity in being old.

'The sunshine may not cheer it, nor the dew;
It cannot help itself in its decay;
Stiff in its members, wither'd, changed of hue,'—
And, in my spleen, I smiled that it was gray.

To be a prodigal's favourite—then, worse truth,
A miser's pensioner—behold our lot!
O Man! that from thy fair and shining youth
Age might but take the things Youth needed not!

Lucy

I

I travell'd among unknown men
   In lands beyond the sea;
Nor, England! did I know till then
   What love I bore to thee.

'Tis past, that melancholy dream!
   Nor will I quit thy shore
A second time; for still I seem
   To love thee more and more.

Among thy mountains did I feel
   The joy of my desire;
And she I cherish'd turn'd her wheel
   Beside an English fire.

Thy mornings show'd, thy nights conceal'd
   The bowers where Lucy play'd;
And thine too is the last green field
   That Lucy's eyes survey'd.

II

She dwelt among the untrodden ways
    Beside the springs of Dove;
A maid whom there were none to praise,
    And very few to love.

A violet by a mossy stone
    Half-hidden from the eye!
—Fair as a star, when only one
    Is shining in the sky.

She lived unknown, and few could know
    When Lucy ceased to be;
But she is in her grave, and, oh,
    The difference to me!

III

A slumber did my spirit seal;
    I had no human fears:
She seem'd a thing that could not feel
    The touch of earthly years.

No motion has she now, no force;
    She neither hears nor sees;
Roll'd round in earth's diurnal course
    With rocks, and stones, and trees.

Ode on Intimations of Immortality from
Recollections of Early Childhood

There was a time when meadow, grove, and stream
    The earth, and every common sight,
        To me did seem
        Apparell'd in celestial light,
The glory and the freshness of a dream.
It is not now as it hath been of yore;—
        Turn wheresoe'er I may,
        By night or day,
The things which I have seen I now can see no more.

The rainbow comes and goes,
    And lovely is the rose;
    The moon doth with delight
Look round her when the heavens are bare;
    Waters on a starry night
        Are beautiful and fair;
    The sunshine is a glorious birth;
    But yet I know, where'er I go,
That there hath pass'd away a glory from the earth.

Now, while the birds thus sing a joyous song,
    And while the young lambs bound
        As to the tabor's sound,
To me alone there came a thought of grief:
A timely utterance gave that thought relief,
        And I again am strong.
The cataracts blow their trumpets from the steep,—
    No more shall grief of mine the season wrong:
    I hear the echoes through the mountains throng,
The winds come to me from the fields of sleep,
        And all the earth is gay;
            Land and sea
        Give themselves up to jollity,
            And with the heart of May
        Doth every beast keep holiday;—
            Thou child of joy,
Shout round me, let me hear thy shouts, thou happy Shepherd-
    boy!
Ye blessèd Creatures, I have heard the call
        Ye to each other make; I see
The heavens laugh with you in your jubilee;
        My heart is at your festival,
        My head hath its coronal,
The fulness of your bliss, I feel—I feel it all.
            O evil day! if I were sullen
            While Earth herself is adorning
                This sweet May morning;
            And the children are culling
                On every side
        In a thousand valleys far and wide
        Fresh flowers; while the sun shines warm,
And the babe leaps up on his mother's arm:—

I hear, I hear, with joy I hear!
—But there's a tree, of many, one,
A single field which I have look'd upon,
Both of them speak of something that is gone:
The pansy at my feet
Doth the same tale repeat:
Whither is fled the visionary gleam?
Where is it now, the glory and the dream?

Our birth is but a sleep and a forgetting;
The Soul that rises with us, our life's Star,
Hath had elsewhere its setting,
And cometh from afar;
Not in entire forgetfulness,
And not in utter nakedness,
But trailing clouds of glory do we come
From God, who is our home:
Heaven lies about us in our infancy!
Shades of the prison-house begin to close
Upon the growing Boy,
But he beholds the light, and whence it flows,
He sees it in his joy;
The Youth, who daily farther from the east
Must travel, still is Nature's priest
And by the vision splendid
Is on his way attended;
At length the Man perceives it die away,
And fade into the light of common day.

Earth fills her lap with pleasurs of her own;
Yearnings she hath in her own enatural kind,
And, even with something of a mother's mind
And no unworthy aim,
The homely nurse doth all she can
To make her foster-child, her inmate, Man,
Forget the glories he hath known,
And that imperial palace whence he came.

Behold the Child among his new-born blisses,
A six years' darling of a pigmy size!
See, where 'mid work of his own hand he lies,
Fretted by sallies of his mother's kisses,

With light upon him from his father's eyes!
See, at his feet, some little plan or chart,
Some fragment from his dream of human life,
Shaped by himself with newly-learned art;
      A wedding or a festival,
      A mourning or a funeral;
         And this hath now his heart,
      And unto this he frames his song:
        Then will he fit his tongue
To dialogues of business, love, or strife;
      But it will not be long
      Ere this be thrown aside,
      And with new joy and pride
The little actor cons another part;
Filling from time to time his 'humorous stage'
With all the Persons, down to palsied Age,
That life brings with her in her equipage;
      As if his whole vocation
      Were endless imitation.

Thou, whose exterior semblance doth belie
      Thy soul's immensity;
Thou best Philosopher, who yet dost keep
Thy heritage, thou Eye among the blind,
That, deaf and silent, read'st the eternal deep,
Haunted for ever by the eternal Mind,—
      Mighty Prophet! Seer blest!
      On whom those truths do rest
Which we are toiling all our lives to find,
In darkness lost, the darkness of the grave;
Thou, over whom thy Immortality
Broods like the Day, a Master o'er a Slave,
A Presence which is not to be put by;
Thou little Child, yet glorious in the might
Of heaven-born freedom on thy being's height,
Why with such earnest pains dost thou provoke
The years to bring the inevitable yoke,
Thus blindly with thy blessedness at strife?
Full soon thy Soul shall have her earthly freight,
And custom lie upon thee with a weight
Heavy as frost, and deep almost as life!

O joy! that in our embers
Is something that doth live,
That Nature yet remembers
What was so fugitive!
The thought of our past years in me doth breed
Perpetual benediction: not indeed
For that which is most worthy to be blest,
Delight and liberty, the simple creed
Of Childhood, whether busy or at rest,
With new-fledged hope still fluttering in his breast:
—Not for these I raise
The song of thanks and praise;
But for those obstinate questionings
Of sense and outward things,
Fallings from us, vanishings,
Blank misgivings of a creature
Moving about in worlds not realised,
High instincts, before which our mortal nature
Did tremble like a guilty thing surprised:
But for those first affections,
Those shadowy recollections,
Which, be they what they may,
Are yet the fountain-light of all our day,
Are yet a master-light of all our seeing;
Uphold us, cherish, and have power to make
Our noisy years seem moments in the being
Of the eternal silence: truths that wake,
To perish never;
Which neither listlessness, nor mad endeavour,
Nor man nor boy
Nor all that is at enmity with joy,
Can utterly abolish or destroy!
Hence in a season of calm weather
Though inland far we be,
Our souls have sight of that immortal sea
Which brought us hither;
Can in a moment travel thither—
And see the children sport upon the shore,
And hear the mighty waters rolling evermore.

Then, sing ye birds, sing, sing a joyous song!
And let the young lambs bound

As to the tabor's sound!
We, in thought, will join your throng
　　Ye that pipe and ye that play,
　　Ye that through your hearts to-day
　　Feel the gladness of the May!
What though the radiance which was once so bright
Be now for ever taken from my sight,
　　Though nothing can bring back the hour
Of splendour in the grass, of glory in the flower;
　　We will grieve not, rather find
　　Strength in what remains behind;
　　In the primal sympathy
　　Which having been must ever be;
　　In the soothing thoughts that spring
　　Out of human suffering;
　　In the faith that looks through death,
　　In years that bring the philosophic mind.

And O, ye Fountains, Meadows, Hills, and Groves,
Forbode not any severing of our loves!
Yet in my heart of hearts I feel your might;
I only have relinquish'd one delight
To live beneath your more habitual sway;
I love the brooks which down their channels fret,
Even more than when I tripp'd lightly as they;
The innocent brightness of a new-born day
　　　　Is lovely yet;
The clouds that gather round the setting sun
Do take a sober colouring from an eye
That hath kept watch o'er man's mortality;
Another race hath been, and other palms are won.
Thanks to the human heart by which we live,
Thanks to its tenderness, its joys, and fears,
To me the meanest flower that blows can give
Thoughts that do often lie too deep for tears.

SIR WALTER SCOTT
1771-1832

Proud Maisie

Proud Maisie is in the wood,
  Walking so early;
Sweet Robin sits on the bush
  Singing so rarely.

'Tell me, thou bonny bird,
  When shall I marry me?'
—'When six braw gentlemen
  Kirkward shall carry ye.'

'Who makes the bridal bed,
  Birdie, say truly?'
—'The grey-headed sexton
  That delves the grave duly.

'The glow-worm o'er grave and stone
  Shall light thee steady;
The owl from the steeple sing
  Welcome, proud lady!'

Rosabelle

O listen, listen, ladies gay!
  No haughty feat of arms I tell;
Soft is the note, and sad the lay,
  That mourns the lovely Rosabelle.—

'Moor, moor the barge, ye gallant crew!
  And, gentle lady, deign to stay!
Rest thee in Castle Ravensheuch,
  Nor tempt the stormy firth to-day.

The blackening wave is edged with white:
  To inch and rock the sea-mews fly;
The fishers have heard the Water-Sprite,
  Whose screams forebode that wreck is nigh.

Last night the gifted Seer did view
  A wet shroud swathed round lady gay;
Then stay thee, Fair, in Ravensheuch:
  Why cross the gloomy firth to-day?'—

' 'Tis not because Lord Lindesay's heir
  To-night at Roslin leads the ball,
But that my ladye-mother there
  Sits lonely in her castle-hall.

'Tis not because the ring they ride,
  And Lindesay at the ring rides well,
But that my sire the wine will chide,
  If 'tis not fill'd by Rosabelle.'—

O'er Roslin all that dreary night
  A wondrous blaze was seen to gleam;
'Twas broader than the watch-fire's light,
  And redder than the bright moonbeam.

It glared on Roslin's castled rock,
  It ruddied all the copse-wood glen;
'Twas seen from Dryden's groves of oak,
  And seen from cavern'd Hawthornden.

Seem'd all on fire that chapel proud,
  Where Roslin's chiefs uncoffin'd lie,
Each Baron, for a sable shroud,
  Sheathed in his iron panoply.

Seem'd all on fire within, around,
  Deep sacristy and altar's pale;
Shone every pillar foliage-bound,
  And glimmer'd all the dead men's mail.

Blazed battlement and pinnet high,
  Blazed every rose-carved buttress fair—
So still they blaze, when fate is nigh
  The lordly line of high St Clair.

There are twenty of Roslin's barons bold
  Lie buried within that proud chapelle;
Each one the holy vault doth hold,
  But the sea holds lovely Rosabelle!

And each St Clair was buried there
  With candle, with book, and with knell;
But the sea-caves rung, and the wild winds sung
  The dirge of lovely Rosabelle.

Lucy Ashton's Song

Look not thou on beauty's charming;
Sit thou still when kings are arming;
Taste not when the wine-cup glistens;
Speak not when the people listens;
Stop thine ear against the singer;
From the red gold keep thy finger;
Vacant heart and hand and eye,
Easy live and quiet die.

The Rover

'A weary lot is thine, fair maid,
  A weary lot is thine!
To pull the thorn thy brow to braid,
  And press the rue for wine.
A lightsome eye, a soldier's mien,
  A feather of the blue,
A doublet of the Lincoln green—
  No more of me you knew
          My Love!
  No more of me you knew.

This morn is merry June, I trow,
  The rose is budding fain;
But she shall bloom in winter snow
  Ere we two meet again.'

He turned his charger as he spake
　　Upon the river shore,
He gave his bridle-reins a shake,
　　Said 'Adieu for evermore
　　　　　　My Love!
And adieu for evermore.'

Bonny Dundee

To the Lords of Convention 'twas Claver'se who spoke,
'Ere the King's crown shall fall there are crowns to be broke;
So let each Cavalier who loves honour and me,
Come follow the bonnet of Bonny Dundee.

　　Come fill up my cup, come fill up my can,
　　Come saddle your horses, and call up your men;
　　Come open the West Port, and let me gang free,
　　And it's room for the bonnets of Bonny Dundee!'

Dundee he is mounted, he rides up the street,
The bells are rung backward, the drums they are beat;
But the Provost, douce man, said, 'Just e'en let him be,
The Gude Town is weel quit of that Deil of Dundee.'

As he rode down the sanctified bends of the Bow,
Ilk carline was flyting and shaking her pow;
But the young plants of grace they looked couthie and slee,
Thinking, luck to thy bonnet, thou Bonny Dundee!

With sour-featured Whigs the Grassmarket was pang'd,
As if half the West had set tryst to be hanged;
There was spite in each look, there was fear in each e'e,
As they watched for the bonnets of Bonny Dundee.

These cowls of Kilmarnock had spits and had spears,
And lang-hafted gullies to kill Cavaliers;
But they shrunk to close-heads, and the causeway was free,
At the toss of the bonnet of Bonny Dundee.

flyting, *scolding*　　　　　pang'd, *stuffed*
set tryst, *arranged*

He spurred to the foot of the proud Castle rock,
And with the gay Gordon he gallantly spoke;
'Let Mons Meg and her marrows speak twa words or three
For the love of the bonnet of Bonny Dundee.'

The Gordon demands of him which way he goes:
'Where'er shall direct me the shade of Montrose!
Your Grace in short space shall hear tidings of me,
Or that low lies the bonnet of Bonny Dundee.

'There are hills beyond Pentland, and lands beyond Forth,
If there's lords in the Lowlands, there's chiefs in the North;
There are wild Duniewassals three thousand times three,
Will cry *hoigh!* for the bonnet of Bonny Dundee.

There's brass on the target of barkened bull-hide;
There's steel in the scabbard that dangles beside;
The brass shall be burnished, the steel shall flash free
At a toss of the bonnet of Bonny Dundee.

Away to the hills, to the caves, to the rocks,
Ere I own an usurper, I'll couch with the fox;
And tremble, false Whigs, in the midst of your glee,
You have not seen the last of my bonnet and me!'

He waved his proud hand, and the trumpets were blown,
The kettle-drums clash'd, and the horsemen rode on,
Till on Ravelston's cliffs and on Clermiston's lee
Died away the wild war-notes of Bonny Dundee.

    Come fill up my cup, come fill up my can,
    Come saddle the horses and call up the men,
    Come open your gates, and let me gae free,
    For it's up with the bonnets of Bonny Dundee!

Jock of Hazeldean

    'Why weep ye by the tide, ladie?
      Why weep ye by the tide?
    I'll wed ye to my youngest son,
      And ye sall be his bride:

Duniewassal, *highland gentleman*

And ye sall be his bride, ladie,
    Sae comely to be seen'—
But aye she loot the tears down fa'
    For Jock of Hazeldean.

Now let this wilfu' grief be done,
    And dry that cheek so pale;
Young Frank is chief of Errington
    And lord of Langley-dale;
His step is first in peaceful ha',
    His sword in battle keen'—
But aye she loot the tears down fa'
    For Jock of Hazeldean.

A chain of gold ye sall not lack,
    Nor braid to bind your hair;
Nor mettled hound, nor managed hawk,
    Nor palfrey fresh and fair;
And you, the foremost o' them a',
    Shall ride our forest queen'—
But aye she loot the tears down fa'
    For Jock of Hazeldean.

The kirk was decked at morning-tide
    The tapers glimmer'd fair;
The priest and bridegroom wait the bride,
    And dame and knight are there.
They sought her baith by bower and ha';
    The ladie was not seen!
She's o'er the border, and awa'
    Wi' Jock of Hazeldean.

Coronach

He is gone on the mountain,
    He is lost to the forest,
Like a summer-dried fountain,
    When our need was the sorest,
The font reappearing
    From the rain-drops shall borrow,
But to us comes no cheering,
    To Duncan no morrow!

The hand of the reaper
    Takes the ears that are hoary,
But the voice of the weeper
    Wails manhood in glory.
The autumn winds rushing
    Waft the leaves that are serest,
But our flower was in flushing,
    When blighting was nearest.

Fleet foot on the corrie,
    Sage counsel in cumber,
Red hand in the foray,
    How sound is thy slumber!
Like the dew on the mountain,
    Like the foam on the river,
Like the bubble on the fountain,
    Thou art gone, and for ever!

SAMUEL TAYLOR COLERIDGE

1772-1834

The Rime of the Ancient Mariner

PART I

<table>
<tr>
<td>An ancient Mariner meeteth three Gallants bidden to a wedding-feast, and detaineth one</td>
<td>

It is an ancient Mariner,
And he stoppeth one of three.
'By thy long grey beard and glittering eye,
Now wherefore stopp'st thou me?

The Bridegroom's doors are opened wide,
And I am next of kin;
The guests are met, the feast is set:
May'st hear the merry din.'

He holds him with his skinny hand,
'There was a ship,' quoth he.
'Hold off! unhand me, grey-beard loon!'
Eftsoons his hand dropt he.

</td>
</tr>
<tr>
<td>The Wedding-Guest is spell-bound by the eye of the old sea-faring man, and constrained to hear his tale.</td>
<td>

He holds him with his glittering eye—
The Wedding-Guest stood still,
And listens like a three years' child:
The Mariner hath his will.

The Wedding-Guest sat on a stone:
He cannot choose but hear;
And thus spake on that ancient man,
The bright-eyed Mariner.

'The ship was cheered, the harbour cleared,
Merrily did we drop
Below the kirk, below the hill,
Below the lighthouse top.

</td>
</tr>
</table>

The Mariner tells
how the ship sailed
southward with a
good wind and fair
weather, till it
reached the Line.

The Sun came up upon the left,
Out of the sea came he!
And he shone bright, and on the right
Went down into the sea.

Higher and higher every day,
Till over the mast at noon—'
The Wedding-Guest here beat his breast,
For he heard the loud bassoon.

The Wedding-
Guest heareth the
bridal music; but
the Mariner con-
tinueth his tale.

The bride hath paced into the hall,
Red as a rose is she;
Nodding their heads before her goes
The merry minstrelsy.

The Wedding-Guest he beat his breast,
Yet he cannot choose but hear;
And thus spake on that ancient man,
The bright-eyed Mariner:

The ship driven
by a storm to-
ward the South
Pole.

'And now the Storm-blast came, and he
Was tyrannous and strong:
He struck with his o'ertaking wings,
And chased us south along.

With sloping masts and dipping prow,
As who pursued with yell and blow
Still treads the shadow of his foe,
And forward bends his head,
The ship drove fast, loud roar'd the blast,
And southward aye we fled.

And now there came both mist and snow
And it grew wondrous cold:
And ice, mast-high, came floating by,
As green as emerald.

The land of ice,
and of fearful
sounds, where
no living thing
was to be seen.

And through the drifts the snowy clifts
Did send a dismal sheen:
Nor shapes of men nor beasts we ken—
The ice was all between.

The ice was here, the ice was there,
The ice was all around:
It crack'd and growl'd, and roar'd and
howl'd,
Like noises in a swound!

Till a great sea-
bird, called the
Albatross, came
through the snow-
fog, and was re-
ceived with great
joy and hospitality.
At length did cross an Albatross,
Thorough the fog it came;
As if it had been a Christian soul,
We hailed it in God's name.

It ate the food it ne'er had eat,
And round and round it flew.
The ice did split with a thunder-fit;
The helmsman steered us through!

And lo! the
Albatross proveth
a bird of good
omen, and fol-
loweth the ship as
it returned north-
ward through fog
and floating ice.
And a good south wind sprung up behind;
The Albatross did follow,
And every day, for food or play,
Came to the mariner's hollo!

In mist or cloud, on mast or shroud,
It perched for vespers nine;
Whiles all the night, through fog-smoke
white,
Glimmered the white moonshine.'

The ancient
Mariner in-
hospitably killeth
the pious bird of
good omen.
'God save thee, ancient Mariner!
From the fiends, that plague thee thus!—
Why look'st thou so?'—'With my cross-
bow
I shot the Albatross.

PART II

'The Sun now rose upon the right:
Out of the sea came he,
Still hid in mist, and on the left
Went down into the sea.

And the good south wind still blew behind,
But no sweet bird did follow,
Nor any day for food or play
Came to the mariner's hollo!

His shipmates
cry out against
the ancient
Mariner for
killing the bird
of good luck.

And I had done a hellish thing,
And it would work 'em woe:
For all averr'd I had killed the bird
That made the breeze to blow.
Ah wretch! said they, the bird to slay
That made the breeze to blow!

But when the
fog cleared off,
they justify the
same, and thus
make them-
selves accom-
plices in the
crime.

Nor dim nor red, like God's own head,
The glorious Sun uprist:
Then all averr'd I had kill'd the bird
That brought the fog and mist.
'Twas right, said they, such birds to slay,
That bring the fog and mist.

The fair breeze
continues; the
ship enters the
Pacific Ocean, and
sails northward,
even till it reaches
the Line.

The fair breeze blew, the white foam flew,
The furrow follow'd free;
We were the first that ever burst
Into that silent sea.

The ship hath
been suddenly
becalmed.

Down dropt the breeze, the sails dropt
    down,
'Twas sad as sad could be;
And we did speak only to break
The silence of the sea!

All in a hot and copper sky
The bloody sun at noon,
Right up against the mast did stand,
No bigger than the Moon.

Day after day, day after day,
We stuck, nor breath nor motion;
As idle as a painted ship
Upon a painted ocean.

And the Albatross
begins to be
avenged.

Water, water, everywhere,
And all the boards did shrink;
Water, water, everywhere,
Nor any drop to drink.

The very deep did rot: O Christ!
That ever this should be!
Yea, slimy things did crawl with legs
Upon the slimy sea.

About, about, in reel and rout
The death-fires danced at night;
The water, like a witch's oils,
Burnt green, and blue and white.

A Spirit had
followed them;
one of the invisible
inhabitants of this
planet, neither de-
parted souls nor
angels; concerning
whom the learned
Jew, Josephus, and
the Platonic Con-
stantinopolitan,
Michael Psellus,
may be consulted.
They are very
numerous, and
there is no climate
or element without
one or more.
The shipmates, in
their sore distress,
would fain throw
the whole guilt
on the ancient
Mariner: in sign
whereof they hang
the dead sea-bird
round his neck.

And some in dreams assurèd were
Of the Spirit that plagued us so;
Nine fathom deep he had followed us
From the land of mist and snow.

And every tongue, through utter drought,
Was withered at the root;
We could not speak, no more than if
We had been choked with soot.

Ah! well a-day! what evil looks
Had I from old and young!
Instead of the cross, the Albatross
About my neck was hung.

PART III

'There passed a weary time. Each throat
Was parched, and glazed each eye.
A weary time! a weary time!
How glazed each weary eye,
When looking westward, I beheld
A something in the sky.

The ancient
Mariner be-
holdeth a sign in
the element afar off.

At first it seemed a little speck,
And then it seemed a mist;
It moved and moved, and took at last
A certain shape, I wist.

A speck, a mist, a shape, I wist!
And still it near'd and near'd:
As if it dodged a water-sprite,
It plung'd, and tack'd, and veer'd.

At its nearer
approach, it
seemeth him
to be a ship;
and at a dear
ransom he
freeth his
speech from the
bonds of thirst.

With throats unslaked, with black lips
    baked,
We could nor laugh nor wail;
Through utter drought all dumb we stood!
I bit my arm, I suck'd the blood,
And cried, "A sail! a sail!"

A flash of joy.

With throats unslaked, with black lips
    baked,
Agape they heard me call:
Gramercy! they for joy did grin,
And all at once their breath drew in,
As they were drinking all.

And horror
follows. For can
it be a ship that
comes onward
without wind or
tide?

"See! See! (I cried) she tacks no more!
Hither to work us weal,
Without a breeze, without a tide,
She steadies with upright keel!"

The western wave was all aflame,
The day was wellnigh done!
Almost upon the western wave
Rested the broad, bright Sun;
When that strange shape drove suddenly
Betwixt us and the Sun.

It seemeth him
but the skeleton
of a ship.

And straight the Sun was fleck'd with bars
(Heaven's Mother send us grace!),
As if through a dungeon-grate he peer'd
With broad and burning face.

Alas! (thought I, and my heart beat loud)
How fast she nears and nears!
Are those *her* sails that glance in the Sun,
Like restless gossameres?

Are those *her* ribs through which the Sun
Did peer, as through a grate?
And is that Woman all her crew?
Is that a DEATH? and are there two?
Is DEATH that woman's mate?

Her lips were red, *her* looks were free,
Her locks were yellow as gold:
Her skin was as white as leprosy,
The Night-mare LIFE-IN-DEATH was she,
Who thicks man's blood with cold.

The naked hulk alongside came,
And the twain were casting dice;
"The game is done! I've won! I've won!"
Quoth she, and whistles thrice.

The Sun's rim dips; the stars rush out:
At one stride comes the dark;
With far-heard whisper, o'er the sea,
Off shot the spectre-bark.

We listened and looked sideways up!
Fear at my heart, as at a cup,
My life-blood seemed to sip!
The stars were dim, and thick the night,
The steersman's face by his lamp gleamed
        white;
From the sails the dew did drip—
Till clomb above the eastern bar
The hornèd Moon, with one bright star
Within the nether tip.

One after one, by the star-dogged Moon,
Too quick for groan or sigh,
Each turned his face with a ghastly pang,
And cursed me with his eye.

Four times fifty living men
(And I heard nor sigh nor groan),
With heavy thump, a lifeless lump,
They dropp'd down one by one.

Side notes:

And its ribs are seen as bars on the face of the setting Sun.

The Spectre-Woman and her Death-mate, and no other on board the skeleton ship. Like vessel, like crew!

Death and Life-in-Death have diced for the ship's crew, and she (the latter) winneth the ancient Mariner.

No twilight within the courts of the Sun.

At the rising of the Moon,

One after another,

His shipmates drop down dead.

256

But Life-in-Death
begins her work
on the ancient
Mariner.
The souls did from their bodies fly—
They fled to bliss or woe!
And every soul, it pass'd me by
Like the whizz of my crossbow!'

PART IV

The Wedding-
Guest feareth that
a spirit is talking
to him.
'I fear thee, ancient Mariner!
I fear thy skinny hand!
And thou art long, and lank, and brown,
As is the ribb'd sea-sand.

I fear thee and thy glittering eye,
And thy skinny hand so brown.'—
'Fear not, fear not, thou Wedding-Guest!
This body dropt not down.

But the ancient
Mariner assureth
him of his bodily
life, and proceed-
eth to relate his
horrible penance.
Alone, alone, all, all alone,
Alone on a wide, wide sea!
And never a saint took pity on
My soul in agony.

The many men, so beautiful!
And they all dead did lie:
And a thousand thousand slimy things
Lived on; and so did I.

And envieth that
they should live,
and so many lie
dead.
I look'd upon the rotting sea,
And drew my eyes away;
I look'd upon the rotting deck,
And there the dead men lay.

I looked to heaven, and tried to pray;
But or ever a prayer had gusht,
A wicked whisper came, and made
My heart as dry as dust.

I closed my lids, and kept them close,
And the balls like pulses beat;
For the sky and the sea, and the sea and
the sky,
Lay like a load on my weary eye,
And the dead were at my feet.

But the curse
liveth for him in
the eye of the
dead men.

The cold sweat melted from their limbs,
Nor rot nor reek did they:
The look with which they looked on me
Had never passed away.

An orphan's curse would drag to hell
A spirit from on high;
But oh! more horrible than that
Is the curse in a dead man's eye!
Seven days, seven nights, I saw that curse,
And yet I could not die.

In his loneliness
and fixedness he
yearneth towards
the journeying
Moon, and the
stars that still
sojourn, yet still
move onward; and
everywhere the
blue sky belongs to
them, and is their
appointed rest, and
their native country
and their own
natural homes,
which they enter
unannounced, as
lords that are cer-
tainly expected and
yet there is a silent
joy at their arrival.

The moving Moon went up the sky,
And nowhere did abide:
Softly she was going up,
And a star or two beside—

Her beams bemocked the sultry main,
Like April hoar-frost spread;
But where the ship's huge shadow lay,
The charmèd water burnt alway
A still and awful red.

By the light of
the Moon he be-
holdeth God's
creatures of the
great calm.

Beyond the shadow of the ship,
I watch'd the water-snakes:
They moved in tracks of shining white,
And when they rear'd, the elfish light
Fell off in hoary flakes.

Within the shadow of the ship
I watch'd their rich attire:
Blue, glossy green, and velvet black,
They coil'd and swam; and every track
Was a flash of golden fire.

Their beauty
and their
happiness

He blesseth them
in his heart.

O happy living things! no tongue
Their beauty might declare:
A spring of love gush'd from my heart,
And I bless'd them unaware:
Sure my kind saint took pity on me,
And I bless'd them unaware.

The selfsame moment I could pray;
And from my neck so free
The Albatross fell off, and sank
Like lead into the sea.

Part V

'O sleep! it is a gentle thing,
Beloved from pole to pole!
To Mary Queen the praise be given!
She sent the gentle sleep from Heaven,
That slid into my soul.

By the grace of
the holy Mother,
the ancient Mariner
is refreshed with
rain.

The silly buckets on the deck,
That had so long remained,
I dreamt that they were filled with dew,
And when I awoke, it rained.

My lips were wet, my throat was cold,
My garments all were dank;
Sure I had drunken in my dreams,
And still my body drank.

I moved, and could not feel my limbs:
I was so light—almost
I thought that I had died in sleep,
And was a blessed ghost.

He heareth sounds
and seeth strange
sights and com-
motions in the sky
and the element.

And soon I heard a roaring wind:
It did not come anear;
But with its sound it shook the sails,
That were so thin and sere.

The upper air burst into life!
And a hundred fire-flags sheen,
To and fro they were hurried about!
And to and fro, and in and out,
The wan stars danced between.

And the coming wind did roar more loud,
And the sails did sigh like sedge;
And the rain poured down from one black
    cloud;
The Moon was at its edge.

The thick black cloud was cleft, and still
The Moon was at its side:
Like waters shot from some high crag,
The lightning fell with never a jag,
A river steep and wide.

The bodies of the ship's crew are inspired, and the ship moves on.

The loud wind never reached the ship,
Yet now the ship moved on!
Beneath the lightning and the Moon
The dead men gave a groan.

They groan'd, they stirr'd, they all uprose,
Nor spake, nor moved their eyes;
It had been strange, even in a dream,
To have seen those dead men rise.

The helmsman steer'd, the ship moved on;
Yet never a breeze up-blew;
The mariners all 'gan work the ropes,
Where they were wont to do;
They raised their limbs like lifeless tools—
We were a ghastly crew.

The body of my brother's son
Stood by me, knee to knee:
The body and I pull'd at one rope,
But he said naught to me.'

But not by the souls of the men, nor by demons of earth or middle air, but by a blessed troop of angelic spirits, sent down by the invocation of the guardian saint.

'I fear thee, ancient Mariner!'
'Be calm, thou Wedding-Guest:
'Twas not those souls that fled in pain,
Which to their corses came again,
But a troop of spirits blest:

For when it dawned—they dropt their
    arms,
And clustered round the mast;
Sweet sounds rose slowly through their
    mouths,
And from their bodies passed.

260

Around, around, flew each sweet sound,
Then darted to the Sun;
Slowly the sounds came back again,
Now mixed, now one by one.

Sometimes a-dropping from the sky
I heard the skylark sing;
Sometimes all little birds that are,
How they seemed to fill the sea and air
With their sweet jargoning!

And now 'twas like all instruments,
Now like a lonely flute;
And now it is an angel's song,
That makes the heavens be mute.

It ceased; yet still the sails made on
A pleasant noise till noon,
A noise like of a hidden brook
In the leafy month of June,
That to the sleeping woods all night
Singeth a quiet tune.

Till noon we quietly sailed on,
Yet never a breeze did breathe:
Slowly and smoothly went the ship,
Moved onward from beneath.

The lonesome Spirit from the South Pole carries on the ship as far as the Line, in obedience to the angelic troop, but still requireth vengeance.

Under the keel nine fathoms deep,
From the land of mist and snow,
The spirit slid: and it was he
That made the ship to go.
The sails at noon left off their tune,
And the ship stood still also.

The Sun, right up above the mast,
Had fixed her to the ocean:
But in a minute she 'gan stir,
With a short uneasy motion—
Backwards and forwards half her length
With a short uneasy motion.

Then like a pawing horse let go,
She made a sudden bound:
It flung the blood into my head,
And I fell down in a swound.

The Polar Spirit's
fellow-demons, the
invisible inhabi-
tants of the ele-
ment, take part
in his wrong; and
two of them relate,
one to the other,
that penance long
and heavy for the
ancient Mariner
hath been accorded
to the Polar Spirit,
who returneth
southward.

How long in that same fit I lay,
I have not to declare;
But e'er my living life return'd,
I heard, and in my soul discern'd
Two voices in the air.

"Is it he?" quoth one, "is this the man?
By Him who died on cross,
With his cruel bow he laid full low
The harmless Albatross.
The Spirit who bideth by himself
In the land of mist and snow,
He loved the bird that loved the man
Who shot him with his bow."

The other was a softer voice,
As soft as honey-dew:
Quoth he, "The man hath penance done,
And penance more will do."

Part VI

First Voice

' "But tell me, tell me! speak again,
Thy soft response renewing—
What makes that ship drive on so fast?
What is the Ocean doing?"

Second Voice

"Still as a slave before his lord,
The Ocean hath no blast;
His great bright eye most silently
Up to the Moon is cast—
If he may know which way to go;
For she guides him smooth or grim.
See, brother, see! how graciously
She looketh down on him."

First Voice

"But why drives on that ship so fast,
Without or wave or wind?"

Second Voice

"The air is cut away before,
And closes from behind.

Fly, brother, fly! more high, more high!
Or we shall be belated:
For slow and slow that ship will go,
When the Mariner's trance is abated."

I woke, and we were sailing on
As in a gentle weather:
'Twas night, calm night, the moon was
    high;
The dead men stood together.

All stood together on the deck,
For a charnel-dungeon fitter:
All fixed on me their stony eyes,
That in the Moon did glitter.

The pang, the curse, with which they died,
Had never passed away:
I could not draw my eyes from theirs,
Nor turn them up to pray.

And now this spell was snapt: once more
I viewed the ocean green,
And looked far forth, yet little saw
Of what had else been seen—

Like one that on a lonesome road
Doth walk in fear and dread,
And having once turn'd round, walks on,
And turns no more his head;
Because he knows a frightful fiend
Doth close behind him tread.

263

But soon there breathed a wind on me,
Nor sound nor motion made:
Its path was not upon the sea,
In ripple or in shade.

It raised my hair, it fann'd my cheek
Like a meadow-gale of spring—
It mingled strangely with my fears,
Yet it felt like a welcoming.

Swiftly, swiftly flew the ship,
Yet she sail'd softly too:
Sweetly, sweetly blew the breeze—
On me alone it blew.

And the ancient Mariner beholdeth his native country.

O dream of joy! is this indeed
The lighthouse top I see?
Is this the hill? is this the kirk?
Is this mine own countree?

We drifted o'er the harbour-bar,
And I with sobs did pray—
O let me be awake, my God!
Or let me sleep alway.

The harbour-bay was clear as glass,
So smoothly it was strewn!
And on the bay the moonlight lay,
And the shadow of the Moon.

The rock shone bright, the kirk no less,
That stands above the rock:
The moonlight steeped in silentness
The steady weathercock.

The angelic spirits leave the dead bodies,

And the bay was white with silent light,
Till rising from the same,
Full many shapes, that shadows were,
In crimson colours came.

And appear in their own forms of light.

A little distance from the prow
Those crimson shadows were:
I turned my eyes upon the deck—
Oh, Christ! what saw I there!

Each corse lay flat, lifeless and flat,
And, by the holy rood!
A man all light, a seraph-man,
On every corse there stood.

This seraph-band, each waved his hand:
It was a heavenly sight!
They stood as signals to the land,
Each one a lovely light;

This seraph-band, each waved his hand,
No voice did they impart—
No voice; but oh! the silence sank
Like music on my heart.

But soon I heard the dash of oars,
I heard the Pilot's cheer;
My head was turned perforce away
And I saw a boat appear.

The Pilot and the Pilot's boy,
I heard them coming fast:
Dear Lord in Heaven! it was a joy
The dead men could not blast.

I saw a third—I heard his voice:
It is the Hermit good!
He singeth loud his godly hymns
That he makes in the wood.
He'll shrieve my soul, he'll wash away
The Albatross's blood.

PART VII

The Hermit
of the Wood

'This hermit good lives in that wood
Which slopes down to the sea.
How loudly his sweet voice he rears!
He loves to talk with mariners
That come from a far countree.

He kneels at morn, and noon, and eve—
He hath a cushion plump:
It is the moss that wholly hides
The rotted old oak-stump.

The skiff-boat near'd: I heard them talk,
"Why, this is strange, I trow!
Where are those lights so many and fair,
That signal made but now?"

Approacheth
the ship with
wonder.
"Strange, by my faith!" the Hermit said—
"And they answer'd not our cheer!
The planks look warp'd! and see those sails,
How thin they are and sere!
I never saw aught like to them,
Unless perchance it were

Brown skeletons of leaves that lag
My forest-brook along;
When the ivy-tod is heavy with snow,
And the owlet whoops to the wolf below,
That eats the she-wolf's young."

"Dear Lord! it hath a fiendish look—
(The Pilot made reply)
I am afeared"—"Push on, push on!"
Said the Hermit cheerily.

The boat came closer to the ship,
But I nor spake nor stirred;
The boat came close beneath the ship,
And straight a sound was heard.

The ship suddenly
sinketh.
Under the water it rumbled on,
Still louder and more dread:
It reached the ship, it split the bay;
The ship went down like lead.

The ancient
Mariner is saved
in the Pilot's boat.
Stunned by that loud and dreadful sound,
Which sky and ocean smote,
Like one that hath been seven days drowned
My body lay afloat;
But swift as dreams, myself I found
Within the Pilot's boat.

266

Upon the whirl, where sank the ship,
The boat spun round and round;
And all was still, save that the hill
Was telling of the sound.

I moved my lips—the Pilot shrieked
And fell down in a fit;
The holy Hermit raised his eyes,
And prayed where he did sit.

I took the oars: the Pilot's boy,
Who now doth crazy go,
Laugh'd loud and long, and all the while
His eyes went to and fro.
"Ha! ha!" quoth he, "full plain I see
The Devil knows how to row."

And now, all in my own countree,
I stood on the firm land!
The Hermit stepp'd forth from the boat,
And scarcely he could stand.

The ancient
Mariner earnestly
entreateth the
Hermit to shrieve
him; and the pen-
ance of life falls
on him.

"O shrieve me, shrieve me, holy man!"
The Hermit cross'd his brow.
"Say quick," quoth he, "I bid thee say—
What manner of man art thou?"

Forthwith this frame of mine was wrench'd
With a woeful agony,
Which forced me to begin my tale;
And then it left me free.

And ever and anon
throughout his
future life an
agony constraineth
him to travel from
land to land;

Since then, at an uncertain hour,
That agony returns:
And till my ghastly tale is told,
This heart within me burns.

I pass, like night, from land to land;
I have strange power of speech;
That moment that his face I see,
I know the man that must hear me:
To him my tale I teach.

What loud uproar bursts from that door!
The wedding-guests are there:
But in the garden-bower the bride
And bride-maids singing are:
And hark, the little vesper bell,
Which biddeth me to prayer!

O Wedding-Guest! this soul hath been
Alone on a wide wide sea:
So lonely 'twas, that God himself
Scarce seemèd there to be.

O sweeter than the marriage-feast,
'Tis sweeter far to me,
To walk together to the kirk
With a goodly company!—

To walk together to the kirk,
And all together pray,
While each to his great Father bends,
Old men, and babes, and loving friends,
And youths and maidens gay!

And to teach, by
his own example,
love and reverence
to all things that
God made and
loveth.

Farewell, farewell! but this I tell
To thee, thou Wedding-Guest!
He prayeth well, who loveth well
Both man and bird and beast.

He prayeth best, who loveth best
All things both great and small;
For the dear God who loveth us,
He made and loveth all.'

The Mariner, whose eye is bright,
Whose beard with age is hoar,
Is gone: and now the Wedding-Guest
Turned from the bridegroom's door.

He went like one that hath been stunned,
And is of sense forlorn:
A sadder and a wiser man
He rose the morrow morn.

Kubla Khan

In Xanadu did Kubla Khan
  A stately pleasure-dome decree:
Where Alph, the sacred river, ran
Through caverns measureless to man
  Down to a sunless sea.

So twice five miles of fertile ground
With walls and towers were girdled round:
And here were gardens bright with sinuous rills
Where blossomed many an incense-bearing tree;
And here were forests ancient as the hills,
Enfolding sunny spots of greenery.

But oh! that deep romantic chasm which slanted
Down the green hill athwart a cedarn cover!
A savage place! as holy and enchanted
As e'er beneath a waning moon was haunted
By woman wailing for her demon-lover!
And from this chasm, with ceaseless turmoil seething,
As if this earth in fast thick pants were breathing,
A mighty fountain momently was forced:
Amid whose swift half-intermitted burst
Huge fragments vaulted like rebounding hail:
Or chaffy grain beneath the thresher's flail:
And mid these dancing rocks at once and ever
It flung up momently the sacred river.
Five miles meandering with a mazy motion
Through wood and dale the sacred river ran,
Then reach'd the caverns measureless to man,
And sank in tumult to a lifeless ocean:
And 'mid this tumult Kubla heard from far
Ancestral voices prophesying war!

  The shadow of the dome of pleasure
  Floated midway on the waves;
  Where was heard the mingled measure
  From the fountain and the caves.
It was a miracle of rare device
A sunny pleasure-dome with caves of ice!

A damsel with a dulcimer
In a vision once I saw:
It was an Abyssinian maid,
And on her dulcimer she play'd,
Singing of Mount Abora.
Could I revive within me
Her symphony and song,
To such a deep delight 'twould win me
That with music loud and long,

I would build that dome in air,
That sunny dome! those caves of ice!
And all who heard should see them there,
And all should cry, Beware! Beware!
His flashing eyes, his floating hair!
Weave a circle round him thrice,
And close your eyes with holy dread,
For he on honey-dew hath fed,
And drunk the milk of Paradise.

PERCY BYSSHE SHELLEY
1792-1822

The Cloud

I bring fresh showers for the thirsting flowers,
    From the seas and the streams;
I bear light shade for the leaves when laid
    In their noonday dreams.
From my wings are shaken the dews that waken
    The sweet buds every one,
When rocked to rest on their mother's breast,
    As she dances about the sun.
I wield the flail of the lashing hail,
    And whiten the green plains under,
And then again I dissolve it in rain,
    And laugh as I pass in thunder.

I sift the snow on the mountains below,
    And their great pines groan aghast;
And all the night 'tis my pillow white,
    While I sleep in the arms of the blast.
Sublime on the towers of my skiey bowers,
    Lightning my pilot sits;
In a cavern under is fettered the thunder,
    It struggles and howls at fits;
Over earth and ocean, with gentle motion,
    This pilot is guiding me,
Lured by the love of the genii that move
    In the depths of the purple sea;
Over the rills and the crags, and the hills,
    Over the lakes and the plains,
Wherever he dream, under mountain or stream,
    The Spirit he loves remains;
And I all the while bask in Heaven's blue smile,
    Whilst he is dissolving in rains.

The sanguine Sunrise, with his meteor eyes,
    And his burning plumes outspread,
Leaps on the back of my sailing rack,
    When the morning star shines dead;
As on the jag of a mountain crag,
    Which an earthquake rocks and swings,
An eagle alit one moment may sit
    In the light of its golden wings.
And when Sunset may breathe, from the lit sea beneath,
    Its ardours of rest and of love,
And the crimson pall of eve may fall
    From the depth of Heaven above,
With wings folded I rest on mine aëry nest,
    As still as a brooding dove.

That orbèd maiden with white fire laden,
    Whom mortals call the Moon,
Glides glimmering o'er my fleece-like floor,
    By the midnight breezes strewn;
And wherever the beat of her unseen feet,
    Which only the angels hear,
May have broken the woof of my tent's thin roof,
    The stars peep behind her and peer;
And I laugh to see them whirl and flee,
    Like a swarm of golden bees,
When I widen the rent in my wind-built tent,
    Till the calm rivers, lakes, and seas,
Like strips of the sky fallen through me on high,
    Are each paved with the moon and these.

I bind the Sun's throne with a burning zone,
    And the Moon's with a girdle of pearl;
The volcanoes are dim, and the stars reel and swim,
    When the whirlwinds my banner unfurl.
From cape to cape, with a bridge-like shape,
    Over a torrent sea,
Sunbeam-proof, I hang like a roof,—
    The mountains its columns be.
The triumphal arch through which I march
    With hurricane, fire, and snow,
When the Powers of the air are chained to my chair,
    Is the million-coloured bow;

The sphere-fire above its soft colours wove,
    While the moist Earth was laughing below.

I am the daughter of Earth and Water,
    And the nursling of the Sky;
I pass through the pores of the ocean and shores;
    I change, but I cannot die.
For after the rain when with never a stain
    The pavilion of Heaven is bare,
And the winds and sunbeams with their convex gleams
    Build up the blue dome of air,
I silently laugh at my own cenotaph,
    And out of the caverns of rain,
Like a child from the womb, like a ghost from the tomb,
    I arise and unbuild it again.

Ode to the West Wind

(1)

O wild West Wind, thou breath of Autumn's being,
Thou, from whose unseen presence the leaves dead
Are driven, like ghosts from an enchanter fleeing,

Yellow, and black, and pale, and hectic red,
Pestilence-stricken multitudes: O thou
Who chariotest to their dark wintry bed

The wingèd seeds, where they lie cold and low,
Each like a corpse within its grave, until
Thine azure sister of the Spring shall blow

Her clarion o'er the dreaming earth, and fill
(Driving sweet buds like flocks to feed in air)
With living hues and odours plain and hill:

Wild Spirit, which art moving everywhere;
Destroyer and Preserver; hear, oh, hear!

(2)

Thou on whose stream, 'mid the steep sky's commotion,
Loose clouds like earth's decaying leaves are shed,
Shook from the tangled boughs of Heaven and Ocean,

Angels of rain and lightning: there are spread
On the blue surface of thine airy surge,
Like the bright hair uplifted from the head

Of some fierce Mænad, even from the dim verge
Of the horizon to the zenith's height,
The locks of the approaching storm. Thou dirge

Of the dying year, to which this closing night
Will be the dome of a vast sepulchre,
Vaulted with all thy congregated might

Of vapours, from whose solid atmosphere
Black rain, and fire, and hail, will burst: oh, hear!

(3)

Thou who didst waken from his summer dreams
The blue Mediterranean, where he lay,
Lull'd by the coil of his crystalline streams,

Beside a pumice isle in Baiæ's bay,
And saw in sleep old palaces and towers
Quivering within the wave's intenser day,

All overgrown with azure moss and flowers
So sweet, the sense faints picturing them! Thou
For whose path the Atlantic's level powers

Cleave themselves into chasms, while far below
The sea-blooms and the oozy woods which wear
The sapless foliage of the ocean, know

Thy voice, and suddenly grow gray with fear,
And tremble and despoil themselves: oh, hear!

(4)

If I were a dead leaf thou mightest bear;
If I were a swift cloud to fly with thee;
A wave to pant beneath thy power, and share

The impulse of thy strength, only less free
Than thou, O uncontrollable! If even
I were as in my boyhood, and could be

The comrade of thy wanderings over Heaven,
As then, when to outstrip thy skiey speed
Scarce seemed a vision; I would ne'er have striven

As thus with thee in prayer in my sore need.
Oh, lift me as a wave, a leaf, a cloud!
I fall upon the thorns of life! I bleed!

A heavy weight of hours has chained and bowed
One too like thee: tameless, and swift, and proud.

(5)

Make me thy lyre, even as the forest is:
What if my leaves are falling like its own!
The tumult of thy mighty harmonies

Will take from both a deep, autumnal tone,
Sweet though in sadness. Be thou, Spirit fierce,
My spirit! Be thou me, impetuous one!

Drive my dead thoughts over the universe
Like withered leaves to quicken a new birth!
And, by the incantation of this verse,

Scatter, as from an unextinguished hearth
Ashes and sparks, my words among mankind!
Be through my lips to unawakened earth

The trumpet of a prophecy! O, Wind,
If Winter comes, can Spring be far behind?

To a Skylark

Hail to thee, blithe Spirit!
Bird thou never wert,
That from heaven, or near it,
Pourest thy full heart
In profuse strains of unpremeditated art.

Higher still and higher
From the earth thou springest,
Like a cloud of fire,
The blue deep thou wingest,
And singing still dost soar, and soaring ever singest,

In the golden lightning
Of the sunken sun
O'er which clouds are brightening,
Thou dost float and run,
Like an unbodied joy whose race is just begun.

The pale purple even
Melts around thy flight;
Like a star of heaven
In the broad daylight
Thou art unseen, but yet I hear thy shrill delight:

Keen as are the arrows
Of that silver sphere,
Whose intense lamp narrows
In the white dawn clear
Until we hardly see, we feel that it is there.

All the earth and air
With thy voice is loud,
As, when night is bare,
From one lonely cloud
The moon rains out her beams, and heaven is overflow'd.

What thou art we know not;
What is most like thee?
From rainbow clouds there flow not
Drops so bright to see
As from thy presence showers a rain of melody;—

Like a poet hidden
In a light of thought,
Singing hymns unbidden,
Till the world is wrought
To sympathy with hopes and fears it heeded not:

Like a high-born maiden
In a palace tower,
Soothing her love-laden
Soul in secret hour
With music sweet as love, which overflows her bower:

Like a glow-worm golden
In a dell of dew,
Scattering unbeholden
Its aerial hue
Among the flowers and grass, which screen it from the view:

Like a rose embowered
In its own green leaves,
By warm winds deflowered,
Till the scent it gives
Makes faint with too much sweet those heavy-wingèd thieves:

Sound of vernal showers
On the twinkling grass,
Rain-awakened flowers,
All that ever was
Joyous, and clear, and fresh, thy music doth surpass:

Teach us, Sprite or Bird,
What sweet thoughts are thine:
I have never heard
Praise of love or wine
That panted forth a flood of rapture so divine.

Chorus Hymeneal,
Or triumphal chant,
Matched with thine would be all
But an empty vaunt,
A thing wherein we feel there is some hidden want.

What objects are the fountains
Of thy happy strain?
What fields, or waves, or mountains?
What shapes of sky or plain?
What love of thine own kind? what ignorance of pain?

With thy clear keen joyance
Languor cannot be:
Shadow of annoyance
Never came near thee:
Thou lovest—but ne'er knew love's sad satiety.

Waking or asleep
Thou of death must deem
Things more true and deep
That we mortals dream,
Or how could thy notes flow in such a crystal stream?

We look before and after,
And pine for what is not:
Our sincerest laughter
With some pain is fraught;
Our sweetest songs are those that tell of saddest thought.

Yet if we could scorn
Hate, and pride, and fear;
If we were things born
Not to shed a tear,
I know not how thy joy we ever should come near.

Better than all measures
Of delightful sound,
Better than all treasures
That in books are found,
Thy skill to poet were, thou scorner of the ground!

Teach me half the gladness
That thy brain must know,
Such harmonious madness
From my lips would flow,
The world should listen then, as I am listening now!

To the Night

Swiftly walk over the western wave,
Spirit of Night!
Out of the misty eastern cave,
Where, all the long and lone daylight,
Thou wovest dreams of joy and fear
Which make thee terrible and dear,—
Swift be thy flight!

Wrap thy form in a mantle grey
Star-inwrought!
Blind with thine hair the eyes of Day,
Kiss her until she be wearied out,

Then wander o'er city, and sea, and land,
Touching all with thine opiate wand—
      Come, long-sought!

When I arose and saw the dawn,
      I sigh'd for thee;
When light rode high, and the dew was gone,
  And noon lay heavy on flower and tree,
And the weary Day turn'd to his rest,
Lingering like an unlov'ed guest,
      I sigh'd for thee.

Thy brother Death came, and cried,
      'Wouldst thou me?'
Thy sweet child Sleep, the filmy-eyed,
  Murmured like a noontide bee,
'Shall I nestle near thy side?
Wouldst thou me?'—And I replied,
      'No, not thee!'

Death will come when thou art dead,
      Soon, too soon—
Sleep will come when thou art fled;
  Of neither would I ask the boon
I ask of thee, belovèd Night—
Swift be thine approaching flight,
      Come soon, soon!

Song

Music, when soft voices die,
Vibrates in the memory—
Odours, when sweet violets sicken,
Live within the sense they quicken.

Rose leaves, when the rose is dead,
Are heaped for the belovèd's bed;
And so thy thoughts, when thou art gone,
Love itself shall slumber on.

JOHN KEATS

1795-1821

The Eve of St. Agnes

St. Agnes' Eve—Ah, bitter chill it was!
The owl, for all his feathers, was a-cold;
The hare limp'd trembling through the frozen grass,
And silent was the flock in woolly fold:
Numb were the Beadsman's fingers, while he told
His rosary, and while his frosted breath,
Like pious incense from a censer old,
Seem'd taking flight for heaven, without a death,
Past the sweet Virgin's picture, while his prayer he saith.

His prayer he saith, this patient, holy man;
Then takes his lamp, and riseth from his knees,
And back returneth, meagre, barefoot, wan,
Along the chapel aisle by slow degrees:
The sculptur'd dead, on each side, seem to freeze,
Emprison'd in black, purgatorial rails:
Knights, ladies, praying in dumb orat'ries,
He passeth by; and his weak spirit fails
To think how they may ache in icy hoods and mails.

Northward he turneth through a little door,
And scarce three steps, ere Music's golden tongue
Flatter'd to tears this aged man and poor;
But no—already had his death-bell rung:
The joys of all his life were said and sung:
His was harsh penance on St. Agnes' Eve:
Another way he went, and soon among
Rough ashes sat he for his soul's reprieve,
And all night kept awake, for sinners' sake to grieve.

That ancient Beadsman heard the prelude soft;
And so it chanc'd, for many a door was wide,
From hurry to and fro. Soon, up aloft,
The silver, snarling trumpets 'gan to chide:

The level chambers, ready with their pride,
Were glowing to receive a thousand guests:
The carved angels, ever eager-eyed,
Star'd, where upon their heads the cornice rests,
With hair blown back, and wings put cross-wise on their
    breasts.

At length burst in the argent revelry,
With plume, tiara, and all rich array,
Numerous as shadows haunting faerily
The brain, new stuff'd, in youth, with triumphs gay
Of old romance. These let us wish away,
And turn, sole-thoughted, to one Lady there,
Whose heart had brooded, all that wintry day,
On love, and wing'd St. Agnes' saintly care,
As she had heard old dames full many times declare.

They told her how, upon St. Agnes' Eve.
Young virgins might have visions of delight,
And soft adorings from their loves receive
Upon the honey'd middle of the night,
If ceremonies due they did aright;
As, supperless to bed they must retire,
And couch supine their beauties, lily white;
Nor look behind, nor sideways, but require
Of Heaven with upward eyes for all that they desire.

Full of this whim was thoughtful Madeline:
The music, yearning like a God in pain,
She scarcely heard: her maiden eyes divine,
Fix'd on the floor, saw many a sweeping train
Pass by—she heeded not at all: in vain
Came many a tiptoe, amorous cavalier,
And back retir'd; not cool'd by high disdain,
But she saw not: her heart was otherwhere:
She sigh'd for Agnes' dreams, the sweetest of the year.

She danc'd along with vague, regardless eyes,
Anxious her lips, her breathing quick and short:
The hallow'd hour was near at hand: she sighs
Amid the timbrels, and the throng'd resort
Of whisperers in anger, or in sport;

'Mid looks of love, defiance, hate, and scorn,
Hoodwink'd with faery fancy; all amort,
Save to St. Agnes and her lambs unshorn,
And all the bliss to be before to-morrow morn.

So, purposing each moment to retire,
She linger'd still. Meantime, across the moors,
Had come young Porphyro, with heart on fire
For Madeline. Beside the portal doors,
Buttress'd from moonlight, stands he, and implores
All saints to give him sight of Madeline,
But for one moment in the tedious hours,
That he might gaze and worship all unseen;
Perchance speak, kneel, touch, kiss—in sooth such things have
    been.

He ventures in: let no buzz'd whisper tell:
All eyes be muffled, or a hundred swords
Will storm his heart, Love's fev'rous citadel:
For him, those chambers held barbarian hordes,
Hyena foemen, and hot-blooded lords,
Whose very dogs would execrations howl
Against his lineage: not one breast affords
Him any mercy, in that mansion foul,
Save one old beldame, weak in body and in soul.

Ah, happy chance! the aged creature came,
Shuffling along with ivory-headed wand,
To where he stood, hid from the torch's flame,
Behind a broad hall-pillar, far beyond
The sound of merriment and chorus bland:
He startled her; but soon she knew his face,
And grasp'd his fingers in her palsied hand,
Saying, 'Mercy, Porphyro! hie thee from this place:
They are all here to-night, the whole blood-thirsty race!

Get hence! get hence! there's dwarfish Hildebrand;
He had a fever late, and in the fit
He cursed thee and thine, both house and land:
Then there's that old Lord Maurice, not a whit
More tame for his gray hairs—Alas me! flit!

Flit like a ghost away.'—'Ah, Gossip dear,
We're safe enough; here in this arm-chair sit,
And tell me how'—'Good Saints! not here, not here;
Follow me, child, or else these stones will be thy bier.'

He follow'd through a lowly arched way,
Brushing the cobwebs with his lofty plume,
And as she mutter'd 'Well-a—well-a-day!'
He found him in a little moonlight room,
Pale, lattic'd, chill, and silent as a tomb.
'Now tell me where is Madeline,' said he,
'O tell me, Angela, by the holy loom
Which none but secret sisterhood may see,
When they St. Agnes' wool are weaving piously.'

'St. Agnes! Ah! it is St. Agnes' Eve—
Yet men will murder upon holy days:
Thou must hold water in a witch's sieve,
And be liege-lord of all the Elves and Fays,
To venture so; it fills me with amaze
To see thee, Porphyro!—St. Agnes' Eve!
God's help! my lady fair the conjuror plays
This very night: good angels her deceive!
But let me laugh awhile, I've mickle time to grieve.'

Feebly she laugheth in the languid moon,
While Porphyro upon her face doth look,
Like puzzled urchin on an aged crone
Who keepeth clos'd a wond'rous riddle-book,
As spectacled she sits in chimney nook.
But soon his eyes grew brilliant, when she told
His lady's purpose; and he scarce could brook
Tears, at the thought of those enchantments cold,
And Madeline asleep in lap of legends old.

Sudden a thought came like a full-blown rose,
Flushing his brow, and in his pained heart
Made purple riot: then doth he propose
A stratagem, that makes the beldame start:
'A cruel man and impious thou art:
Sweet lady, let her pray, and sleep, and dream
Alone with her good angels, far apart

From wicked men like thee. Go, go!—I deem
Thou canst not surely be the same that thou didst seem.'

'I will not harm her, by all saints I swear,'
Quoth Porphyro: 'O may I ne'er find grace
When my weak voice shall whisper its last prayer,
If one of her soft ringlets I displace,
Or look with ruffian passion in her face:
Good Angela, believe me by these tears;
Or I will, even in a moment's space,
Awake, with horrid shout, my foemen's ears,
And beard them, though they be more fang'd than wolves
    and bears.'

'Ah! why wilt thou affright a feeble soul?
A poor, weak, palsy-stricken, churchyard thing,
Whose passing-bell may ere the midnight toll;
Whose prayers for thee, each morn and evening,
Were never miss'd.'—Thus plaining, doth she bring
A gentler speech from burning Porphyro;
So woeful, and of such deep sorrowing,
That Angela gives promise she will do
Whatever he shall wish, betide her weal or woe.

Which was, to lead him, in close secrecy,
Even to Madeline's chamber, and there hide
Him in a closet, of such privacy
That he might see her beauty unespied,
And win perhaps that night a peerless bride,
While legion'd faeries pac'd the coverlet,
And pale enchantment held her sleepy-eyed.
Never on such a night have lovers met,
Since Merlin paid his Demon all the monstrous debt.

'It shall be as thou wishest,' said the Dame:
'All cates and dainties shall be stored there
Quickly on this feast-night: by the tambour frame
Her own lute thou wilt see: no time to spare,
For I am slow and feeble, and scarce dare
On such a catering trust my dizzy head.
Wait here, my child, with patience; kneel in prayer
The while: Ah! thou must needs the lady wed,
Or may I never leave my grave among the dead.'

So saying, she hobbled off with busy fear.
The lover's endless minutes slowly pass'd;
The dame return'd, and whisper'd in his ear
To follow her; with aged eyes aghast
From fright of dim espial. Safe at last,
Through many a dusky gallery, they gain
The maiden's chamber, silken, hush'd, and chaste;
Where Porphyro took covert, pleas'd amain.
His poor guide hurried back with agues in her brain.

Her falt'ring hand upon the balustrade,
Old Angela was feeling for the stair,
When Madeline, St. Agnes' charmed maid,
Rose, like a mission'd spirit, unaware:
With silver taper's light, and pious care,
She turn'd, and down the aged gossip led
To a safe level matting. Now prepare,
Young Porphyro, for gazing on that bed;
She comes, she comes again, like ring-dove fray'd and fled.

Out went the taper as she hurried in;
Its little smoke, in pallid moonshine, died:
She clos'd the door, she panted, all akin
To spirits of the air, and visions wide:
No uttered syllable, or, woe betide!
But to her heart, her heart was voluble,
Paining with eloquence her balmy side;
As though a tongueless nightingale should swell
Her throat in vain, and die, heart-stifled, in her dell.

A casement high and triple-arch'd there was,
All garlanded with carven imag'ries
Of fruits, and flowers, and bunches of knot-grass,
And diamonded with panes of quaint device,
Innumerable of stains and splendid dyes,
As are the tiger-moth's deep-damask'd wings;
And in the midst, 'mong thousand heraldries,
And twilight saints, and dim emblazonings,
A shielded scutcheon blush'd with blood of queens and kings.

Full on this casement shone the wintry moon,
And threw warm gules on Madeline's fair breast,

As down she knelt for heaven's grace and boon;
Rose-bloom fell on her hands, together prest,
And on her silver cross soft amethyst,
And on her hair a glory, like a saint:
She seem'd a splendid angel, newly drest,
Save wings, for heaven:—Porphyro grew faint:
She knelt, so pure a thing, so free from mortal taint.

Anon his heart revives: her vespers done,
Of all its wreathed pearls her hairs she frees;
Unclasps her warmed jewels one by one;
Loosens her fragrant bodice; by degrees
Her rich attire creeps rustling to her knees:
Half-hidden, like a mermaid in sea-weed,
Pensive awhile she dreams awake, and sees,
In fancy, fair St. Agnes in her bed,
But dares not look behind, or all the charm is fled.

Soon, trembling in her soft and chilly nest,
In sort of wakeful swoon, perplex'd she lay,
Until the poppied warmth of sleep oppress'd
Her soothed limbs, and soul fatigued away;
Flown, like a thought, until the morrow-day;
Blissfully haven'd both from joy and pain;
Clasp'd like a missal where swart Paynims pray;
Blinded alike from sunshine and from rain,
As though a rose should shut, and be a bud again.

Stol'n to this paradise, and so entranced,
Porphyro gazed upon her empty dress,
And listen'd to her breathing, if it chanced
To wake into a slumberous tenderness;
Which when he heard, that minute did he bless,
And breath'd himself: then from the closet crept,
Noiseless as fear in a wide wilderness,
And over the hush'd carpet, silent, stept,
And 'tween the curtains peep'd, where, lo!—how fast she
    slept.

Then by the bed-side, where the faded moon
Made a dim, silver twilight, soft he set
A table, and, half-anguish'd, threw thereon
A cloth of woven crimson, gold, and jet:—

O for some drowsy Morphean amulet!
The boisterous, midnight, festive clarion,
The kettle-drum, and far-heard clarinet,
Affray his ears, though but in dying tone:—
The hall door shuts again, and all the noise is gone.

And still she slept an azure-lidded sleep,
In blanched linen, smooth, and lavender'd,
While he from forth the closet brought a heap
Of candied apple, quince, and plum, and gourd;
With jellies soother than the creamy curd,
And lucent syrops, tinct with cinnamon;
Manna and dates, in argosy transferr'd
From Fez; and spiced dainties, every one,
From silken Samarcand to cedar'd Lebanon.

These delicates he heap'd with glowing hand
On golden dishes and in baskets bright
Of wreathed silver: sumptuous they stand
In the retired quiet of the night,
Filling the chilly room with perfume light.—
'And now, my love, my seraph fair, awake!
Thou art my heaven, and I thine eremite:
Open thine eyes, for meek St. Agnes' sake,
Or I shall drowse beside thee, so my soul doth ache.'

Thus whispering, his warm, unnerved arm
Sank in her pillow. Shaded was her dream
By the dusk curtains:—'twas a midnight charm
Impossible to melt as iced stream:
The lustrous salvers in the moonlight gleam;
Broad golden fringe upon the carpet lies:
It seem'd he never, never could redeem
From such a steadfast spell his lady's eyes;
So mus'd awhile, entoil'd in woofed phantasies.

Awakening up, he took her hollow lute,—
Tumultuous,—and, in chords that tenderest be,
He play'd an ancient ditty, long since mute,
In Provence call'd, 'La belle dame sans mercy':
Close to her ear touching the melody;—
Wherewith disturb'd, she utter'd a soft moan:

He ceased—she panted quick—and suddenly
Her blue affrayed eyes wide open shone:
Upon his knees he sank, pale as smooth-sculptured stone.

Her eyes were open, but she still beheld,
Now wide awake, the vision of her sleep:
There was a painful change, that nigh expell'd
The blisses of her dream so pure and deep.
At which fair Madeline began to weep,
And moan forth witless words with many a sigh;
While still her gaze on Porphyro would keep;
Who knelt, with joined hands and piteous eye,
Fearing to move or speak, she look'd so dreamingly.

'Ah, Porphyro!' said she, 'but even now
Thy voice was at sweet tremble in mine ear,
Made tuneable with every sweetest vow;
And those sad eyes were spiritual and clear:
How chang'd thou art! how pallid, chill, and drear!
Give me that voice again, my Porphyro,
Those looks immortal, those complainings dear!
Oh leave me not in this eternal woe,
For if thou diest, my Love, I know not where to go.'

Beyond a mortal man impassion'd far
At these voluptuous accents, he arose,
Ethereal, flush'd, and like a throbbing star
Seen mid the sapphire heaven's deep repose;
Into her dream he melted, as the rose
Blendeth its odour with the violet,—
Solution sweet; meantime the frost-wind blows
Like Love's alarum pattering the sharp sleet
Against the window-panes; St. Agnes' moon hath set.

'Tis dark: quick pattereth the flaw-blown sleet:
'This is no dream, my bride, my Madeline!'
'Tis dark: the iced gusts still rave and beat:
'No dream, alas! alas! and woe is mine!
Porphyro will leave me here to fade and pine.—
Cruel! what traitor could thee hither bring?
I curse not, for my heart is lost in thine,
Though thou forsakest a deceived thing;—
A dove forlorn and lost with sick unpruned wing.'

'My Madeline! sweet dreamer! lovely bride!
Say, may I be for aye thy vassal blest?
Thy beauty's shield, heart-shap'd and vermeil dyed?
Ah, silver shrine, here will I take my rest
After so many hours of toil and quest,
A famish'd pilgrim,—sav'd by miracle.
Though I have found, I will not rob thy nest
Saving of thy sweet self; if thou think'st well
To trust, fair Madeline, to no rude infidel.

'Hark! 'tis an elfin-storm from faery land,
Of haggard seeming, but a boon indeed:
Arise—arise! the morning is at hand;—
The bloated wassaillers will never heed:—
Let us away, my love, with happy speed;
There are no ears to hear, or eyes to see,—
Drown'd all in Rhenish and the sleepy mead:
Awake! arise! my love, and fearless be,
For o'er the southern moors I have a home for thee.'

She hurried at his words, beset with fears,
For there were sleeping dragons all around,
At glaring watch, perhaps, with ready spears—
Down the wide stairs a darkling way they found.—
In all the house was heard no human sound.
A chain-droop'd lamp was flickering by each door;
The arras, rich with horseman, hawk, and hound,
Flutter'd in the besieging wind's uproar;
And the long carpets rose along the gusty floor.

They glide, like phantoms, into the wide hall;
Like phantoms, to the iron porch, they glide:
Where lay the Porter, in uneasy sprawl,
With a huge empty flagon by his side:
The wakeful bloodhound rose, and shook his hide,
But his sagacious eye an inmate owns:
By one, and one, the bolts full easy slide:—
The chains lie silent on the footworn stones;—
The key turns, and the door upon its hinges groans.

And they are gone: aye, ages long ago
These lovers fled away into the storm.

That night the Baron dreamt of many a woe,
And all his warrior-guests, with shade and form
Of witch, and demon, and large coffin-worm,
Were long be-nightmar'd. Angela the old
Died palsy-twitch'd, with meagre face deform;
The Beadsman, after thousand aves told,
For aye unsought for slept among his ashes cold.

La Belle Dame sans Merci

'O what can ail thee, knight-at-arms,
    Alone and palely loitering?
The sedge has wither'd from the Lake,
    And no birds sing.

O what can ail thee, knight-at-arms!
    So haggard and so woebegone?
The squirrel's granary is full,
    And the harvest's done.

I see a lily on thy brow
    With anguish moist and fever dew,
And on thy cheeks a fading rose
    Fast withereth too.'

'I met a Lady in the Meads,
    Full beautiful—a fairy's child,
Her hair was long, her foot was light,
    And her eyes were wild.

I made a garland for her head,
    And bracelets too, and fragrant zone;
She look'd at me as she did love,
    And made sweet moan.

I set her on my pacing steed
    And nothing else saw all day long,
For sidelong would she bend, and sing
    A fairy's song.

She found me roots of relish sweet,
    And honey wild and manna dew,
And sure in language strange she said
    "I love thee true."

She took me to her elfin grot,
    And there she wept, and sigh'd full sore,
And there I shut her wild wild eyes
    With kisses four.

And there she lullèd me asleep,
    And there I dream'd—Ah! woe betide!
The latest dream I ever dreamt
    On the cold hill-side.

I saw pale Kings and Princes too,
    Pale warriors, death-pale were they all;
They cried—"La belle Dame sans Merci
    Hath thee in thrall!"

I saw their starved lips in the gloam
    With horrid warning gapèd wide,
And I awoke and found me here
    On the cold hill's side.

And this is why I sojourn here
    Alone and palely loitering,
Though the sedge is wither'd from the Lake
    And no birds sing.'

On first looking into Chapman's Homer

Much have I travell'd in the realms of gold
And many goodly states and kingdoms seen;
Round many western islands have I been
Which bards in fealty to Apollo hold.
Oft of one wide expanse had I been told
That deep-brow'd Homer ruled as his demesne;
Yet did I never breathe its pure serene
Till I heard Chapman speak out loud and bold:
Then felt I like some watcher of the skies
When a new planet swims into his ken;
Or like stout Cortez, when with eagle eyes
He stared at the Pacific—and all his men
Look'd at each other with a wild surmise—
Silent, upon a peak in Darien.

Ode to a Nightingale

My heart aches, and a drowsy numbness pains
　　My sense, as though of hemlock I had drunk,
Or emptied some dull opiate to the drains
　　One minute past, and Lethe-wards had sunk:
'Tis not through envy of thy happy lot,
　　But being too happy in thine happiness,—
　　　　That thou, light-winged Dryad of the trees,
　　　　　　In some melodious plot
　　Of beechen green, and shadows numberless,
　　　　Singest of summer in full-throated ease.

O for a draught of vintage! that hath been
　　Cool'd a long age in the deep-delved earth,
Tasting of Flora and the country green,
　　Dance, and Provençal song, and sunburnt mirth!
O for a beaker full of the warm South,
　　Full of the true, the blushful Hippocrene,
　　　　With beaded bubbles winking at the brim,
　　　　　　And purple-stained mouth;
　　That I might drink, and leave the world unseen,
　　　　And with thee fade away into the forest dim:

Fade far away, dissolve, and quite forget
　　What thou among the leaves hast never known,
The weariness, the fever, and the fret
　　Here, where men sit and hear each other groan;
Where palsy shakes a few, sad, last gray hairs,
　　Where youth grows pale, and spectre-thin, and dies;
　　　　Where but to think is to be full of sorrow
　　　　　　And leaden-eyed despairs,
　　Where Beauty cannot keep her lustrous eyes,
　　　　Or new Love pine at them beyond to-morrow.

Away! away! for I will fly to thee,
　　Not charioted by Bacchus and his pards,
But on the viewless wings of Poesy,
　　Though the dull brain perplexes and retards:
Already with thee! tender is the night,
　　And haply the Queen-Moon is on her throne,

Cluster'd around by all her starry Fays;
But here there is no light,
Save what from heaven is with the breezes blown
Through verdurous blooms and winding mossy ways.

I cannot see what flowers are at my feet,
Nor what soft incense hangs upon the boughs,
But, in embalmed darkness, guess each sweet
Wherewith the seasonable month endows
The grass, the thicket, and the fruit-tree wild;
White hawthorn, and the pastoral eglantine;
Fast fading violets cover'd up in leaves;
And mid-May's eldest child,
The coming musk-rose, full of dewy wine,
The murmurous haunt of flies on summer eves.

Darkling I listen; and, for many a time
I have been half in love with easeful Death,
Call'd him soft names in many a mused rhyme,
To take into the air my quiet breath;
Now more than ever seems it rich to die,
To cease upon the midnight with no pain,
While thou art pouring forth thy soul abroad
In such an ecstasy!
Still wouldst thou sing, and I have ears in vain—
To thy high requiem become a sod.

Thou wast not born for death, immortal Bird!
No hungry generations tread thee down;
The voice I hear this passing night was heard
In ancient days by emperor and clown:
Perhaps the self-same song that found a path
Through the sad heart of Ruth, when, sick for home,
She stood in tears amid the alien corn;
The same that oft-times hath
Charm'd magic casements, opening on the foam
Of perilous seas, in faery lands forlorn.

Forlorn! the very word is like a bell
To toll me back from thee to my sole self!
Adieu! the fancy cannot cheat so well
As she is fam'd to do, deceiving elf.

Adieu! adieu! thy plaintive anthem fades
　　Past the near meadows, over the still stream,
　　　　Up the hill-side; and now 'tis buried deep
　　　　　　In the next valley-glades:
　　Was it a vision, or a waking dream?
　　　　Fled is that music:—Do I wake or sleep?

Ode on a Grecian Urn

Thou still unravish'd bride of quietness,
　　Thou foster-child of silence and slow time,
Sylvan historian, who canst thus express
　　A flowery tale more sweetly than our rhyme:
What leaf-fring'd legend haunts about thy shape
　　Of deities or mortals, or of both,
　　　　In Tempe or the dales of Arcady?
　　What men or gods are these? What maidens loth?
What mad pursuit? What struggle to escape?
　　　　What pipes and timbrels? What wild ecstasy?

Heard melodies are sweet, but those unheard
　　Are sweeter; therefore, ye soft pipes, play on;
Not to the sensual ear, but, more endear'd,
　　Pipe to the spirit ditties of no tone:
Fair youth, beneath the trees, thou canst not leave
　　Thy song, nor ever can those trees be bare;
　　　　Bold Lover, never, never canst thou kiss,
Though winning near the goal—yet, do not grieve;
　　　　She cannot fade, though thou hast not thy bliss,
　　For ever wilt thou love, and she be fair!

Ah, happy, happy boughs! that cannot shed
　　Your leaves, nor ever bid the Spring adieu;
And, happy melodist, unwearied,
　　For ever piping songs for ever new;
More happy love! more happy, happy love!
　　For ever warm and still to be enjoy'd,
　　　　For ever panting, and for ever young;
All breathing human passion far above,
　　That leaves a heart high-sorrowful and cloy'd,
　　　　A burning forehead, and a parching tongue.

Who are these coming to the sacrifice?
  To what green altar, O mysterious priest,
Lead'st thou that heifer lowing at the skies,
  And all her silken flanks with garlands drest?
What little town by river or sea-shore,
  Or mountain-built with peaceful citadel,
    Is emptied of this folk, this pious morn?
And, little town, thy streets for evermore
  Will silent be; and not a soul to tell
    Why thou art desolate, can e'er return.

O Attic shape! Fair attitude! with brede
  Of marble men and maidens overwrought,
With forest branches and the trodden weed;
  Thou, silent form, dost tease us out of thought
As doth eternity: Cold Pastoral!
  When old age shall this generation waste,
    Thou shalt remain, in midst of other woe
Than ours, a friend to man, to whom thou say'st,
'Beauty is truth, truth beauty,'—that is all
    Ye know on earth, and all ye need to know.

Ode to Autumn

Season of mists and mellow fruitfulness!
  Close bosom-friend of the maturing sun;
Conspiring with him how to load and bless
  With fruit the vines that round the thatch-eaves run;
To bend with apples the moss'd cottage-trees,
  And fill all fruit with ripeness to the core;
    To swell the gourd, and plump the hazel shells
With a sweet kernel; to set budding more,
And still more, later flowers for the bees,
Until they think warm days will never cease,
    For Summer has o'er -brimm'd their clammy cells.

Who hath not seen thee oft amid thy store?
  Sometimes whoever seeks abroad may find
Thee sitting careless on a granary floor,
  Thy hair soft-lifted by the winnowing wind;

Or on a half-reap'd furrow sound asleep,
　Drowsed with the fumes of poppies, while thy hook
　　Spares the next swath and all its twinèd flowers;
And sometimes like a gleaner thou dost keep
　Steady thy laden head across a brook;
　Or by a cider-press, with patient look,
　　Thou watchest the last oozings, hours by hours.

Where are the songs of Spring? Ay, where are they?
　Think not of them, thou hast thy music too,
While barrèd clouds bloom the soft-dying day,
　And touch the stubble-plains with rosy hue;
Then in a wailful choir the small gnats mourn
　Among the river sallows, borne aloft
　　Or sinking as the light wind lives or dies;
And full-grown lambs loud bleat from hilly bourn;
　Hedge-crickets sing; and now with treble soft
　The redbreast whistles from a garden-croft,
　　And gathering swallows twitter in the skies.

ALFRED, LORD TENNYSON
1809-1892

The Splendour falls on Castle Walls

The splendour falls on castle walls
    And snowy summits old in story:
The long light shakes across the lakes,
    And the wild cataract leaps in glory.
Blow, bugle, blow, set the wild echoes flying,
Blow, bugle; answer, echoes, dying, dying, dying

O hark, O hear! how thin and clear,
    And thinner, clearer, farther going!
O sweet and far from cliff and scar
    The horns of Elfland faintly blowing!
Blow, let us hear the purple glens replying:
Blow, bugle; answer, echoes, dying, dying, dying.

O love, they die in yon rich sky,
    They faint on hill or field or river:
Our echoes roll from soul to soul,
    And grow for ever and for ever.
Blow, bugle, blow, set the wild echoes flying,
And answer, echoes, answer, dying, dying, dying.

Break, Break, Break

Break, break, break,
    On thy cold grey stones, O Sea!
And I would that my tongue could utter
    The thoughts that arise in me.

O well for the fisherman's boy,
    That he shouts with his sister at play!
O well for the sailor lad,
    That he sings in his boat on the bay!

And the stately ships go on
    To their haven under the hill;
But O for the touch of a vanish'd hand,
    And the sound of a voice that is still!

Break, break, break,
    At the foot of the crags, O Sea!
But the tender grace of a day that is dead
    Will never come back to me

Now sleeps the Crimson Petal

Now sleeps the crimson petal, now the white;
Nor waves the cypress in the palace walk;
Nor winks the gold fin in the porphyry font:
The fire-fly wakens: waken thou with me.

Now droops the milk-white peacock like a ghost,
And like a ghost she glimmers on to me.

Now lies the earth all Danaë to the stars,
And all thy heart lies open unto me.

Now slides the silent meteor on, and leaves
A shining furrow, as thy thoughts in me.

Now folds the lily all her sweetness up,
And slips into the bosom of the lake:
So fold thyself, my dearest thou, and slip
Into my bosom and be lost in me.

Morte d'Arthur

So all day long the noise of battle roll'd
Among the mountains by the winter sea;
Until King Arthur's table, man by man,
Had fall'n in Lyonnesse about their Lord,
King Arthur: then, because his wound was deep,
The bold Sir Bedivere uplifted him,
Sir Bedivere, the last of all his knights,

And bore him to a chapel nigh the field,
A broken chancel with a broken cross,
That stood on a dark strait of barren land.
On one side lay the Ocean, and on one
Lay a great water, and the moon was full.
  Then spake King Arthur to Sir Bedivere:
'The sequel of to-day unsolders all
The goodliest fellowship of famous knights
Whereof this world holds record. Such a sleep
They sleep—the men I loved. I think that we
Shall never more, at any future time,
Delight our souls with talk of knightly deeds,
Walking about the gardens and the halls
Of Camelot, as in the days that were.
I perish by this people which I made,—
Tho' Merlin sware that I should come again
To rule once more—but let what will be, be,
I am so deeply smitten thro' the helm
That without help I cannot last till morn.
Thou therefore take my brand Excalibur,
Which was my pride: for thou rememberest how
In those old days, one summer noon, an arm
Rose up from out the bosom of the lake,
Clothed in white samite, mystic, wonderful,
Holding the sword—and how I row'd across
And took it, and have worn it, like a king:
And, wheresoever I am sung or told
In aftertime, this also shall be known:
But now delay not: take Excalibur,
And fling him far into the middle mere:
Watch what thou seest, and lightly bring me word.'

  To him replied the bold Sir Bedivere:
'It is not meet, Sir King, to leave thee thus,
Aidless, alone, and smitten thro' the helm.
A little thing may harm a wounded man.
Yet I thy hest will all perform at full,
Watch what I see, and lightly bring thee word.'

  So saying, from the ruin'd shrine he stept
And in the moon athwart the place of tombs,
Where lay the mighty bones of ancient men,

Old knights, and over them the sea-wind sang
Shrill, chill, with flakes of foam. He, stepping down
By zig-zag paths, and juts of pointed rock,
Came on the shining levels of the lake.

There drew he forth the brand Excalibur,
And o'er him, drawing it, the winter moon,
Brightening the skirts of a long cloud, ran forth
And sparkled keen with frost against the hilt:
For all the haft twinkled with diamond sparks,
Myriads of topaz-lights, and jacinth-work
Of subtlest jewellery. He gazed so long
That both his eyes were dazzled, as he stood,
This way and that dividing the swift mind,
In act to throw: but at the last it seem'd
Better to leave Excalibur conceal'd
There in the many-knotted water-flags,
That whistled stiff and dry about the marge.
So strode he back slow to the wounded King.

Then spake King Arthur to Sir Bedivere:
'Hast thou performed my mission which I gave?
What is it thou hast seen? or what hast heard?'
And answer made the bold Sir Bedivere:
'I heard the ripple washing in the reeds,
And the wild water lapping on the crag.'

To whom replied King Arthur, faint and pale:
'Thou hast betray'd thy nature and thy name,
Not rendering true answer, as beseem'd
Thy fealty, nor like a noble knight:
For surer sign had follow'd, either hand,
Or voice, or else a motion of the mere.
This is shameful thing for men to lie.
Yet now, I charge thee, quickly go again
As thou art lief and dear, and do the thing
I bad thee, watch, and lightly bring me word.'

Then went Sir Bedivere the second time
Across the ridge, and paced beside the mere,
Counting the dewy pebbles, fix'd in thought;
But when he saw the wonder of the hilt,

How curiously and strangely chased, he smote
His palms together, and he cried aloud:
'And if indeed I cast the brand away,
Surely a precious thing, one worthy note,
Should thus be lost for ever from the earth,
Which might have pleased the eyes of many men.
What good should follow this, if this were done?
What harm, undone? deep harm to disobey,
Seeing obedience is the bond of rule.
Were it well to obey, then, if a king demand
An act unprofitable, against himself?
The King is sick, and knows not what he does.
What record, or what relic of my lord
Should be to aftertime, but empty breath
And rumours of a doubt? but were this kept,
Stored in some treasure-house of mighty kings,
Some one might show it at a joust of arms,
Saying, "King Arthur's sword, Excalibur,
Wrought by the lonely maiden of the Lake.
Nine years she wrought it, sitting in the deeps
Upon the hidden bases of the hills."
So might some old man speak in the aftertime
To all the people, winning reverence.
But now much honour and much fame were lost.'

    So spake he, clouded with his own conceit,
And hid Excalibur the second time,
And so strode back slow to the wounded King.

    Then spoke King Arthur, breathing heavily:
'What is it thou hast seen? or what hast heard?'
    And answer made the bold Sir Bedivere:
'I heard the water lapping on the crag,
And the long ripple washing in the reeds.'

    To whom replied King Arthur, much in wrath:
'Ah, miserable and unkind, untrue,
Unknightly, traitor-hearted! Woe is me!
Authority forgets a dying king,
Laid widow'd of the power in his eye
That bow'd the will. I see thee what thou art,
For thou, the latest-left of all my knights,
In whom should meet the offices of all,

Thou wouldst betray me for the precious hilt;
Either from lust of gold, or like a girl
Valuing the giddy pleasure of the eyes.
Yet, for a man may fail in duty twice,
And the third time may prosper, get thee hence:
But if thou spare to fling Excalibur,
I will arise and slay thee with my hands.'

Then quickly rose Sir Bedivere, and ran,
And, leaping down the ridges lightly, plunged
Among the bulrush-beds, and clutch'd the sword,
And strongly wheel'd and threw it. The great brand
Made lightnings in the splendour of the moon,
And flashing round and round, and whirl'd in an arch,
Shot like a streamer of the northern morn,
Seen where the moving isles of winter shock
By night, with noises of the northern sea.
So flash'd and fell the brand Excalibur:
But ere he dipt the surface, rose an arm
Clothed in white samite, mystic, wonderful,
And caught him by the hilt, and brandish'd him
Three times, and drew him under in the mere.
And lightly went the other to the King.

Then spoke King Arthur, drawing thicker breath:
'Now see I by thine eyes that this is done.
Speak out: what is it thou hast heard, or seen?'
And answer made the bold Sir Bedivere:
'Sir King, I closed mine eyelids, lest the gems
Should blind my purpose, for I never saw,
Nor shall see, here or elsewhere, till I die,
Not tho' I live three lives of mortal men,
So great a miracle as yonder hilt.
Then with both hands I flung him, wheeling him;
But when I look'd again, behold an arm,
Clothed in white samite, mystic, wonderful,
That caught him by the hilt, and brandish'd him
Three times, and drew him under in the mere.'
And answer made King Arthur, breathing hard:
'My end draws nigh; 'tis time that I were gone.
Make broad thy shoulders to receive my weight,
And bear me to the margin; yet I fear
My wound hath taken cold, and I shall die.'

So saying, from the pavement he half rose,
Slowly, with pain, reclining on his arm,
And looking wistfully with wide blue eyes
As in a picture. Him Sir Bedivere
Remorsefully regarded thro' his tears,
And would have spoken, but he found not words,
Then took with care, and kneeling on one knee,
O'er both his shoulders drew the languid hands,
And rising bore him thro' the place of tombs.

But, as he walk'd, King Arthur panted hard,
Like one that feels a nightmare on his bed
When all the house is mute. So sigh'd the King,
Muttering and murmuring at his ear, 'Quick, quick!
I fear it is too late, and I shall die.'
But the other swiftly strode from ridge to ridge,
Clothed with his breath, and looking, as he walk'd,
Larger than human on the frozen hills.
He heard the deep behind him, and a cry
Before. His own thought drove him, like a goad.
Dry clash'd his harness in the icy caves
And barren chasms, and all to left and right
The bare black cliff clang'd round him, as he based
His feet on juts of slippery crag that rang
Sharp-smitten with the dint of armed heels—
And on a sudden, lo! the level lake,
And the long glories of the winter moon.

Then saw they how there hove a dusky barge,
Dark as a funeral scarf from stem to stern,
Beneath them; and descending they were ware
That all the decks were dense with stately forms
Black-stoled, black-hooded, like a dream—by these
Three Queens with crowns of gold—and from them
    rose
A cry that shiver'd to the tingling stars,
And, as it were one voice, an agony
Of lamentation, like a wind, that shrills
All night in a waste land, where no one comes,
Or hath come, since the making of the world.

Then murmur'd Arthur, 'Place me in the barge,
And to the barge they came. There those three Queen's
Put forth their hands, and took the King, and wept.

But she, that rose the tallest of them all
And fairest, laid his head upon her lap,
And loosed the shatter'd casque, and chafed his hands,
And call'd him by his name, complaining loud,
And dropping bitter tears against his brow
Striped with dark blood: for all his face was white
And colourless, and like the wither'd moon
Smote by the fresh beam of the springing east;
And all his greaves and cuisses dash'd with drops
Of onset; and the light and lustrous curls—
That made his forehead like a rising sun
High from the dais-throne—were parch'd with dust;
Or, clotted into points and hanging loose,
Mix'd with the knightly growth that fringed his lips.
So like a shatter'd column lay the King;
Not like that Arthur who, with lance in rest,
From spur to plume a star of tournament,
Shot thro' the lists at Camelot, and charged
Before the eyes of ladies and of kings.

Then loudly cried the bold Sir Bedivere:
'Ah! my Lord Arthur, whither shall I go?
Where shall I hide my forehead and my eyes?
For now I see the true old times are dead,
When every morning brought a noble chance,
And every chance brought out a noble knight.
Such times have been not since the light that led
The holy Elders with the gift of myrrh.
But now the whole ROUND TABLE is dissolved
Which was an image of the mighty world;
And I, the last, go forth companionless,
And the days darken round me, and the years,
Among new men, strange faces, other minds.'

And slowly answer'd Arthur from the barge:
'The old order changeth, yielding place to new,
And God fulfils Himself in many ways,
Lest one good custom should corrupt the world.
Comfort thyself: what comfort is in me?
I have lived my life, and that which I have done
May He within Himself make pure! but thou,
If thou shouldst never see my face again,
Pray for my soul. More things are wrought by prayer

Than this world dreams of. Wherefore, let thy voice
Rise like a fountain for me night and day.
For what are men better than sheep or goats
That nourish a blind life within the brain,
If, knowing God, they lift not hands of prayer
Both for themselves and those who call them friend?
For so the whole round earth is every way
Bound by gold chains about the feet of God.
But now farewell. I am going a long way
With those thou seest—if indeed I go—
(For all my mind is clouded with a doubt)
To the island-valley of Avilion;
Where falls not hail, or rain, or any snow,
Nor ever wind blows loudly; but it lies
Deep-meadow'd, happy, fair with orchard-lawns
And bowery hollows crown'd with summer sea,
Where I will heal me of my grievous wound.'

So said he, and the barge with oar and sail
Moved from the brink, like some full-breasted swan,
That, fluting a wild carol ere her death,
Ruffles her pure cold plume, and takes the flood
With swarthy webs. Long stood Sir Bedivere
Revolving many memories, till the hull
Look'd one black dot against the verge of dawn,
And on the mere the wailing died away.

The Lady of Shalott

Part I

On either side the river lie
Long fields of barley and of rye,
That clothe the wold and meet the sky;
And thro' the field the road runs by
    To many-tower'd Camelot;
And up and down the people go,
Gazing where the lilies blow,
Round an island there below,
    The island of Shalott.

Willows whiten, aspens quiver,
Little breezes dusk and shiver
Thro' the wave that runs for ever
By the island in the river
    Flowing down to Camelot.
Four grey walls, and four grey towers,
Overlook a space of flowers,
And the silent isle imbowers
    The Lady of Shalott.

By the margin, willow-veil'd,
Slide the heavy barges trail'd
By slow horses; and unhail'd
The shallop flitteth silken-sail'd
    Skimming down to Camelot:
But who hath seen her wave her hand?
Or at the casement seen her stand?
Or is she known in all the land,
    The Lady of Shalott?

Only reapers, reaping early
In among the bearded barley,
Hear a song that echoes cheerly
From the river winding clearly,
    Down to tower'd Camelot:
And by the moon the reaper weary,
Piling sheaves in uplands airy,
Listening, whispers, ' 'Tis the fairy
    Lady of Shalott.'

PART II

There she weaves by night and day
A magic web with colours gay.
She has heard a whisper say,
A curse is on her if she stay
    To look down to Camelot.
She knows not what the curse may be,
And so she weaveth steadily,
And little other care hath she,
    The Lady of Shalott.

And moving thro' a mirror clear
That hangs before her all the year,
Shadows of the world appear.
There she sees the highway near
     Winding down to Camelot:
There the river eddy whirls,
And there the surly village-churls,
And the red cloaks of market girls,
     Pass onward from Shalott.

Sometimes a troop of damsels glad,
An abbot on an ambling pad,
Sometimes a curly shepherd-lad,
Or long-hair'd page in crimson clad,
     Goes by to tower'd Camelot;
And sometimes thro' the mirror blue
The knights come riding two and two:
She hath no loyal knight and true,
     The Lady of Shalott.

But in her web she still delights
To weave the mirror's magic sights,
For often thro' the silent nights
A funeral, with plumes and lights
     And music, went to Camelot:
Or when the moon was overhead,
Came two young lovers lately wed;
'I am half sick of shadows,' said
     The Lady of Shalott.

PART III

A bow-shot from her bower-eaves,
He rode between the barley-sheaves,
The sun came dazzling thro' the leaves,
And flamed upon the brazen greaves
     Of bold Sir Lancelot.
A red-cross knight for ever kneel'd
To a lady in his shield,
That sparkled on the yellow field,
     Beside remote Shalott.

The gemmy bridle glitter'd free,
Like to some branch of stars we see
Hung in the golden Galaxy.
The bridle bells rang merrily
  As he rode down to Camelot:
And from his blazon'd baldric slung
A mighty silver bugle hung,
And as he rode his armour rung,
  Beside remote Shalott.

All in the blue unclouded weather
Thick-jewell'd shone the saddle leather,
The helmet and the helmet-feather
Burn'd like one burning flame together,
  As he rode down to Camelot.
As often thro' the purple night,
Below the starry clusters bright,
Some bearded meteor, trailing light,
  Moves over still Shalott.

His broad clear brow in sunlight glow'd;
On burnished hooves his war-horse trode;
From underneath his helmet flow'd
His coal-black curls as on he rode,
  As he rode down to Camelot.
From the bank and from the river
He flash'd into the crystal mirror.
'Tirra lirra', by the river
  Sang Sir Lancelot.

She left the web, she left the loom,
She made three paces thro' the room,
She saw the water-lily bloom,
She saw the helmet and the plume,
  She look'd down to Camelot.
Out flew the web and floated wide;
The mirror crack'd from side to side;
'The curse is come upon me,' cried
  The Lady of Shalott.

Part IV

In the stormy east-wind straining,
The pale yellow woods were waning,
The broad stream in his banks complaining,
Heavily the low sky raining
    Over tower'd Camelot;
Down she came and found a boat
Beneath a willow left afloat,
And round about the prow she wrote
    The Lady of Shalott.

And down the river's dim expanse
Like some bold seer in a trance,
Seeing all his own mischance—
With a glassy countenance
    Did she look to Camelot.
And at the closing of the day
She loosed the chain, and down she lay;
The broad stream bore her far away,
    The Lady of Shalott.

Lying, robed in snowy white
That loosely flew to left and right—
The leaves upon her falling light—
Thro' the noises of the night
    She floated down to Camelot:
And as the boat-head wound along
The willowy hills and fields among,
They heard her singing her last song,
    The Lady of Shalott.

Heard a carol, mournful, holy,
Chanted loudly, chanted lowly,
Till her blood was frozen slowly,
And her eyes were darken'd wholly,
    Turn'd to tower'd Camelot.
For ere she reach'd upon the tide
The first house by the water-side,
Singing, in her song she died,
    The Lady of Shalott.

Under tower and balcony,
By garden wall and gallery,
A gleaming shape she floated by,
Dead-pale between the houses high,
    Silent into Camelot.
Out upon the wharfs they came,
Knight and burgher, lord and dame,
And round the prow they read her name,
    The Lady of Shalott.

Who is this? and what is here?
And in the lighted palace near
Died the sound of royal cheer;
And they cross'd themselves for fear,
    All the knights at Camelot:
But Lancelot mused a little space;
He said, 'She has a lovely face;
God in His mercy lend her grace,
    The Lady of Shalott.'

The Lotos-Eaters

'Courage!' he said, and pointed toward the land,
'This mounting wave will roll us shoreward soon.'
In the afternoon they came unto a land
In which it seemed always afternoon.
All round the coast the languid air did swoon,
Breathing like one that hath a weary dream.
Full-faced above the valley stood the moon;
And like a downward smoke, the slender stream
Along the cliff to fall and pause and fall did seem.

A land of streams! some, like a downward smoke,
Slow-dropping veils of thinnest lawn, did go;
And some thro' wavering lights and shadows broke,
Rolling a slumbrous sheet of foam below.
They saw the gleaming river seaward flow
From the inner land: far off, three mountain-tops,
Three silent pinnacles of aged snow,
Stood sunset-flush'd: and, dew'd with showery drops,
Up-clomb the shadowy pine above the woven copse.

The charmed sunset linger'd low adown
In the red West: thro' mountain clefts the dale
Was seen far inland, and the yellow down
Border'd with palm, and many a winding vale
And meadow, set with slender galingale;
A land where all things always seem'd the same!
And round about the keel with faces pale,
Dark faces pale against that rosy flame,
The mild-eyed melancholy Lotos-eaters came.

Branches they bore of that enchanted stem,
Laden with flower and fruit, whereof they gave
To each, but whoso did receive of them,
And taste, to him the gushing of the wave
Far far away did seem to mourn and rave
On alien shores; and if his fellow spake,
His voice was thin, as voices from the grave;
And deep-asleep he seem'd, yet all awake,
And music in his ears his beating heart did make.

They sat them down upon the yellow sand,
Between the sun and moon upon the shore;
And sweet it was to dream of Fatherland,
Of child, and wife, and slave; but evermore
Most weary seem'd the sea, weary the oar,
Weary the wandering fields of barren foam.
Then some one said, 'We will return no more';
And all at once they sang, 'Our island home
Is far beyond the wave; we will no longer roam.'

CHORIC SONG

I

There is sweet music here that softer falls
Than petals from blown roses on the grass,
Or night-dews on still waters between walls
Of shadowy granite, in a gleaming pass;
Music that gentlier on the spirit lies,
Than tir'd eyelids upon tir'd eyes;
Music that brings sweet sleep down from the blissful skies.
Here are cool mosses deep,
And thro' the moss the ivies creep,

And in the stream the long-leaved flowers weep,
And from the craggy ledge the poppy hangs in sleep.

II

Why are we weigh'd upon with heaviness,
And utterly consumed with sharp distress,
While all things else have rest from weariness?
All things have rest: why should we toil alone,
We only toil, who are the first of things,
And make perpetual moan,
Still from one sorrow to another thrown:
Nor ever fold our wings,
And cease from wanderings,
Nor steep our brows in slumber's holy balm;
Nor hearken what the inner spirit sings,
'There is no joy but calm!'
Why should we only toil, the roof and crown of things?

III

Lo! in the middle of the wood,
The folded leaf is woo'd from out the bud
With winds upon the branch, and there
Grows green and broad, and takes no care,
Sun-steep'd at noon, and in the moon
Nightly dew-fed; and turning yellow
Falls, and floats adown the air.
Lo! sweeten'd with the summer light,
The full-juiced apple, waxing over-mellow,
Drops in a silent autumn night.
All its allotted length of days,
The flower ripens in its place,
Ripens and fades, and falls, and hath no toil,
Fast-rooted in the fruitful soil.

IV

Hateful is the dark-blue sky,
Vaulted o'er the dark-blue sea.
Death is the end of life; ah, why
Should life all labour be?
Let us alone. Time driveth onward fast,
And in a little while our lips are dumb.
Let us alone. Wnat is it that will last?

All things are taken from us, and become
Portions and parcels of the dreadful Past.
Let us alone. What pleasure can we have
To war with evil? Is there any peace
In ever climbing up the climbing wave?
All things have rest, and ripen toward the grave
In silence; ripen, fall and cease:
Give us long rest or death, dark death, or dreamful ease.

V

How sweet it were, hearing the downward stream,
With half-shut eyes ever to seem
Falling asleep in a half-dream!
To dream and dream, like yonder amber light,
Which will not leave the myrrh-bush on the height;
To hear each other's whisper'd speech;
Eating the Lotos day by day,
To watch the crisping ripples on the beach,
And tender curving lines of creamy spray;
To lend our hearts and spirits wholly
To the influence of mild-minded melancholy;
To muse and brood and live again in memory,
With those old faces of our infancy
Heap'd over with a mound of grass,
Two handfuls of white dust, shut in an urn of brass!

VI

Dear is the memory of our wedded lives,
And dear the last embraces of our wives
And their warm tears: but all hath suffer'd change;
For surely now our household hearths are cold:
Our sons inherit us: our looks are strange:
And we should come like ghosts to trouble joy.
Or else the island princes over-bold
Have eat our substance, and the minstrel sings
Before them of the ten-years' war in Troy,
And our great deeds, as half-forgotten things.
Is there confusion in the little isle?
Let what is broken so remain.
The Gods are hard to reconcile:
'Tis hard to settle order once again.

There *is* confusion worse than death,
Trouble on trouble, pain on pain,
Long labour unto aged breath,
Sore task to hearts worn out with many wars
And eyes grown dim with gazing on the pilot-stars.

VII

But, propt on beds of amaranth and moly,
How sweet (while warm airs lull us, blowing lowly)
With half-dropt eyelids still,
Beneath a heaven dark and holy,
To watch the long bright river drawing slowly
His waters from the purple hill—
To hear the dewy echoes calling
From cave to cave thro' the thick-twined vine—
To watch the emerald-colour'd water falling
Thro' many a wov'n acanthus-wreath divine!
Only to hear and see the far-off sparkling brine,
Only to hear were sweet, stretch'd out beneath the pine.

VIII

The Lotos blooms below the barren peak:
The Lotos blows by every winding creek:
All day the wind breathes low with mellower tone:
Thro' every hollow cave and alley lone
Round and round the spicy downs the yellow Lotos-dust is
blown.
We have had enough of action, and of motion we,
Roll'd to starboard, roll'd to larboard, when the surge was
seething free,
Where the wallowing monster spouted his foam-fountains in
the sea.
Let us swear an oath, and keep it with an equal mind,
In the hollow Lotos-land to live and lie reclined
On the hills like Gods together, careless of mankind.
For they lie beside their nectar, and the bolts are hurl'd
Far below them in the valleys, and the clouds are lightly curl'd
Round their golden houses, girdled with the gleaming world:
Where they smile in secret, looking over wasted lands,
Blight and famine, plague and earthquake, roaring deeps and
fiery sands,

Clanging fights, and flaming towns, and sinking ships, and
    praying hands.
But they smile, they find a music centred in a doleful song
Steaming up, a lamentation and an ancient tale of wrong,
Like a tale of little meaning tho' the words are strong;
Chanted from an ill-used race of men that cleave the soil,
Sow the seed, and reap the harvest with enduring toil,
Storing yearly little dues of wheat, and wine and oil;
Till they perish and they suffer—some, 'tis whisper'd—down
    in hell
Suffer endless anguish, others in Elysian valleys dwell,
Resting weary limbs at last on beds of asphodel.
Surely, surely, slumber is more sweet than toil, the shore
Than labour in the deep mid-ocean, wind and wave and oar;
Oh rest ye, brother mariners, we will not wander more.

Ulysses

It little profits that an idle king,
By this still hearth, among these barren crags,
Match'd with an aged wife, I mete and dole
Unequal laws unto a savage race,
That hoard, and sleep, and feed, and know not me.
I cannot rest from travel: I will drink
Life to the lees: all times I have enjoy'd
Greatly, have suffer'd greatly, both with those
That loved me, and alone; on shore, and when
Thro' scudding drifts the rainy Hyades
Vext the dim sea: I am become a name;
For always roaming with a hungry heart
Much have I seen and known; cities of men
And manners, climates, councils, governments,
Myself not least, but honour'd of them all;
And drunk delight of battle with my peers,
Far on the ringing plains of windy Troy.
I am a part of all that I have met;
Yet all experience is an arch wherethro'
Gleams that untravell'd world, whose margin fades
For ever and for ever when I move.
How dull it is to pause, to make an end,
To rust unburnish'd, not to shine in use!

As tho' to breathe were life. Life piled on life
Were all too little, and of one to me
Little remains: but every hour is saved
From that eternal silence, something more,
A bringer of new things; and vile it were
For some three suns to store and hoard myself,
And this gray spirit yearning in desire
To follow knowledge, like a sinking star,
Beyond the utmost bound of human thought.

This is my son, mine own Telemachus,
To whom I leave the sceptre and the isle—
Well-loved of me, discerning to fulfil
This labour, by slow prudence to make mild
A rugged people, and thro' soft degrees
Subdue them to the useful and the good.
Most blameless is he, centred in the sphere
Of common duties, decent not to fail
In offices of tenderness, and pay
Meet adoration to my household gods,
When I am gone. He works his work, I mine.

There lies the port: the vessel puffs her sail:
There gloom the dark broad seas. My mariners,
Souls that have toil'd, and wrought, and thought with
    me—
That ever with a frolic welcome took
The thunder and the sunshine, and opposed
Free hearts, free foreheads—you and I are old;
Old age hath yet his honour and his toil;
Death closes all: but something ere the end,
Some work of noble note, may yet be done,
Not unbecoming men that strove with Gods.
The lights begin to twinkle from the rocks:
The long day wanes: the slow moon climbs: the deep
Moans round with many voices. Come, my friends,
'Tis not too late to seek a newer world.
Push off, and sitting well in order smite
The sounding furrows; for my purpose holds
To sail beyond the sunset, and the baths
Of all the western stars, until I die.
It may be that the gulfs will wash us down:
It may be we shall touch the Happy Isles,
And see the great Achilles, whom we knew.

Tho' much is taken, much abides; and tho'
We are not now that strength which in old days
Moved earth and heaven; that which we are, we are;
One equal temper of heroic hearts
Made weak by time and fate, but strong in will
To strive, to seek, to find, and not to yield.

ROBERT BROWNING

1812-1889

Pippa's Song

The year's at the spring
And day's at the morn;
Morning's at seven;
The hill-side's dew-pearled;
The lark's on the wing;
The snail's on the thorn;
God's in His heaven—
All's right with the world!

My Last Duchess

FERRARA

That's my last Duchess painted on the wall,
Looking as if she were alive; I call
That piece a wonder, now: Frá Pandolf's hands
Worked busily a day, and there she stands.
Will't please you sit and look at her? I said
'Frá Pandolf' by design, for never read
Strangers like you that pictured countenance,
The depth and passion of its earnest glance,
But to myself they turned (since none puts by
The curtain I have drawn for you, but I)
And seemed as they would ask me, if they durst,
How such a glance came there; so, not the first
Are you to turn and ask thus. Sir, 'twas not
Her husband's presence only, called that spot
Of joy into the Duchess' cheek: perhaps
Frá Pandolf chanced to say 'Her mantle laps
Over my Lady's wrist too much', or 'Paint
Must never hope to reproduce the faint
Half-flush that dies along her throat'; such stuff
Was courtesy, she thought, and cause enough
For calling up that spot of joy. She had

A heart . . . how shall I say? . . . too soon made glad,
Too easily impressed; she liked whate'er
She looked on, and her looks went everywhere.
Sir, 'twas all one! My favour at her breast,
The dropping of the daylight in the West,
The bough of cherries some officious fool
Broke in the orchard for her, the white mule
She rode with round the terrace—all and each
Would draw from her alike the approving speech,
Or blush, at least. She thanked men,—good; but thanked
Somehow . . . I know not how . . . as if she ranked
My gift of a nine-hundred-years-old name
With anybody's gift. Who'd stoop to blame
This sort of trifling? Even had you skill
In speech—(which I have not)—to make your will
Quite clear to such an one, and say 'Just this
Or that in you disgusts me; here you miss,
Or there exceed the mark'—and if she let
Herself be lessoned so, nor plainly set
Her wits to yours, forsooth, and made excuse,
—E'en then would be some stooping, and I chuse
Never to stoop. Oh, Sir, she smiled, no doubt,
Whene'er I passed her; but who passed without
Much the same smile? This grew; I gave commands;
Then all smiles stopped together. There she stands
As if alive. Will't please you rise? We'll meet
The company below, then. I repeat,
The Count your Master's known munificence
Is ample warrant that no just pretence
Of mine for dowry will be disallowed;
Though his fair daughter's self, as I avowed
At starting, is my object. Nay, we'll go
Together down, Sir! Notice Neptune, though,
Taming a sea-horse, thought a rarity,
Which Claus of Innsbruck cast in bronze for me.

Prospice

Fear death?—to feel the fog in my throat,
      The mist in my face,
When the snows begin, and the blasts denote
      I am nearing the place,

The power of the night, the press of the storm,
    The post of the foe;
Where he stands, the Arch Fear in a visible form,
    Yet the strong man must go:
For the journey is done and the summit attained,
    And the barriers fall,
Though a battle's to fight ere the guerdon be gained,
    The reward of it all.
I was ever a fighter, so—one fight more,
    The best and the last!
I would hate that death bandaged my eyes, and forbore,
    And bade me creep past.
No! let me taste the whole of it, fare like my peers
    The heroes of old,
Bear the brunt, in a minute pay glad life's arrears
    Of pain, darkness, and cold.
For sudden the worst turns the best to the brave,
    The black minute's at end,
And the elements' rage, the fiend-voices that rave,
    Shall dwindle, shall blend,
Shall change, shall become first a peace out of pain
    Then a light, then thy breast,
O thou soul of my soul! I shall clasp thee again,
    And with God be the rest!

The Bishop Orders his Tomb at St. Praxed's Church

ROME, 15—

Vanity, saith the preacher, vanity!
Draw round my bed; is Anselm keeping back?
Nephews—sons mine . . . ah God, I know not! well—
She, men would have to be your mother once,
Old Gandolf envied me, so fair she was!
What's done is done, and she is dead beside,
Dead long ago, and I am bishop since,
And as she died so must we die ourselves,
And thence ye may perceive the world's a dream.
Life, how and what is it? As here I lie
In this state-chamber, dying by degrees,
Hours and long hours in the dead night, I ask
'Do I live, am I dead?' Peace, peace seems all.

St. Praxed's ever was the church for peace;
And so, about this tomb of mine. I fought
With tooth and nail to save my niche, ye know:
—Old Gandolf cozened me, despite my care;
Shrewd was that snatch from out the corner South
He graced his carrion with, God curse the same!
Yet still my niche is not so cramped but thence
One sees the pulpit o' the epistle side,
And somewhat of the choir, those silent seats,
And up into the aery dome where live
The angels, and a sunbeam's sure to lurk
And I shall fill my slab of basalt there,
And 'neath my tabernacle take my rest,
With those nine columns round me, two and two
The odd one at my feet where Anselm stands:
Peach-blossom marble all, the rare, the ripe
As fresh-poured red wine of a mighty pulse
—Old Gandolf with his paltry onion-stone,
Put me where I may look at him! True peach,
Rosy and flawless: how I earned the prize!
Draw close; that conflagration of my church
—What then? So much was saved if aught were missed!
My sons, ye would not be my death? Go dig
The white-grape vineyard where the oil-press stood,
Drop water gently till the surface sinks,
And if ye find . . . Ah, God I know not, I! . . .
Bedded in store of rotten figleaves soft,
And corded up in a tight olive-frail
Some lump, ah God, of *lapis lazuli*,
Big as a Jew's head cut off at the nape,
Blue as a vein o'er the Madonna's breast—
Sons, all have I bequeathed you, villas, all,
That brave Frascati villa with its bath,
So, let the blue lump poise between my knees,
Like God the Father's globe on both his hands
Ye worship in the Jesu Church so gay,
For Gandolf shall not choose but see and burst!
Swift as a weaver's shuttle fleet our years:
Man goeth to the grave, and where is he?
Did I say basalt for my slab, sons? Black—
'Twas ever antique black I meant! How else
Shall ye contrast my frieze to come beneath?

The bas-relief in bronze ye promised me,
Those Pans and nymphs ye wot of, and perchance
Some tripod, thyrsus, with a vase or so,
The Saviour at his sermon on the mount,
St. Praxed in a glory, and one Pan
Ready to twitch the nymph's last garment off,
And Moses with the tables . . . but I know
Ye mark me not! What do they whisper thee,
Child of my bowels, Anselm? Ah, ye hope
To revel down my villas, while I gasp
Bricked o'er with beggar's mouldy travertine
Which Gandolf from his tomb-top chuckles at!
Nay, boys, ye love me—all of jasper, then!
'Tis jasper ye stand pledged to, lest I grieve
My bath must needs be left behind, alas!
One block, pure green as a pistachio-nut,
There's plenty jasper somewhere in the world—
And have I not St. Praxed's ear to pray
Horses for ye, and brown Greek manuscripts,
And mistresses with great smooth marbly limbs?
—That's if ye carve my epitaph aright,
Choice Latin, picked phrase, Tully's every word,
No gaudy ware like Gandolf's second line—
Tully, my masters? Ulpian serves his need!
And then how shall I lie through centuries,
And hear the blessed mutter of the mass,
And see God made and eaten all day long,
And feel the steady candle-flame, and taste
Good strong thick stupefying incense-smoke!
For as I lie here, hours of the dead night,
Dying in state and by such slow degrees,
I fold my arms as if they clasped a crook,
And stretch my feet forth straight as stone can point,
And let the bedclothes for a mortcloth drop
Into great laps and folds of sculptor's-work:
And as your tapers dwindle, and strange thoughts
Grow, with a certain humming in my ears,
About the life before I lived this life,
And this life too, Popes, Cardinals and Priests,
St. Praxed at his sermon on the mount,
Your tall pale mother with her talking eyes,
And new-found agate urns as fresh as day,

And marble's language, Latin pure, discreet,
—Aha ELUCESCEBAT quoth our friend?
No Tully, said I, Ulpian at the best!
Evil and brief hath been my pilgrimage.
All *lapis*, all, sons! Else I give the Pope
My villas: will ye ever eat my heart?
Ever your eyes were as a lizard's quick,
They glitter like your mother's for my soul,
Or ye would heighten my impoverished frieze,
Piece out its starved design, and fill my vase
With grapes, and add a vizor and a term,
And to the tripod ye would tie a lynx
That in his struggle throws the thyrsus down,
To comfort me on my entablature
Whereon I am to lie till I must ask
'Do I live, am I dead?' There, leave me, there!
For ye have stabbed me with ingratitude
To death—ye wish it—God, ye wish it! Stone—
Gritstone, a-crumble! Clammy squares which sweat
As if the corpse they keep were oozing through—
And no more *lapis* to delight the world!
Well, go! I bless ye. Fewer tapers there,
But in a row: and, going, turn your backs
—Ay, like departing altar-ministrants,
And leave me in my church, the church for peace,
That I may watch at leisure if he leers—
Old Gandolf, at me, from his onion-stone,
As still he envied me, so fair she was!

Up at a Villa—Down in the City
(as distinguished by an Italian Person of Quality)

I

Had I plenty of money, money enough and to spare
The house for me, no doubt, were a house in the city-square.
Ah, such a life, such a life, as one leads at the window there!

II

Something to see, by Bacchus, something to hear, at least!
There, the whole day long, one's life is a perfect feast;
While up at a villa one lives, I maintain it, no more than a
beast.

323

III

Well now, look at our villa, stuck like the horn of a bull
Just on a mountain's edge as bare as the creature's skull,
Save a mere shag of a bush with hardly a leaf to pull!
—I scratch my own, sometimes, to see if the hair's turned
    wool.

IV

But the city, oh the city—the square with the houses! Why?
They are stone-faced, white as a curd, there's something to
    take the eye!
Houses in four straight lines, not a single front awry!
You watch who crosses and gossips, who saunters, who hur-
    ries by:
Green blinds, as a matter of course, to draw when the sun
    gets high;
And the shops with fanciful signs which are painted properly.

V

What of a villa? Though winter be over in March by rights,
'Tis May perhaps ere the snow shall have withered well off
    the heights:
You've the brown ploughed land before, where the oxen
    steam and wheeze,
And the hills over-smoked behind by the faint grey olive trees.

VI

Is it better in May, I ask you? You've summer all at once;
In a day he leaps complete with a few strong April suns!
'Mid the sharp short emerald wheat, scarce risen three fingers
    well,
The wild tulip, at end of its tube, blows out its great red bell,
Like a thin clear bubble of blood, for the children to pick and
    sell.

VII

Is it ever hot in the square? There's a fountain to spout and
    splash!
In the shade it sings and springs; in the shine such foam-
    bows flash
On the horses with curling fish-tails, that prance and paddle
    and pash

Round the lady atop in the conch—fifty gazers do not abash,
Though all that she wears is some weeds round her waist in
a sort of a sash!

VIII

All the year long at the villa, nothing's to see though you
linger,
Except yon cypress that points like Death's lean lifted fore-
finger.
Some think fireflies pretty, when they mix in the corn and
mingle,
Or thread the stinking hemp till the stalks of it seem a-tingle.
Late August or early September, the stunning cicala is shrill,
And the bees keep their tiresome whine round the resinous
firs on the hill.
Enough of the seasons,—I spare you the months of the fever
and chill.

IX

Ere opening your eyes in the city, the blessed church-bells
begin
No sooner the bells leave off, than the diligence rattles in:
You get the pick of the news, and it costs you never a pin.
By and by there's the travelling doctor gives pills, lets blood,
draws teeth;
Or the Pulcinello-trumpet breaks up the market beneath.
At the post-office such a scene-picture—the new play, piping
hot!
And a notice how, only this morning, three liberal thieves
were shot.
Above it, behold the Archbishop's most fatherly of rebukes,
And beneath, with his crown and his lion, some little new law
of the Duke's!
Or a sonnet with flowery marge, to the Reverend Don So-
and-so
Who is Dante, Boccaccio, Petrarca, Saint Jerome and Cicero,
'And moreover,' (the sonnet goes rhyming), 'the skirts of
St. Paul has reached,
Having preached us those six Lent-lectures more unctuous
than ever he preached.'
Noon strikes,—here sweeps the procession! our Lady borne
smiling and smart

325

With a pink gauze gown all spangles, and seven swords stuck
in her heart!
Bang, whang, whang, goes the drum, *tootle-te-tootle* the fife;
No keeping one's haunches still: it's the greatest pleasure in
life.

x

But bless you, it's dear—it's dear! fowls, wine, at double the
rate.
They have clapped a new tax upon salt, and what oil pays
passing the gate
It's a horror to think of. And so, the villa for me, not the
city!
Beggars can scarcely be choosers—but still—ah, the pity, the
pity!
Look, two and two go the priests, then the monks with cowls
and sandals,
And the penitents dressed in white shirts, a-holding the yellow
candles.
One, he carries a flag up straight, and another a cross with
handles,
And the Duke's guard brings up the rear, for the better pre-
vention of scandals.
Bang, whang, whang, goes the drum, *tootle-te-tootle* the fife.
Oh, a day in the city-square, there is no such pleasure in life!

MATTHEW ARNOLD
1822-1888

Sohrab and Rustum

AN EPISODE

And the first grey of morning fill'd the east,
And the fog rose out of the Oxus stream.
But all the Tartar camp along the stream
Was hush'd, and still the men were plunged in sleep:
Sohrab alone, he slept not: all night long
He had lain wakeful, tossing on his bed;
But when the grey dawn stole into his tent,
He rose, and clad himself, and girt his sword,
And took his horseman's cloak, and left his tent,
And went abroad into the cold wet fog,
Through the dim camp to Peran-Wisa's tent.

Through the black Tartar tents he pass'd, which stood
Clustering like beehives on the low flat strand
Of Oxus, where the summer floods o'erflow
When the sun melts the snows in high Pamere:
Through the black tents he pass'd, o'er that low strand,
And to a hillock came, a little back
From the stream's brink, the spot where first a boat,
Crossing the stream in summer, scrapes the land.
The men of former times had crown'd the top
With a clay fort: but that was fall'n; and now
The Tartars built there Peran-Wisa's tent,
A dome of laths, and o'er it felts were spread.
And Sohrab came there, and went in, and stood
Upon the thick-pil'd carpets in the tent,
And found the old man sleeping on his bed
Of rugs and felts, and near him lay his arms.
And Peran-Wisa heard him, though the step
Was dull'd; for he slept light, an old man's sleep;
And he rose quickly on one arm, and said:—

327

'Who art thou? for it is not yet clear dawn.
Speak! is there news, or any night alarm?'

But Sohrab came to the bedside, and said:—
'Thou know'st me, Peran-Wisa: it is I.
The sun is not yet risen, and the foe
Sleep; but I sleep not; all night long I lie
Tossing and wakeful, and I come to thee.
For so did King Afrasiab bid me seek
Thy counsel, and to heed thee as thy son,
In Samarcand, before the army march'd;
And I will tell thee what my heart desires.
Thou knowest if, since from Ader-baijan first
I came among the Tartars, and bore arms,
I have still serv'd Afrasiab well, and shown,
At my boy's years, the courage of a man.
This too thou know'st, that, while I still bear on
The conquering Tartar ensigns through the world,
And beat the Persians back on every field,
I seek one man, one man, and one alone—
Rustum, my father; who, I hop'd, should greet,
Should one day greet, upon some well-fought field,
His not unworthy, not inglorious son.
So I long hop'd, but him I never find.
Come then, hear now, and grant me what I ask.
Let the two armies rest to-day: but I
Will challenge forth the bravest Persian lords
To meet me, man to man: if I prevail,
Rustum will surely hear it; if I fall—
Old man, the dead need no one, claim no kin.
Dim is the rumour of a common fight,
Where host meets host, and many names are sunk;
But of a single combat Fame speaks clear.'

He spoke; and Peran-Wisa took the hand
Of the young man in his, and sigh'd, and said:—
'O Sohrab, an unquiet heart is thine!
Canst thou not rest among the Tartar chiefs
And share the battle's common chance with us
Who love thee, but must press for ever first,
In single fight incurring single risk,
To find a father thou hast never seen?

That were far best, my son, to stay with us
Unmurmuring; in our tents, while it is war,
And when 'tis truce, then in Afrasiab's towns.
But, if this one desire indeed rules all,
To seek out Rustum—seek him not through fight!
Seek him in peace, and carry to his arms,
O Sohrab, carry an unwounded son!
But far hence seek him, for he is not here.
For now it is not as when I was young,
When Rustum was in front of every fray:
But now he keeps apart, and sits at home,
In Seistan, with Zal, his father old.
Whether that his own mighty strength at last
Feels the abhorr'd approaches of old age;
Or in some quarrel with the Persian King.
There go:—Thou wilt not? Yet my heart forebodes
Danger or death awaits thee on this field.
Fain would I know thee safe and well, though lost
To us: fain therefore send thee hence, in peace
To seek thy father, not seek single fights
In vain:—but who can keep the lion's cub
From ravening? and who govern Rustum's son?
Go: I will grant thee what thy heart desires.'

So said he, and dropp'd Sohrab's hand, and left
His bed, and the warm rugs whereon he lay;
And o'er his chilly limbs his woollen coat
He pass'd, and tied his sandals on his feet,
And threw a white cloak round him, and he took
In his right hand a ruler's staff, no sword;
And on his head he plac'd his sheep-skin cap,
Black, glossy, curl'd, the fleece of Kara-Kul;
And rais'd the curtain of his tent, and call'd
His herald to his side, and went abroad.

The sun by this had risen, and clear'd the fog
From the broad Oxus and the glittering sands:
And from their tents the Tartar horsemen fil'd
Into the open plain; so Haman bade;
Haman, who next to Peran-Wisa rul'd
The host, and still was in his lusty prime.
From their black tents, long files of horse, they stream'd:
As when, some grey November morn, the files,

In marching order spread, of long-neck'd cranes
Stream over Casbin, and the southern slopes
Of Elburz, from the Aralian estuaries,
Or some frore Caspian reed-bed, southward bound
For the warm Persian sea-board: so they stream'd.
The Tartars of the Oxus, the King's guard,
First, with black sheep-skin caps and with long spears;
Large men, large steeds; who from Bokhara come
And Khiva, and ferment the milk of mares.
Next the more temperate Toorkmuns of the south,
The Tukas, and the lances of Salore,
And those from Attruck and the Caspian sands;
Light men, and on light steeds, who only drink
The acrid milk of camels, and their wells.
And then a swarm of wandering horse, who came
From far, and a more doubtful service own'd;
The Tartars of Ferghana, from the banks
Of the Jaxartes, men with scanty beards
And close-set skull-caps; and those wilder hordes
Who roam o'er Kipchak and the northern waste,
Kalmuks and unkempt Kuzzaks, tribes who stray
Nearest the Pole, and wandering Kirghizzes,
Who come on shaggy ponies from Pamere.
These all fil'd out from camp into the plain.
And on the other side the Persians form'd:
First a light cloud of horse, Tartars they seem'd,
The Ilyats of Khorassan: and behind,
The royal troops of Persia, horse and foot,
Marshall'd battalions bright in burnish'd steel.
But Peran-Wisa with his herald came
Threading the Tartar squadrons to the front,
And with his staff kept back the foremost ranks.
And when Ferood, who led the Persians, saw
That Peran-Wisa kept the Tartars back,
He took his spear, and to the front he came,
And check'd his ranks, and fix'd them where they stood.
And the old Tartar came upon the sand
Betwixt the silent hosts, and spake, and said:—
    'Ferood, and ye, Persians and Tartars, hear!
Let there be truce between the hosts to-day.
But choose a champion from the Persian lords
To fight our champion Sohrab, man to man.'

As, in the country, on a morn in June,
When the dew glistens on the pearled ears,
A shiver runs through the deep corn for joy—
So, when they heard what Peran-Wisa said,
A thrill through all the Tartar squadrons ran
Of pride and hope for Sohrab, whom they lov'd.
But as a troop of pedlars, from Cabool,
Cross underneath the Indian Caucasus,
That vast sky-neighbouring mountain of milk snow:
Winding so high, that, as they mount, they pass
Long flocks of travelling birds dead on the snow,
Chok'd by the air, and scarce can they themselves
Slake their parch'd throats with sugar'd mulberries—
In single file they move, and stop their breath,
For fear they should dislodge the o'erhanging snows—
So the pale Persians held their breath with fear.

And to Ferood his brother Chiefs came up
To counsel: Gudurz and Zoarrah came,
And Feraburz, who rul'd the Persian host
Second, and was the uncle of the King:
These came and counsell'd; and then Gudurz said:—
'Ferood, shame bids us take their challenge up,
Yet champion have we none to match this youth.
He has the wild stag's foot, the lion's heart.
But Rustum came last night; aloof he sits
And sullen, and has pitch'd his tents apart:
Him will I seek, and carry to his ear
The Tartar challenge, and this young man's name.
Haply he will forget his wrath, and fight.
Stand forth the while, and take their challenge up.'
So spake he; and Ferood stood forth and cried:—
'Old man, be it agreed as thou hast said.
Let Sohrab arm, and we will find a man.'

He spake; and Peran-Wisa turn'd, and strode
Back through the opening squadrons to his tent.
But through the anxious Persians Gudurz ran,
And cross'd the camp which lay behind, and reach'd,
Out on the sands beyond it, Rustum's tents.
Of scarlet cloth they were, and glittering gay,
Just pitch'd: the high pavilion in the midst

Was Rustum's, and his men lay camp'd around.
And Gudurz enter'd Rustum's tent, and found
Rustum: his morning meal was done, but still
The table stood beside him, charg'd with food;
A side of roasted sheep, and cakes of bread,
And dark green melons; and there Rustum sate
Listless, and held a falcon on his wrist,
And play'd with it; but Gudurz came and stood
Before him; and he look'd, and saw him stand;
And with a cry sprang up, and dropp'd the bird,
And greeted Gudurz with both hands, and said:—

'Welcome! these eyes could see no better sight.
What news? but sit down first, and eat and drink.'

But Gudurz stood in the tent door, and said:—
'Not now: a time will come to eat and drink,
But not to-day: to-day has other needs.
The armies are drawn out, and stand at gaze:
For from the Tartars is a challenge brought
To pick a champion from the Persian lords
To fight their champion—and thou know'st his name—
Sohrab men call him, but his birth is hid.
O Rustum, like thy might is this young man's!
He has the wild stag's foot, the lion's heart.
And he is young, and Iran's chiefs are old,
Or else too weak; and all eyes turn to thee.
Come down and help us, Rustum, or we lose.'

He spoke: but Rustum answered with a smile:—
'Go to! if Iran's chiefs are old, then I
Am older: if the young are weak, the King
Errs strangely: for the King, for Kai Khosroo,
Himself is young, and honours younger men,
And lets the agèd moulder to their graves.
Rustum he loves no more, but loves the young—
The young may rise at Sohrab's vaunts, not I.
For what care I, though all speak Sohrab's fame?
For would that I myself had such a son,
And not that one slight helpless girl I have,
A son so fam'd, so brave, to send to war,
And I to tarry with the snow-hair'd Zal,
My father, whom the robber Afghans vex,
And clip his borders short, and drive his herds,

And he has none to guard his weak old age.
There would I go, and hang my armour up,
And with my great name fence that weak old man,
And spend the goodly treasures I have got,
And rest my age, and hear of Sohrab's fame,
And leave to death the hosts of thankless kings,
And with these slaughterous hands draw sword no more.'

He spoke, and smil'd; and Gudurz made reply:—
'What then, O Rustum, will men say to this,
When Sohrab dares our bravest forth, and seeks
Thee most of all, and thou, whom most he seeks,
Hidest thy face? Take heed, lest men should say:
Like some old miser, Rustum hoards his fame,
And shuns to peril it with younger men.'

And, greatly mov'd, then Rustum made reply:—
'O Gudurz, wherefore dost thou say such words?
Thou knowest better words than this to say.
What is one more, one less, obscure or fam'd,
Valiant or craven, young or old, to me?
Are not they mortal, am not I myself?
But who for men of naught would do great deeds?
Come, thou shalt see how Rustum hoards his fame.
But I will fight unknown, and in plain arms;
Let not men say of Rustum, he was match'd
In single fight with any mortal man.'

He spoke, and frown'd; and Gudurz turn'd, and ran
Back quickly through the camp in fear and joy,
Fear at his wrath, but joy that Rustum came.
But Rustum strode to his tent door, and call'd
His followers in, and bade them bring his arms,
And clad himself in steel: the arms he chose
Were plain, and on his shield was no device,
Only his helm was rich, inlaid with gold,
And from the fluted spine atop a plume
Of horsehair wav'd, a scarlet horsehair plume.
So arm'd, he issued forth; and Ruksh, his horse,
Follow'd him, like a faithful hound, at heel—
Ruksh, whose renown was nois'd through all the earth,
The horse, whom Rustum on a foray once
Did in Bokhara by the river find
A colt beneath its dam, and drove him home,

And rear'd him; a bright bay, with lofty crest;
Dight with a saddle-cloth of broider'd green
Crusted with gold, and on the ground were work'd
All beasts of chase, all beasts which hunters know:
So follow'd, Rustum left his tents, and cross'd
The camp, and to the Persian host appear'd.
And all the Persians knew him, and with shouts
Hail'd; but the Tartars knew not who he was.
And dear as the wet diver to the eyes
Of his pale wife who waits and weeps on shore,
By sandy Bahrein, in the Persian Gulf,
Plunging all day in the blue waves, at night,
Having made up his tale of precious pearls,
Rejoins her in their hut upon the sands—
So dear to the pale Persians Rustum came.

And Rustum to the Persian front advanc'd,
And Sohrab arm'd in Haman's tent, and came.
And as afield the reapers cut a swathe
Down through the middle of a rich man's corn,
And on each side are squares of standing corn,
And in the midst a stubble, short and bare;
So on each side were squares of men, with spears
Bristling, and in the midst, the open sand.
And Rustum came upon the sand, and cast
His eyes towards the Tartar tents, and saw
Sohrab come forth, and ey'd him as he came.

As some rich woman, on a winter's morn,
Eyes through her silken curtains the poor drudge
Who with numb blacken'd fingers makes her fire—
At cock-crow, on a starlit winter's morn,
When the frost flowers the whiten'd window panes—
And wonders how she lives, and what the thoughts
Of that poor drudge may be; so Rustum ey'd
The unknown adventurous youth, who from afar
Came seeking Rustum, and defying forth
All the most valiant chiefs: long he perus'd
His spirited air, and wonder'd who he was.
For very young he seem'd, tenderly rear'd;
Like some young cypress, tall, and dark, and straight,
Which in a queen's secluded garden throws
Its slight dark shadow on the moonlit turf,

By midnight, to a bubbling fountain's sound—
So slender Sohrab seem'd, so softly rear'd.
And a deep pity enter'd Rustum's soul
As he beheld him coming; and he stood,
And beckon'd to him with his hand, and said:—
   'O thou young man, the air of Heaven is soft,
And warm, and pleasant; but the grave is cold.
Heaven's air is better than the cold dead grave.
Behold me: I am vast, and clad in iron,
And tried; and I have stood on many a field
Of blood, and I have fought with many a foe:
Never was that field lost, or that foe sav'd.
O Sohrab, wherefore wilt thou rush on death?
Be govern'd: quit the Tartar host, and come
To Iran, and be as my son to me,
And fight beneath my banner till I die.
There are no youths in Iran brave as thou.'

   So he spake, mildly: Sohrab heard his voice,
The mighty voice of Rustum; and he saw
His giant figure planted on the sand,
Sole, like some single tower, which a chief
Has builded on the waste in former years
Against the robbers; and he saw that head,
Streak'd with its first grey hairs: hope fill'd his soul;
And he ran forwards and embrac'd his knees,
And clasp'd his hand within his own, and said:—
   'Oh, by thy father's head! by thine own soul!
Art thou not Rustum? Speak! art thou not he?'

   But Rustum ey'd askance the kneeling youth,
And turn'd away, and spoke to his own soul:—
   'Ah me, I muse what this young fox may mean.
False, wily, boastful, are these Tartar boys.
For if I now confess this thing he asks,
And hide it not, but say: *Rustum is here!*
He will not yield indeed, nor quit our foes,
But he will find some pretext not to fight,
And praise my fame, and proffer courteous gifts,
A belt or sword perhaps, and go his way.
And on a feast day, in Afrasiab's hall,
In Samarcand, he will arise and cry—

"I challeng'd once, when the two armies camp'd
Beside the Oxus, all the Persian lords
To cope with me in single fight; but they
Shrank; only Rustum dar'd: then he and I
Chang'd gifts, and went on equal terms away."
So will he speak, perhaps, while men applaud.
Then were the chiefs of Iran sham'd through me.'
    And then he turn'd, and sternly spake aloud:—
'Rise! wherefore dost thou vainly question thus
Of Rustum? I am here, whom thou hast call'd
By challenge forth: make good thy vaunt, or yield.
Is it with Rustum only thou wouldst fight?
Rash boy, men look on Rustum's face and flee.
For well I know, that did great Rustum stand
Before thy face this day, and were reveal'd,
There would be then no talk of fighting more.
But being what I am, I tell thee this;
Do thou record it in thine inmost soul:
Either thou shalt renounce thy vaunt, and yield;
Or else thy bones shall strew this sand, till winds
Bleach them, or Oxus with his summer floods,
Oxus in summer wash them all away.'

    He spoke: and Sohrab answer'd, on his feet:—
'Art thou so fierce? Thou wilt not fright me so.
I am no girl, to be made pale by words.
Yet this thou hast said well, did Rustum stand
Here on this field, there were no fighting then.
But Rustum is far hence, and we stand here.
Begin: thou art more vast, more dread than I,
And thou art prov'd, I know, and I am young—
But yet success sways with the breath of Heaven.
And though thou thinkest that thou knowest sure
Thy victory, yet thou canst not surely know.
For we are all, like swimmers in the sea,
Pois'd on the top of a huge wave of Fate,
Which hangs uncertain to which side to fall.
And whether it will heave us up to land,
Or whether it will roll us out to sea,
Back out to sea, to the deep waves of death,
We know not, and no search will make us know:
Only the event will teach us in its hour.'

He spoke; and Rustum answer'd not, but hurl'd
His spear: down from the shoulder, down it came,
As on some partridge in the corn a hawk
That long has tower'd in the airy clouds
Drops like a plummet: Sohrab saw it come,
And sprang aside, quick as a flash: the spear
Hiss'd, and went quivering down into the sand
Which it sent flying wide:—then Sohrab threw
In turn, and full struck Rustum's shield: sharp rang,
The iron plates rang sharp, but turn'd the spear.
And Rustum seiz'd his club, which none but he
Could wield: an unlopp'd trunk it was, and huge,
Still rough; like those which men in treeless plains
To build them boats fish from the flooded rivers,
Hyphasis or Hydaspes, when, high up
By their dark springs, the wind in winter-time
Has made in Himalayan forests wrack,
And strewn the channels with torn boughs—so huge
The club which Rustum lifted now, and struck
One stroke; but again Sohrab sprang aside
Lithe as the glancing snake, and the club came
Thundering to earth, and leapt from Rustum's hand.
And Rustum follow'd his own blow, and fell
To his knees, and with his fingers clutch'd the sand:
And now might Sohrab have unsheath'd his sword,
And pierc'd the mighty Rustum while he lay
Dizzy, and on his knees, and chok'd with sand:
But he look'd on, and smil'd, nor bar'd his sword,
But courteously drew back, and spoke, and said:—
'Thou strik'st too hard: that club of thine will float
Upon the summer floods, and not my bones.
But rise, and be not wroth; not wroth am I:
No, when I see thee, wrath forsakes my soul.
Thou say'st, thou art not Rustum: be it so.
Who art thou then, that canst so touch my soul?
Boy as I am, I have seen battles too;
Have waded foremost in their bloody waves,
And heard their hollow roar of dying men;
But never was my heart thus touch'd before.
Are they from Heaven, these softenings of the heart?
O thou old warrior, let us yield to Heaven!
Come, plant we here in earth our angry spears,

And make a truce, and sit upon this sand,
And pledge each other in red wine, like friends,
And thou shalt talk to me of Rustum's deeds.
There are enough foes in the Persian host
Whom I may meet, and strike, and feel no pang;
Champions enough Afrasiab has, whom thou
Mayst fight; fight them, when they confront thy spear.
But oh, let there be peace 'twixt thee and me!'

He ceas'd: but while he spake, Rustum had risen,
And stood erect, trembling with rage: his club
He left to lie, but had regain'd his spear,
Whose fiery point now in his mail'd right hand
Blaz'd bright and baleful, like that autumn Star,
The baleful sign of fevers: dust had soil'd
His stately crest, and dimm'd his glittering arms.
His breast heav'd; his lips foam'd; and twice his voice
Was chok'd with rage: at last these words broke way:—
    'Girl! nimble with thy feet, not with thy hands!
Curl'd minion, dancer, coiner of sweet words!
Fight; let me hear thy hateful voice no more!
Thou art not in Afrasiab's gardens now
With Tartar girls, with whom thou art wont to dance;
But on the Oxus sands, and in the dance
Of battle, and with me, who make no play
Of war: I fight it out, and hand to hand.
Speak not to me of truce, and pledge, and wine!
Remember all thy valour: try thy feints
And cunning: all the pity I had is gone:
Because thou hast sham'd me before both the hosts
With thy light skipping tricks, and thy girl's wiles.'

He spoke; and Sohrab kindled at his taunts,
And he too drew his sword: at once they rush'd
Together, as two eagles on one prey
Come rushing down together from the clouds,
One from the east, one from the west: their shields
Dash'd with a clang together, and a din
Rose, such as that the sinewy woodcutters
Make often in the forest's heart at morn,
Of hewing axes, crashing trees; such blows
Rustum and Sohrab on each other hail'd.

And you would say that sun and stars took part
In that unnatural conflict; for a cloud
Grew suddenly in Heaven, and dark'd the sun
Over the fighters' heads; and a wind rose
Under their feet, and moaning swept the plain,
And in a sandy whirlwind wrapp'd the pair.
In gloom they twain were wrapp'd, and they alone;
For both the onlooking hosts on either hand
Stood in broad daylight, and the sky was pure,
And the sun sparkled on the Oxus stream.
But in the gloom they fought, with bloodshot eyes
And labouring breath: first Rustum struck the shield
Which Sohrab held stiff out: the steel-spik'd spear
Rent the tough plates, but fail'd to reach the skin,
And Rustum pluck'd it back with angry groan.
Then Sohrab with his sword smote Rustum's helm,
Nor clove its steel quite through; but all the crest
He shore away, and that proud horsehair plume,
Never till now defil'd, sunk to the dust;
And Rustum bow'd his head; but then the gloom
Grew blacker: thunder rumbled in the air,
And lightnings rent the cloud; and Ruksh, the horse,
Who stood at hand, utter'd a dreadful cry:
No horse's cry was that, most like the roar
Of some pain'd desert lion, who all day
Has trail'd the hunter's javelin in his side,
And comes at night to die upon the sand:—
The two hosts heard that cry, and quak'd for fear,
And Oxus curdled as it cross'd his stream.
But Sohrab heard, and quail'd not, but rush'd on,
And struck again; and again Rustum bow'd
His head; but this time all the blade, like glass,
Sprang in a thousand shivers on the helm,
And in his hand the hilt remain'd alone.
Then Rustum rais'd his head: his dreadful eyes
Glar'd, and he shook on high his menacing spear,
And shouted, *Rustum!* Sohrab heard that shout,
And shrank amaz'd: back he recoil'd one step,
And scann'd with blinking eyes the advancing form:
And then he stood bewilder'd; and he dropp'd
His covering shield, and the spear pierc'd his side.
He reel'd, and staggering back, sunk to the ground.

And then the gloom dispers'd, and the wind fell,
And the bright sun broke forth, and melted all
The cloud; and the two armies saw the pair;
Saw Rustum standing, safe upon his feet,
And Sohrab, wounded, on the bloody sand.

Then, with a bitter smile, Rustum began:—
'Sohrab, thou thoughtest in thy mind to kill
A Persian lord this day, and strip his corpse,
And bear thy trophies to Afrasiab's tent.
Or else that the great Rustum would come down
Himself to fight, and that thy wiles would move
His heart to take a gift, and let thee go.
And then that all the Tartar host would praise
Thy courage or thy craft, and spread thy fame,
To glad thy father in his weak old age.
Fool! thou art slain, and by an unknown man!
Dearer to the red jackals shalt thou be,
Than to thy friends, and to thy father old.'

And with a fearless mien Sohrab replied:—
'Unknown thou art; yet thy fierce vaunt is vain.
Thou dost not slay me, proud and boastful man!
No! Rustum slays me, and this filial heart.
For were I match'd with ten such men as thou,
And I were he who till to-day I was,
They should be lying here, I standing there.
But that belovèd name unnerv'd my arm—
That name, and something, I confess, in thee,
Which troubles all my heart, and made my shield
Fall; and thy spear transfix'd an unarm'd foe.
And now thou boastest, and insult'st my fate.
But hear thou this, fierce man, tremble to hear!
The mighty Rustum shall avenge my death!
My father, whom I seek through all the world,
He shall avenge my death, and punish thee!'

As when some hunter in the spring hath found
A breeding eagle sitting on her nest,
Upon the craggy isle of a hill lake,
And pierc'd her with an arrow as she rose,
And follow'd her to find her where she fell
Far off;—anon her mate comes winging back
From hunting, and a great way off descries

His huddling young left sole; at that, he checks
His pinion, and with short uneasy sweeps
Circles above his eyry, with loud screams
Chiding his mate back to her nest; but she
Lies dying, with the arrow in her side,
In some far stony gorge out of his ken,
A heap of fluttering feathers: never more
Shall the lake glass her, flying over it;
Never the black and dripping precipices
Echo her stormy scream as she sails by:—
As that poor bird flies home, nor knows his loss—
So Rustum knew not his own loss, but stood
Over his dying son, and knew him not.
　　But with a cold, incredulous voice, he said:—
'What prate is this of fathers and revenge?
The mighty Rustum never had a son.'

　　And, with a failing voice, Sohrab replied:—
'Ah yes, he had! and that lost son am I.
Surely the news will one day reach his ear,
Reach Rustum, where he sits, and tarries long,
Somewhere, I know not where, but far from here;
And pierce him like a stab, and make him leap
To arms, and cry for vengeance upon thee.
Fierce man, bethink thee, for an only son!
What will that grief, what will that vengeance be!
Oh, could I live, till I that grief had seen!
Yet him I pity not so much, but her
My mother, who in Ader-baijan dwells
With that old King, her father, who grows grey
With age, and rules over the valiant Koords.
Her most I pity, who no more will see
Sohrab returning from the Tartar camp,
With spoils and honour, when the war is done.
But a dark rumour will be bruited up,
From tribe to tribe, until it reach her ear;
And then will that defenceless woman learn
That Sohrab will rejoice her sight no more:
But that in battle with a nameless foe,
By the far distant Oxus, he is slain.'

　　He spoke; and as he ceas'd he wept aloud,
Thinking of her he left, and his own death.

He spoke; but Rustum listen'd, plung'd in thought
Nor did he yet believe it was his son
Who spoke, although he call'd back names he knew;
For he had had sure tidings that the babe,
Which was in Ader-baijan born to him,
Had been a puny girl, no boy at all:
So that sad mother sent him word, for fear
Rustum should take the boy, to train in arms;
And so he deem'd that either Sohrab took,
By a false boast, the style of Rustum's son;
Or that men gave it him, to swell his fame.
So deem'd he; yet he listen'd, plung'd in thought;
And his soul set to grief, as the vast tide
Of the bright rocking Ocean sets to shore
At the full moon: tears gather'd in his eyes;
For he remember'd his own early youth,
And all its bounding rapture; as, at dawn,
The shepherd from his mountain lodge descries
A far bright city, smitten by the sun,
Through many rolling clouds;—so Rustum saw
His youth; saw Sohrab's mother, in her bloom;
And that old King, her father, who lov'd well
His wandering guest, and gave him his fair child
With joy; and all the pleasant life they led,
They three, in that long-distant summer-time—
The castle, and the dewy woods, and hunt
And hound, and morn on those delightful hills
In Ader-baijan. And he saw that Youth,
Of age and looks to be his own dear son,
Piteous and lovely, lying on the sand,
Like some rich hyacinth, which by the scythe
Of an unskilful gardener has been cut,
Mowing the garden grass-plots near its bed,
And lies, a fragrant tower of purple bloom,
On the mown, dying grass;—so Sohrab lay,
Lovely in death, upon the common sand.
And Rustum gaz'd on him with grief, and said:—

'O Sohrab, thou indeed art such a son
Whom Rustum, wert thou his, might well have lov'd!
Yet here thou errest, Sohrab, or else men
Have told thee false;—thou art not Rustum's son.
For Rustum had no son: one child he had—

But one—a girl; who with her mother now
Plies some light female task, nor dreams of us—
Of us she dreams not, nor of wounds, nor war.'

But Sohrab answer'd him in wrath; for now
The anguish of the deep-fix'd spear grew fierce,
And he desirèd to draw forth the steel,
And let the blood flow free, and so to die;
But first he would convince his stubborn foe—
And, rising sternly on one arm, he said:—
    'Man, who art thou who dost deny my words?
Truth sits upon the lips of dying men,
And Falsehood, while I liv'd, was far from mine.
I tell thee, prick'd upon this arm I bear
That seal which Rustum to my mother gave,
That she might prick it on the babe she bore.'

He spoke: and all the blood left Rustum's cheeks;
And his knees totter'd, and he smote his hand
Against his breast, his heavy mailèd hand,
That the hard iron corslet clank'd aloud:
And to his heart he press'd the other hand,
And in a hollow voice he spake, and said:—
    'Sohrab, that were a proof which could not lie.
If thou shew this, then art thou Rustum's son.'

Then, with weak hasty fingers, Sohrab loos'd
His belt, and near the shoulder bar'd his arm,
And show'd a sign in faint vermilion points
Prick'd: as a cunning workman, in Pekin,
Pricks with vermilion some clear porcelain vase,
An emperor's gift—at early morn he paints,
And all day long, and, when night comes, the lamp
Lights up his studious forehead and thin hands:—
So delicately prick'd the sign appear'd
On Sohrab's arm, the sign of Rustum's seal.
It was that Griffin, which of old rear'd Zal,
Rustum's great father, whom they left to die,
A helpless babe, among the mountain rocks.
Him that kind creature found, and rear'd, and lov'd—
Then Rustum took it for his glorious sign.
And Sohrab bar'd that figure on his arm,

And himself scann'd it long with mournful eyes,
And then he touch'd it with his hand and said:—
  'How say'st thou? Is that sign the proper sign
Of Rustum's son, or of some other man's?'

  He spoke: but Rustum gaz'd, and gaz'd, and stood
Speechless; and then he utter'd one sharp cry—
O Boy—thy Father!—and his voice chok'd there.
And then a dark cloud pass'd before his eyes,
And his head swam, and he sunk down to earth.
But Sohrab crawl'd to where he lay, and cast
His arms about his neck, and kiss'd his lips,
And with fond faltering fingers strok'd his cheeks,
Trying to call him back to life: and life
Came back to Rustum, and he op'd his eyes,
And they stood wide with horror; and he seiz'd
In both his hands the dust which lay around,
And threw it on his head, and smirch'd his hair—
His hair, and face, and beard, and glittering arms:
And strong convulsive groanings shook his breast,
And his sobs chok'd him; and he clutch'd his sword,
To draw it, and for ever let life out.
But Sohrab saw his thought, and held his hands,
And with a soothing voice he spoke, and said:—
  'Father, forbear: for I but meet to-day
The doom that at my birth was written down
In Heaven, and thou art Heaven's unconscious hand.
Surely my heart cried out that it was thou,
When first I saw thee; and thy heart spoke too,
I know it: but Fate trod those promptings down
Under its iron heel; Fate, Fate engag'd
The strife, and hurl'd me on my father's spear.
But let us speak no more of this: I find
My father; let me feel that I have found.
Come, sit beside me on this sand, and take
My head betwixt thy hands, and kiss my cheeks,
And wash them with thy tears, and say: *My son!*
Quick! quick! for number'd are my sands of life,
And swift; for like the lightning to this field
I came, and like the wind I go away—
Sudden, and swift, and like a passing wind.
But it was writ in Heaven that this should be.'

So said he: and his voice releas'd the heart
Of Rustum, and his tears broke forth; he cast
His arms round his son's neck, and wept aloud,
And kiss'd him. And awe fell on both the hosts
When they saw Rustum's grief: and Ruksh, the horse,
With his head bowing to the ground, and mane
Sweeping the dust, came near, and in mute woe
First to the one then to the other mov'd
His head, as if enquiring what their grief
Might mean; and from his dark, compassionate eyes,
The big warm tears roll'd down, and cak'd the sand.
But Rustum chid him with stern voice, and said:—

'Ruksh, now thou grievest; but, O Ruksh, thy feet
Should then have rotted on thy nimble joints,
When first they bore thy master to this field.'

But Sohrab look'd upon the horse and said:—
'Is this then Ruksh? How often, in past days,
My mother told me of thee, thou brave Steed!
My terrible father's terrible horse; and said,
That I should one day find thy lord and thee.
Come, let me lay my hand upon thy mane.
O Ruksh, thou art more fortunate than I;
For thou hast gone where I shall never go,
And snuff'd the breezes of my father's home.
And thou hast trod the sands of Seistan,
And seen the River of Helmund, and the Lake
Of Zirrah; and the aged Zal himself
Has often strok'd thy neck, and given thee food,
Corn in a golden platter soak'd with wine,
And said—"O Ruksh! bear Rustum well!"—but I
Have never known my grandsire's furrow'd face,
Nor seen his lofty house in Seistan,
Nor slak'd my thirst at the clear Helmund stream:
But lodg'd among my father's foes, and seen
Afrasiab's cities only, Samarcand,
Bokhara, and lone Khiva in the waste,
And the black Toorkmun tents; and only drunk
The desert rivers, Moorghab and Tejend,
Kohik, and where the Kalmuks feed their sheep,
The northern Sir; and this great Oxus stream—
The yellow Oxus, by whose brink I die.'

Then, with a heavy groan, Rustum bewail'd:—
'Oh that its waves were flowing over me!
Oh that I saw its grains of yellow silt
Roll tumbling in the current o'er my head!'

And, with a grave mild voice, Sohrab replied:—
'Desire not that, my father; thou must live.
For some are born to do great deeds, and live,
As some are born to be obscur'd, and die.
Do thou the deeds I die too young to do,
And reap a second glory in thine age.
Thou art my father, and thy gain is mine.
But come: thou seest this great host of men
Which follow me; I pray thee, slay not these:
Let me entreat for them: what have they done?
They follow'd me, my hope, my fame, my star.
Let them all cross the Oxus back in peace.
But me thou must bear hence, not send with them,
But carry me with thee to Seistan,
And place me on a bed, and mourn for me,
Thou, and the snow-hair'd Zal, and all thy friends.
And thou must lay me in that lovely earth,
And heap a stately mound above my bones,
And plant a far-seen pillar over all:
That so the passing horseman on the waste
May see my tomb a great way off, and cry—
Sohrab, the mighty Rustum's son, lies there,
Whom his great father did in ignorance kill—
And I be not forgotten in my grave.'

And, with a mournful voice, Rustum replied:—
'Fear not; as thou hast said, Sohrab, my son,
So shall it be: for I will burn my tents,
And quit the host, and bear thee hence with me,
And carry thee away to Seistan,
And place thee on a bed, and mourn for thee,
With the snow-headed Zal, and all my friends.
And I will lay thee in that lovely earth,
And heap a stately mound above thy bones,
And plant a far-seen pillar over all:
And men shall not forget thee in thy grave.
And I will spare thy host: yea, let them go:

Let them all cross the Oxus back in peace.
What should I do with slaying any more?
For would that all whom I have ever slain
Might be once more alive; my bitterest foes,
And they who were call'd champions in their time,
And through whose death I won that fame I have;
And I were nothing but a common man,
A poor, mean soldier, and without renown;
So thou mightest live too, my son, my son!
Or rather would that I, even I myself,
Might now be lying on this bloody sand,
Near death, and by an ignorant stroke of thine,
Not thou of mine; and I might die, not thou;
And I, not thou, be borne to Seistan;
And Zal might weep above my grave, not thine;
And say—*O son, I weep thee not too sore,
For willingly, I know, thou met'st thine end.*—
But now in blood and battles was my youth,
And full of blood and battles is my age;
And I shall never end this life of blood.'

Then, at the point of death, Sohrab replied:—
'A life of blood indeed, thou dreadful man;
But thou shalt yet have peace; only not now,
Not yet: but thou shalt have it on that day,
When thou shalt sail in a high-masted ship,
Thou and the other peers of Kai Khosroo,
Returning home over the salt blue sea,
From laying thy dear master in his grave.'

And Rustum gaz'd on Sohrab's face, and said:—
'Soon be that day, my son, and deep that sea!
Till then, if Fate so wills, let me endure.'

He spoke; and Sohrab smil'd on him, and took
The spear, and drew it from his side, and eas'd
His wound's imperious anguish: but the blood
Came welling from the open gash, and life
Flow'd with the stream: all down his cold white side
The crimson torrent ran, dim now, and soil'd,
Like the soil'd tissue of white violets
Left, freshly gather'd, on their native bank,
By romping children, whom their nurses call

347

From the hot fields at noon: his head droop'd low,
His limbs grew slack; motionless, white, he lay—
White, with eyes closed; only when heavy gasps,
Deep, heavy gasps, quivering through all his frame,
Convuls'd him back to life, he open'd them,
And fix'd them feebly on his father's face:
Till now all strength was ebb'd, and from his limbs
Unwillingly the spirit fled away,
Regretting the warm mansion which it left,
And youth and bloom, and this delightful world.

So, on the bloody sand, Sohrab lay dead.
And the great Rustum drew his horseman's cloak
Down o'er his face, and sate by his dead son.
As those black granite pillars, once high-rear'd
By Jemshid in Persepolis, to bear
His house, now, 'mid their broken flights of steps,
Lie prone, enormous, down the mountain side—
So in the sand lay Rustum by his son.

And night came down over the solemn waste,
And the two gazing hosts, and that sole pair,
And darken'd all; and a cold fog, with night,
Crept from the Oxus. Soon a hum arose,
As of a great assembly loos'd, and fires
Began to twinkle through the fog: for now
Both armies mov'd to camp, and took their meal:
The Persians took it on the open sands
Southward; the Tartars by the river marge:
And Rustum and his son were left alone.

But the majestic River floated on,
Out of the mist and hum of that low land,
Into the frosty starlight, and there mov'd,
Rejoicing, through the hush'd Chorasmian waste,
Under the solitary moon: he flow'd
Right for the Polar Star, past Orgunjé,
Brimming, and bright, and large; then sands begin
To hem his watery march, and dam his streams,
And split his currents; that for many a league
The shorn and parcell'd Oxus strains along
Through beds of sand and matted rushy isles—

Oxus, forgetting the bright speed he had
In his high mountain cradle in Pamere,
A foil'd circuitous wanderer:—till at last
The long'd-for dash of waves is heard, and wide
His luminous home of waters opens, bright
And tranquil, from whose floor the new-bath'd stars
Emerge, and shine upon the Aral Sea.

The Scholar Gipsy

Go, for they call you, shepherd, from the hill;
  Go, shepherd, and untie the wattled cotes:
    No longer leave thy wistful flock unfed,
  Nor let thy bawling fellows rack their throats,
    Nor the cropp'd grasses shoot another head!
      But when the fields are still,
  And the tired men and dogs all gone to rest,
    And only the white sheep are sometimes seen
    Cross and recross the strips of moon-blanch'd green,
  Come, shepherd, and again begin the quest!

Here, where the reaper was at work of late—
  In this high field's dark corner, where he leaves
    His coat, his basket, and his earthen cruse,
  And in the sun all morning binds the sheaves,
    Then here, at noon, comes back his stores to use—
      Here will I sit and wait,
  While to my ear from uplands far away
    The bleating of the folded flocks is borne,
    With distant cries of reapers in the corn—
  All the live murmur of a summer's day.

Screen'd is this nook o'er the high, half-reap'd field,
  And here till sun-down, shepherd, will I be!
    Through the thick corn the scarlet poppies peep,
  And round green roots and yellowing stalks I see
    Pale blue convolvulus in tendrils creep;
      And air-swept lindens yield
  Their scent, and rustle down their perfumed showers
    Of bloom on the bent grass where I am laid,
    And bower me from the August sun with shade;
  And the eye travels down to Oxford's towers.

And near me on the grass lies Glanvil's book—
　Come, let me read the oft-read tale again!
　　The story of that Oxford scholar poor,
　Of shining parts and quick inventive brain,
　　Who, tired of knocking at preferment's door,
　　　One summer morn forsook
　His friends, and went to learn the gipsy lore,
　　And roam'd the world with that wild brotherhood,
　　And came as, most men deem'd, to little good,
　But came to Oxford and his friends no more.

But once, years after, in the country-lanes,
　Two scholars whom at college erst he knew
　　Met him, and of his way of life inquir'd.
　Whereat he answer'd, that the gipsy crew,
　　His mates, had arts to rule as they desired
　　　The workings of men's brains;
　And they can bind them to what thoughts they will.
　　'And I,' he said, 'the secret of their art,
　　When fully learn'd, will to the world impart;
　But it needs heaven-sent moments for this skill.'

This said, he left them, and return'd no more.—
　But rumours hung about the country-side
　　That the lost Scholar long was seen to stray,
　Seen by rare glimpses, pensive and tongue-tied,
　　In hat of antique shape, and cloak of gray,
　　　The same the gipsies wore.
　Shepherds had met him on the Hurst in spring;
　　At some lone alehouse in the Berkshire moors,
　　On the warm ingle-bench, the smock-frock'd boors
　Had found him seated at their entering,

But, mid their drink and clatter, he would fly;—
　And I myself seem half to know thy looks,
　　And put the shepherds, wanderer, on thy trace;
　And boys who in lone wheatfields scare the rooks
　　I ask if thou hast pass'd their quiet place;
　　　Or in my boat I lie
　Moor'd to the cool bank in the summer heats,
　　Mid wide grass meadows which the sunshine fills,
　　And watch the warm green-muffled Cumner hills,
　And wonder if thou haunt'st their shy retreats.

For most, I know, thou lov'st retired ground!
  Thee, at the ferry, Oxford riders blithe,
    Returning home on summer nights, have met
  Crossing the stripling Thames at Bab-lock-hithe,
    Trailing in the cool stream thy fingers wet,
      As the slow punt swings round
  And leaning backward in a pensive dream,
    And fostering in thy lap a heap of flowers
    Pluck'd in shy fields and distant Wychwood bowers,
  And thine eyes resting on the moonlit stream!

And then they land, and thou art seen no more!
  Maidens who from the distant hamlets come
    To dance around the Fyfield elm in May,
  Oft through the darkening fields have seen thee roam,
    Or cross a stile into the public way.
      Oft thou hast given them store
  Of flowers—the frail-leaf'd, white anemone,
    Dark bluebells drench'd with dews of summer eves,
    And purple orchises with spotted leaves—
  But none has words she can report of thee.

And, above Godstow Bridge, when hay-time's here
  In June, and many a scythe in sunshine flames,
    Men who through those wide fields of breezy grass
  Where black-wing'd swallows haunt the glittering Thames,
    To bathe in the abandon'd lasher pass,
      Have often pass'd thee near
  Sitting upon the river bank o'ergrown;
    Mark'd thine outlandish garb, thy figure spare,
    Thy dark vague eyes, and soft abstracted air—
  But, when they came from bathing, thou wert gone!

At some lone homestead in the Cumner hills,
  Where at her open door the housewife darns,
    Thou hast been seen, or hanging on a gate
  To watch the threshers in the mossy barns.
    Children, who early range these slopes and late
      For cresses from the rills,
  Have known thee watching, all an April day,
    The springing pastures and the feeding kine;
    And mark'd thee, when the stars come out and shine,
  Through the long dewy grass move slow away.

In autumn, on the skirts of Bagley-wood,
  Where most the gipsies by the turf-edged way
    Pitch their smoked tents, and every bush you see
  With scarlet patches tagg'd and shreds of gray,
    Above the forest-ground call'd Thessaly—
      The blackbird picking food
  Sees thee, nor stops his meal, nor fears at all;
    So often has he known thee past him stray
    Rapt, twirling in thy hand a wither'd spray,
  And waiting for the spark from Heaven to fall.

And once, in winter, on the causeway chill
  Where home through flooded fields foot-travellers go,
    Have I not pass'd thee on the wooden bridge
  Wrapt in thy cloak and battling with the snow,
    Thy face towards Hinksey and its wintry ridge?
      And thou hast climb'd the hill
  And gain'd the white brow of the Cumner range;
    Turn'd once to watch, while thick the snowflakes fall,
    The line of festal light in Christ-Church hall—
  Then sought thy straw in some sequester'd grange.

But what—I dream! Two hundred years are flown
  Since first thy story ran through Oxford halls,
    And the grave Glanvil did the tale inscribe
  That thou wert wander'd from the studious walls
    To learn strange arts, and join a gipsy tribe.
      And thou from earth art gone
  Long since, and in some quiet churchyard laid!
    Some country nook, where o'er thy unknown grave
    Tall grasses and white flowering nettles wave—
  Under a dark red-fruited yew-tree's shade.

—No, no, thou hast not felt the lapse of hours!
  For what wears out the life of mortal men?
    'Tis that from change to change their being rolls;
  'Tis that repeated shocks, again, again,
    Exhaust the energy of strongest souls,
      And numb the elastic powers.
  Till having used our nerves with bliss and teen,
    And tired upon a thousand schemes our wit,
    To the just-pausing Genius we remit
  Our well-worn life, and are—what we have been!

Thou hast not lived, why shouldst thou perish, so?
  Thou hadst *one* aim, *one* business, *one* desire!
    Else wert thou long since number'd with the dead—
  Else hadst thou spent, like other men, thy fire!
    The generations of thy peers are fled,
      And we ourselves shall go;
  But thou possessest an immortal lot,
    And we imagine thee exempt from age
    And living as thou liv'st on Glanvil's page,
  Because thou hadst—what we, alas, have not!

For early didst thou leave the world, with powers
  Fresh, undiverted to the world without,
    Firm to their mark, not spent on other things;
  Free from the sick fatigue, the languid doubt,
    Which much to have tried, in much been baffled, brings.
      O life unlike to ours!
  Who fluctuate idly without term or scope,
    Of whom each strives, nor knows for what he strives,
    And each half lives a hundred different lives;
  Who wait like thee, but not, like thee, in hope.

Thou waitest for the spark from Heaven: and we,
  Vague half-believers of our casual creeds,
    Who never deeply felt, nor clearly will'd,
  Whose insight never has borne fruit in deeds,
    Whose weak resolves never have been fulfill'd;
      For whom each year we see
  Breeds new beginnings, disappointments new;
    Who hesitate and falter life away,
    And lose to-morrow the ground won to-day—
  Ah, do not we, wanderer, await it too?

Yes! we await it, but it still delays,
  And then we suffer! and amongst us one,
    Who most has suffer'd, takes dejectedly
  His seat upon the intellectual throne;
    And all his store of sad experience he
      Lays bare of wretched days;
  Tells us his misery's birth and growth and signs,
    And how the dying spark of hope was fed,
    And how the breast was soothed, and how the head,
  And all his hourly varied anodynes.

This for our wisest! and we others pine,
    And wish the long unhappy dream would end,
      And waive all claim to bliss, and try to bear
With close-lipp'd patience for our only friend,
      Sad patience, too near neighbour to despair;
        But none has hope like thine!
Thou through the fields and through the woods dost stray,
    Roaming the country-side, a truant boy,
    Nursing thy project in unclouded joy,
And every doubt long blown by time away.

O born in days when wits were fresh and clear,
    And life ran gaily as the sparkling Thames;
      Before this strange disease of modern life,
With its sick hurry, its divided aims,
      Its heads o'ertax'd, its palsied hearts, was rife—
        Fly hence, our contact fear!
Still fly, plunge deeper in the bowering wood!
    Averse, as Dido did with gesture stern
    From her false friend's approach in Hades turn,
Wave us away, and keep thy solitude!

Still nursing the unconquerable hope,
    Still clutching the inviolable shade,
      With a free onward impulse brushing through,
By night, the silver'd branches of the glade—
      Far on the forest-skirts, where none pursue,
        On some mild pastoral slope
Emerge, and resting on the moonlit pales,
    Freshen thy flowers, as in former years,
    With dew, or listen with enchanted ears,
From the dark dingles, to the nightingales!

But fly our paths, our feverish contact fly!
    For strong the infection of our mental strife,
      Which, though it gives no bliss, yet spoils for rest;
And we should win thee from thy own fair life,
      Like us distracted, and like us unblest!
        Soon, soon thy cheer would die,
Thy hopes grow timorous, and unfix'd thy powers,
    And thy clear aims be cross and shifting made;
    And then thy glad perennial youth would fade,
Fade, and grow old at last, and die like ours.

Then fly our greetings, fly our speech and smiles!
　—As some grave Tyrian trader, from the sea,
　　Descried at sunrise an emerging prow
　Lifting the cool-hair'd creepers stealthily,
　　The fringes of a southward-facing brow
　　　Among the Aegean isles;
　And saw the merry Grecian coaster come,
　　Freighted with amber grapes, and Chian wine,
　　Green bursting figs, and tunnies steep'd in brine;
　And knew the intruders on his ancient home,

The young light-hearted masters of the waves;
　And snatch'd his rudder, and shook out more sail,
　　And day and night held on indignantly
　O'er the blue Midland waters with the gale,
　　Betwixt the Syrtes and soft Sicily,
　　　To where the Atlantic raves
　Outside the western straits, and unbent sails
　　There, where down cloudy cliffs, through sheets of
　　　foam,
　　Shy traffickers, the dark Iberians come;
　And on the beach undid his corded bales.

Thyrsis

A MONODY, *to commemorate the author's friend*, ARTHUR HUGH CLOUGH
who died at Florence, 1861

> Thus yesterday, to-day, to-morrow come,
> They hustle one another and they pass;
> But all our hustling morrows only make
> The smooth to-day of God.
> 　　　　　*From* LUCRETIUS, *an unpublished Tragedy.*

How changed is here each spot man makes or fills!
　In the two Hinkseys nothing keeps the same;
　　The village-street its haunted mansion lacks,
　And from the sign is gone Sibylla's name,
　　And from the roofs the twisted chimney-stacks;
　　　Are ye too changed, ye hills?
　See, 'tis no foot of unfamiliar men
　　To-night from Oxford up your pathway strays!
　　Here came I often, often, in old days;
　Thyrsis and I; we still had Thyrsis then.

Runs it not here, the track by Childsworth Farm,
Up past the wood, to where the elm-tree crowns
The hill behind whose ridge the sunset flames?
The signal-elm, that looks on Ilsley Downs,
The Vale, the three lone weirs, the youthful Thames?—
This winter-eve is warm,
Humid the air; leafless, yet soft as spring,
The tender purple spray on copse and briers;
And that sweet City with her dreaming spires,
She needs not June for beauty's heightening,

Lovely all times she lies, lovely to-night!
Only, methinks, some loss of habit's power
Befalls me wandering through this upland dim;
Once pass'd I blindfold here, at any hour,
Now seldom come I, since I came with him.
That single elm-tree bright
Against the west—I miss it! is it gone?
We prized it dearly; while it stood, we said,
Our friend, the Scholar-Gipsy, was not dead;
While the tree lived, he in these fields lived on.

Too rare, too rare, grow now my visits here!
But once I knew each field, each flower, each stick;
And with the country-folk acquaintance made
By barn in threshing-time, by new-built rick.
Here, too, our shepherd-pipes we first assay'd.
Ah me! this many a year
My pipe is lost, my shepherd's-holiday!
Needs must I lose them, needs with heavy heart
Into the world and wave of men depart;
But Thyrsis of his own will went away.

It irk'd him to be here, he could not rest.
He loved each simple joy the country yields,
He loved his mates; but yet he could not keep,
For that a shadow lower'd on the fields,
Here with the shepherds and the silly sheep.
Some life of men unblest
He knew, which made him droop, and fill'd his head.
He went; his piping took a troubled sound
Of storms that rage outside our happy ground;
He could not wait their passing, he is dead!

So, some tempestuous morn in early June,
  When the year's primal burst of bloom is o'er,
    Before the roses and the longest day—
  When garden-walks, and all the grassy floor,
    With blossoms, red and white, of fallen May,
      And chestnut-flowers are strewn—
  So have I heard the cuckoo's parting cry,
    From the wet field, through the vext garden-trees,
    Come with the volleying rain and tossing breeze:
  The bloom is gone, and with the bloom go I.

Too quick despairer, wherefore wilt thou go?
  Soon will the high Midsummer pomps come on,
    Soon will the musk carnations break and swell,
  Soon shall we have gold-dusted snapdragon,
    Sweet-William with its homely cottage-smell,
      And stocks in fragrant blow;
  Roses that down the alleys shine afar,
    And open, jasmine-muffled lattices,
    And groups under the dreaming garden-trees,
  And the full moon, and the white evening-star.

He hearkens not! light comer, he is flown!
  What matters it? next year he will return,
    And we shall have him in the sweet spring-days,
  With whitening hedges, and uncrumpling fern,
    And blue-bells trembling by the forest-ways,
      And scent of hay new-mown.
  But Thyrsis never more we swains shall see!
    See him come back, and cut a smoother reed,
    And blow a strain the world at last shall heed—
  For Time, not Corydon, hath conquer'd thee.

Alack, for Corydon no rival now!—
  But when Sicilian shepherds lost a mate,
    Some good survivor with his flute would go,
  Piping a ditty sad for Bion's fate,
    And cross the unpermitted ferry's flow,
      And relax Pluto's brow,
  And make leap up with joy the beauteous head
    Of Proserpine, among whose crownèd hair
    Are flowers, first open'd on Sicilian air,
  And flute his friend, like Orpheus, from the dead.

O easy access to the hearer's grace
  When Dorian shepherds sang to Proserpine!
    For she herself had trod Sicilian fields,
  She knew the Dorian water's gush divine,
    She knew each lily white which Enna yields,
      Each rose with blushing face;
  She loved the Dorian pipe, the Dorian strain.
    But ah, of our poor Thames she never heard!
    Her foot the Cumner cowslips never stirr'd!
  And we should tease her with our plaint in vain.

Well! wind-dispers'd and vain the words will be,
  Yet, Thyrsis, let me give my grief its hour
    In the old haunt, and find our tree-topp'd hill!
  Who, if not I, for questing here hath power?
    I know the wood which hides the daffodil,
      I know the Fyfield tree,
  I know what white, what purple fritillaries
    The grassy harvest of the river-fields,
    Above by Ensham, down by Sandford, yields,
  And what sedg'd brooks are Thames's tributaries;

I know these slopes; who knows them if not I?—
  But many a dingle on the loved hill-side,
    With thorns once studded, old, white-blossom'd trees,
  Where thick the cowslips grew, and, far descried,
    High tower'd the spikes of purple orchises,
      Hath since our day put by
  The coronals of that forgotten time.
    Down each green bank hath gone the ploughboy's
      team,
    And only in the hidden brookside gleam
  Primroses, orphans of the flowery prime.

Where is the girl, who, by the boatman's door,
  Above the locks, above the boating throng,
    Unmoor'd our skiff, when, through the Wytham flats,
  Red loosestrife and blond meadow-sweet among,
    And darting swallows, and light water-gnats,
      We track'd the shy Thames shore?
  Where are the mowers, who, as the tiny swell
    Of our boat passing heav'd the river-grass,
    Stood with suspended scythe to see us pass?—
  They all are gone, and thou art gone as well.

Yes, thou art gone! and round me too the night
 In ever-nearing circle weaves her shade.
  I see her veil draw soft across the day,
 I feel her slowly chilling breath invade
   The cheek grown thin, the brown hair sprent with grey;
    I feel her finger light
 Laid pausefully upon life's headlong train;
   The foot less prompt to meet the morning dew,
   The heart less bounding at emotion new,
 And hope, once crush'd, less quick to spring again.

And long the way appears, which seem'd so short
 To the unpractis'd eye of sanguine youth;
  And high the mountain-tops, in cloudy air,
 The mountain-tops where is the throne of Truth,
   Tops in life's morning-sun so bright and bare!
    Unbreachable the fort
 Of the long-batter'd world uplifts its wall.
   And strange and vain the earthly turmoil grows,
   And near and real the charm of thy repose,
 And night as welcome as a friend would fall.

But hush! the upland hath a sudden loss
 Of quiet;—Look! adown the dusk hill-side,
  A troop of Oxford hunters going home,
 As in old days, jovial and talking, ride!
   From hunting with the Berkshire hounds they come—
    Quick, let me fly, and cross
 Into yon further field!—'Tis done; and see,
   Back'd by the sunset, which doth glorify
   The orange and pale violet evening-sky,
 Bare on its lonely ridge, the Tree! the Tree!

I take the omen! Eve lets down her veil,
 The white fog creeps from bush to bush about,
  The west unflushes, the high stars grow bright,
 And in the scatter'd farms the lights come out.
   I cannot reach the Signal-Tree to-night,
    Yet, happy omen, hail!
 Hear it from thy broad lucent Arno vale
   (For there thine earth-forgetting eyelids keep
   The morningless and unawakening sleep
 Under the flowery oleanders pale),

Hear it, O Thyrsis, still our Tree is there!—
　　Ah, vain! These English fields, this upland dim,
　　　These brambles pale with mist engarlanded,
　　That lone, sky-pointing tree, are not for him.
　　　To a boon southern country he is fled,
　　　　And now in happier air,
　　Wandering with the great Mother's train divine
　　　(And purer or more subtle soul than thee,
　　　I trow, the mighty Mother doth not see!)
　　Within a folding of the Apennine,

Thou hearest the immortal strains of old.
　　Putting his sickle to the perilous grain
　　　In the hot cornfield of the Phrygian king,
　　For thee the Lityerses song again
　　　Young Daphnis with his silver voice doth sing;
　　　　Sings his Sicilian fold,
　　His sheep, his hapless love, his blinded eyes;
　　　And how a call celestial round him rang
　　　And heavenward from the fountain-brink he sprang,
　　And all the marvel of the golden skies.

There thou art gone, and me thou leavest here
　　Sole in these fields; yet will I not despair;
　　　Despair I will not, while I yet descry
　　'Neath the soft canopy of English air
　　　That lonely Tree against the western sky.
　　　　Still, still these slopes, 'tis clear,
　　Our Gipsy-Scholar haunts, outliving thee!
　　　Fields where soft sheep from cages pull the hay,
　　　Woods with anemonies in flower till May,
　　Know him a wanderer still; then why not me?

A fugitive and gracious light he seeks,
　　Shy to illumine; and I seek it too.
　　　This does not come with houses or with gold,
　　With place, with honour, and a flattering crew;
　　　'Tis not in the world's market bought and sold.
　　　　But the smooth-slipping weeks
　　Drop by, and leave its seeker still untired;
　　　Out of the heed of mortals he is gone,
　　　He wends unfollow'd, he must house alone;
　　Yet on he fares, by his own heart inspired.

360

Thou too, O Thyrsis, on like quest wert bound,
  Thou wanderedst with me for a little hour;
    Men gave thee nothing, but this happy quest,
If men esteem'd thee feeble, gave thee power,
    If men procured thee trouble, gave thee rest.
      And this rude Cumner ground,
  Its fir-topped Hurst, its farms, its quiet fields,
    Here cam'st thou in thy jocund youthful time,
    Here was thine height of strength, thy golden prime;
And still the haunt beloved a virtue yields.

What though the music of thy rustic flute
  Kept not for long its happy, country tone,
    Lost it too soon, and learnt a stormy note
Of men contention-tost, of men who groan,
    Which task'd thy pipe too sore, and tired thy throat—
      It fail'd, and thou wast mute,
  Yet hadst thou alway visions of our light,
    And long with men of care thou couldst not stay,
    And soon thy foot resumed its wandering way,
Left human haunt, and on alone till night.

Too rare, too rare, grow now my visits here!
  'Mid city-noise, not, as with thee of yore,
    Thyrsis, in reach of sheep-bells is my home!
Then through the great town's harsh, heart-wearying
      roar,
    Let in thy voice a whisper often come,
      To chase fatigue and fear:
  Why faintest thou? I wander'd till I died.
    Roam on! the light we sought is shining still.
    Dost thou ask proof? Our Tree yet crowns the hill,
Our Scholar travels yet the loved hillside.

Dover Beach

The sea is calm to-night.
The tide is full, the moon lies fair
Upon the Straits;—on the French coast the light
Gleams and is gone; the cliffs of England stand,
Glimmering and vast, out in the tranquil bay.
Come to the window, sweet is the night-air!

Only, from the long line of spray
Where the sea meets the moon-blanch'd sand,
Listen! You hear the grating roar
Of pebbles which the waves suck back, and fling,
At their return, up the high strand,
Begin, and cease, and then again begin,
With tremulous cadence slow, and bring
The eternal note of sadness in.

Sophocles long ago
Heard it on the Aegean, and it brought
Into his mind the turbid ebb and flow
Of human misery; we
Find also in the sound a thought,
Hearing it by this distant northern sea.

The sea of faith
Was once, too, at the full, and round earth's shore
Lay like the folds of a bright girdle furl'd.
But now I only hear
Its melancholy, long, withdrawing roar,
Retreating to the breath
Of the night-wind down the vast edges drear
And naked shingles of the world.

Ah, love, let us be true
To one another! for the world, which seems
To lie before us like a land of dreams,
So various, so beautiful, so new,
Hath really neither joy, nor love, nor light,
Nor certitude, nor peace, nor help for pain;
And we are here as on a darkling plain
Swept with confused alarms of struggle and flight,
Where ignorant armies clash by night.

THOMAS HARDY
1840-1928

The Oxen

Christmas Eve, and twelve of the clock.
　'Now they are all on their knees,'
An elder said as we sat in a flock
　By the embers in hearthside ease.

We pictured the meek mild creatures where
　They dwelt in their strawy pen,
Nor did it occur to one of us there
　To doubt they were kneeling then.

So fair a fancy few would weave
　In these years! Yet, I feel,
If someone said on Christmas Eve,
　'Come; see the oxen kneel.

In the lonely barton by yonder coomb
　Our children used to know,'
I should go with him in the gloom,
　Hoping it might be so.

When I set out for Lyonnesse

When I set out for Lyonnesse,
　A hundred miles away,
　The rime was on the spray,
And starlight lit my lonesomeness
When I set out for Lyonnesse
　A hundred miles away.

What would bechance at Lyonnesse
　　While I should sojourn there
　　No prophet durst declare,
Nor did the wisest wizard guess
What would bechance at Lyonnesse
　　While I should sojourn there.

When I came back from Lyonnesse
　　With magic in my eyes,
　　All marked with mute surmise
My radiance rare and fathomless,
When I came back from Lyonnesse
　　With magic in my eyes!

Snow in the Suburbs

Every branch big with it,
　　Bent every twig with it;
Every fork like a white web-foot;
Every street and pavement mute:
Some flakes have lost their way, and grope back upward, when
Meeting those meandering down they turn and descend again.
　　The palings are glued together like a wall,
　　And there is no waft of wind with the fleecy fall.

A sparrow enters the tree,
　　Whereon immediately
A snow-lump thrice his own slight size
Descends on him and showers his head and eyes,
　　And overturns him,
　　And near inurns him,
And lights on a nether twig, when its brush
Starts off a volley of other lodging lumps with a rush.

The steps are a blanched slope,
　　Up which, with feeble hope,
A black cat comes, wide-eyed and thin;
　　And we take him in.

In Time of 'The Breaking of Nations'

I

Only a man harrowing clods
　In a slow silent walk
With an old horse that stumbles and nods
　Half asleep as they stalk.

II

Only thin smoke without flame
　From the heaps of couch grass;
Yet this will go onward the same
　Though Dynasties pass.

III

Yonder a maid and her wight
　Come whispering by:
War's annals will fade into night
　Ere their story die.

The Darkling Thrush

I leant upon a coppice gate
　When Frost was spectre-grey,
And Winter's dregs made desolate
　The weakening eye of day.
The tangled bine-stems scored the sky
　Like strings from broken lyres,
And all mankind that haunted nigh
　Had sought their household fires.

The land's sharp features seemed to be
　The Century's corpse outleant,
His crypt the cloudy canopy,
　The wind his death-lament,
The ancient pulse of germ and birth
　Was shrunken hard and dry,
And every spirit upon earth
　Seemed fervourless as I.

At once a voice arose among
    The bleak twigs overhead
In a full-hearted evensong
    Of joy illimited;
An aged thrush, frail, gaunt, and small,
    In blast-beruffled plume,
Has chosen thus to fling his soul
    Upon the growing gloom.

So little cause for carollings
    Of such ecstatic sound
Was written on terrestrial things
    Afar or nigh around,
That I could think there trembled through
    His happy good-night air
Some blessed Hope, whereof he knew
    And I was unaware.

We Field Women

How it rained
When we worked at Flintcomb-Ash,
And could not stand upon the hill
Trimming swedes for the slicing-mill.
The wet washed through us—plash, plash, plash:
    How it rained!

How it snowed
When we crossed from Flintcomb-Ash
To the Great Barn for drawing reed,
Since, we could nowise chop a swede.—
Flakes in each doorway and casement-sash:
    How it snowed!

How it shone
When we went from Flintcomb-Ash
To start at dairywork once more
In the laughing meads, with cows three-score,
And pails, and songs, and love—too rash:
    How it shone!

GERARD MANLEY HOPKINS
1844-1889

Inversnaid

This darksome burn, horseback brown,
His rollrock highroad roaring down,
In coop and in comb the fleece of his foam
Flutes and low to the lake falls home.

A windpuff-bonnet of fawn-froth
Turns and twindles over the broth
Of a pool so pitchblack, fell-frowning,
It rounds and rounds Despair to drowning.

Degged with dew, dappled with dew
Are the groins of the braes that the brook treads through,
Wiry heathpacks, flitches of fern,
And the beadbonny ash that sits over the burn.

What would the world be, once bereft
Of wet and of wildness? Let them be left,
O let them be left, wildness and wet;
Long live the weeds and the wilderness yet.

Pied Beauty

Glory be to God for dappled things—
  For skies of couple-colour as a brindled cow;
    For rose-moles all in stipple upon trout that swim;
Fresh-firecoal chestnut-falls; finches' wings;
    Landscape plotted and pieced—fold, fallow and plough;
    And all trades, their gear and tackle and trim.

All things counter, original, spare, strange;
  Whatever is fickle, freckled (who knows how?)
    With swift, slow; sweet, sour; adazzle, dim;
He fathers-forth whose beauty is past change:
        Praise Him.

ROBERT BRIDGES

1844-1930

A Passer-by

Whither, O splendid ship, thy white sails crowding,
   Leaning across the bosom of the urgent West,
That fearest nor sea rising, nor sky clouding,
   Whither away, fair rover, and what thy quest?
   Ah! soon, when Winter has all our vales opprest,
When skies are cold and misty, and hail is hurling,
   Wilt thou glide on the blue Pacific, or rest
In a summer haven asleep, thy white sails furling.

I there before thee, in the country that well thou knowest,
   Already arrived am inhaling the odorous air:
I watch thee enter unerringly where thou goest,
   And anchor queen of the strange shipping there,
   Thy sails for awnings spread, thy masts bare;
Nor is aught from the foaming reef to the snow-capped,
      grandest
   Peak, that is over the feathery palms more fair
Than thou, so upright, so stately, and still thou standest.

And yet, O splendid ship, unhailed and nameless,
   I know not if, aiming a fancy, I rightly divine
That thou hast a purpose joyful, a courage blameless,
   Thy port assured in a happier land than mine.
   But for all I have given thee, beauty enough is thine,
As thou, aslant with trim tackle and shrouding,
   From the proud nostril curve of a prow's line
In the offing scatterest foam, thy white sails crowding.

Nightingales

Beautiful must be the mountains whence ye come,
And bright in the fruitful valleys the streams, wherefrom
　　　Ye learn your song:
Where are those starry woods? O might I wander there,
　Among the flowers, which in that heavenly air
　　　Bloom the year long!

Nay, barren are those mountains and spent the streams:
Our song is the voice of desire, that haunts our dreams,
　　　A throe of the heart,
Whose pining visions dim, forbidden hopes profound,
　No dying cadence nor long sigh can sound,
　　　For all our art.

Alone, aloud in the raptured ear of men
We pour our dark nocturnal secret; and then,
　　　As night is withdrawn
From these sweet-springing meads and bursting boughs of
　　May,
　Dream, while the innumerable choir of day
　　　Welcome the dawn.

Triolet

When first we met we did not guess
That Love would prove so hard a master;
Of more than common friendliness
When first we met we did not guess.
Who could foretell this sore distress,
This irretrievable disaster
When first we met?—We did not guess
That Love would prove so hard a master.

Triolet

All women born are so perverse
No man need boast their love possessing.
If nought seem better, nothing's worse;
All women born are so perverse.

From Adam's wife, that proved a curse
Though God had made her for a blessing,
All women born are so perverse
No man need boast their love possessing.

London Snow

When men were all asleep the snow came flying,
In large white flakes falling on the city brown,
Stealthily and perpetually settling and loosely lying,
   Hushing the latest traffic of the drowsy town;
Deadening, muffling, stifling its murmurs failing;
Lazily and incessantly floating down and down:
   Silently sifting and veiling road, roof and railing;
Hiding difference, making unevenness even,
Into angles and crevices softly drifting and sailing.
   All night it fell, and when full inches seven
It lay in the depth of its uncompacted lightness,
The clouds blew off from a high and frosty heaven;
   And all woke earlier for the unaccustomed brightness
Of the winter dawning, the strange unheavenly glare:
The eye marvelled—marvelled at the dazzling whiteness;
   The ear hearkened to the stillness of the solemn air,
No sound of wheel rumbling nor of foot falling,
And the busy morning cries came thin and spare.
   Then boys I heard, as they went to school, calling,
They gathered up the crystal manna to freeze
Their tongues with tasting, their hands with snowballing;
   Or rioted in a drift, plunging up to the knees;
Or peering up from under the white-mossed wonder,
'O look at the trees!' they cried, 'O look at the trees!'
   With lessened load a few carts creak and blunder,
Following along the white deserted way,
A country company long dispersed asunder:
   When now already the sun, in pale display
Standing by Paul's high dome, spread forth below
His sparkling beams, and awoke the stir of the day.
   For now doors open, and war is waged with the snow;
And trains of sombre men, past tale of number,
Tread long brown paths, as toward their toil they go:

But even for them awhile no cares encumber
Their minds diverted; the daily word is unspoken,
The daily thoughts of labour and sorrow slumber
At the sight of the beauty that greets them, for the charm
    they have broken.

I Never Shall Love the Snow Again

I never shall love the snow again
    Since Maurice died:
With corniced drift it blocked the lane,
And sheeted in a desolate plain
    The country side.

The trees with silvery rime bedight
    Their branches bare.
By day no sun appeared; by night
The hidden moon shed thievish light
    In the misty air.

We fed the birds that flew around
    In flocks to be fed:
No shelter in holly or brake they found.
The speckled thrush on the frozen ground
    Lay frozen and dead.

We skated on stream and pond; we cut
    The crinching snow
To Doric temple or Arctic hut;
We laughed and sang at nightfall, shut
    By the fireside glow.

Yet grudged we our keen delights before
    Maurice should come.
We said, In-door or out-of-door
We shall love life for a month or more,
    When he is home.

They brought him home; 'twas two days late
    For Christmas day:
Wrapped in white, in solemn state,
A flower in his hand, all still and straight
    Our Maurice lay.

And two days ere the year outgave
    We laid him low.
The best of us truly were not brave,
When we laid Maurice down in his grave
    Under the snow.

Awake, my Heart

Awake, my heart, to be loved, awake, awake!
The darkness silvers away, the morn doth break,
It leaps in the sky: unrisen lustres slake
The o'ertaken moon. Awake, O heart, awake!

She too that loveth awaketh and hopes for thee;
Her eyes already have sped the shades that flee,
Already they watch the path thy feet shall take:
Awake, O heart, to be loved, awake, awake!

And if thou tarry from her,—if this could be,—
She cometh herself, O heart, to be loved, to thee;
For thee would unashamèd herself forsake:
Awake to be loved, my heart, awake, awake!

Awake, the land is scattered with light, and see,
Uncanopied sleep is flying from field and tree;
And blossoming boughs of April in laughter shake;
Awake, O heart, to be loved, awake, awake!

Lo all things wake and tarry and look for thee:
She looketh and saith, 'O sun, now bring him to me
Come more adored, O adored, for his coming's sake,
And awake my heart to be loved: awake, awake!'

A. E. HOUSMAN
1859-1936

The Chestnut casts his Flambeaux

The chestnut casts his flambeaux, and the flowers
  Stream from the hawthorn in the wind away,
The doors clap to, the pane is blind with showers.
  Pass me the can, lad; there's an end of May.

There's one spoilt spring to scant our mortal lot,
  One season ruined of our little store.
May will be fine next year as like as not:
  Oh ay, but then we shall be twenty-four.

We for a certainty are not the first
  Have sat in taverns while the tempest hurled
Their hopeful plans to emptiness, and cursed
  Whatever brute and blackguard made the world.

It is in truth iniquity on high
  To cheat our sentenced souls of aught they crave,
And mar the merriment as you and I
  Fare on our long fool's errand to the grave.

Iniquity it is; but pass the can.
  My lad, no pair of kings our mother bore;
Our only portion is the estate of man:
  We want the moon, but we shall get no more.

If here to-day the cloud of thunder lours
  To-morrow it will hie on far behests;
The flesh will grieve on other bones than ours
  Soon, and the soul will mourn in other breasts.

The troubles of our proud and angry dust
  Are from eternity, and shall not fail.
Bear them we can, and if we can we must.
  Shoulder the sky, my lad, and drink your ale.

Bredon Hill

In summertime in Bredon
  The bells they sound so clear;
Round both the shires they ring them
  In steeples far and near,
  A happy noise to hear.

Here of a Sunday morning
  My love and I would lie,
And see the coloured counties,
  And hear the larks so high
  About us in the sky.

The bells would ring to call her
  In valleys miles away:
'Come all to church, good people;
Good people come and pray.'
  But here my love would stay.

And I would turn and answer
  Among the springing thyme,
'Oh, peal upon our wedding,
  And we will hear the chime,
  And come to church in time.'

But when the snows at Christmas
  On Bredon top were strown,
My love rose up so early
  And stole out unbeknown
  And went to church alone.

They tolled the one bell only,
  Groom was there none to see,
The mourners followed after,
  And so to church went she,
  And would not wait for me.

The bells they sound on Bredon,
  And still the steeples hum.
'Come all to church, good people,'—
  Oh, noisy bells, be dumb;
  I hear you, I will come.

On Wenlock Edge

On Wenlock Edge the wood's in trouble;
   His forest fleece the Wrekin heaves;
The gale, it plies the saplings double,
   And thick on Severn snow the leaves.

'Twould blow like this through holt and hanger
   When Uricon the city stood:
'Tis the old wind in the old anger,
   But then it threshed another wood.

Then, 'twas before my time, the Roman
   At yonder heaving hill would stare:
The blood that warms an English yeoman,
   The thoughts that hurt him, they were there.

There, like the wind through woods in riot,
   Through him the gale of life blew high;
The tree of man was never quiet:
   Then 'twas the Roman, now 'tis I.

The gale, it plies the saplings double,
   It blows so hard, 'twill soon be gone:
To-day the Roman and his trouble
   Are ashes under Uricon.

Loveliest of Trees, the Cherry now

Loveliest of trees, the cherry now
Is hung with bloom along the bough,
And stands about the woodland ride
Wearing white for Eastertide.

Now, of my threescore years and ten,
Twenty will not come again,
And take from seventy springs a score,
It only leaves me fifty more.

And since to look at things in bloom
Fifty springs are little room,
About the woodlands I will go
To see the cherry hung with snow.

Yonder see the Morning blink

Yonder see the morning blink:
    The sun is up, and up must I,
To wash and dress and eat and drink
And look at things and talk and think
    And work, and God knows why.

Oh often have I washed and dressed
    And what's to show for all my pain?
Let me lie abed and rest:
Ten thousand times I've done my best
    And all's to do again.

WILLIAM BUTLER YEATS
1865-1939

The Wild Swans at Coole

The trees are in their autumn beauty,
The woodland paths are dry,
Under the October twilight the water
Mirrors a still sky;
Upon the brimming water among the stones
Are nine and fifty swans.

The nineteenth autumn has come upon me
Since I first made my count;
I saw, before I had well finished,
All suddenly mount
And scatter wheeling in great broken rings
Upon their clamorous wings.

I have looked upon these brilliant creatures,
And now my heart is sore.
All's changed since I, hearing at twilight,
The first time on this shore,
The bell-beat of their wings above my head,
Trod with a lighter tread.

Unwearied still, lover by lover,
They paddle in the cold
Companionable streams or climb the air;
Their hearts have not grown old;
Passion or conquest, wander where they will,
Attend upon them still.

But now they drift on the still water,
Mysterious, beautiful;
Among what rushes they will build,
By what lake's edge or pool
Delight men's eyes when I awake some day
To find they have flown away?

Easter, 1916

I have met them at close of day
Coming with vivid faces
From counter or desk among grey
Eighteenth century houses.
I have passed with a nod of the head
Or polite, meaningless words,
Or have lingered awhile and said
Polite meaningless words,
And thought before I had done
Of a mocking tale or a jibe
To please a companion
Around the fire at the club,
Being certain that they and I
But lived where motley is worn:
All changed, changed utterly:
A terrible beauty is born.

That woman's days were spent
In ignorant good-will,
Her nights in argument
Until her voice grew shrill.
What voice more sweet than hers
When, young and beautiful,
She rode to harriers?
This man had kept a school
And rode our winged horse;
This other his helper and friend
Was coming into his force;
He might have won fame in the end,
So sensitive his nature seemed,
So daring and sweet his thought.
This other man I had dreamed
A drunken, vainglorious lout.
He had done most bitter wrong
To some who are near my heart,
Yet I number him in the song;
He, too, has resigned his part
In the casual comedy;
He, too, has been changed in his turn,
Transformed utterly:
A terrible beauty is born.

Hearts with one purpose alone
Through summer and winter seem
Enchanted to a stone
To trouble the living stream.
The horse that comes from the road,
The rider, the birds that range
From cloud to tumbling cloud,
Minute by minute they change;
A shadow of cloud on the stream
Changes minute by minute;
A horse-hoof slides on the brim,
And a horse plashes within it;
The long-legged moor-cocks call;
Minute by minute they live:
The stone's in the midst of all.

Too long a sacrifice
Can make a stone of the heart.
O when may it suffice?
That is Heaven's part, our part
To murmur name upon name,
As a mother names her child
When sleep at last has come
On limbs that had run wild.
What is it but nightfall?
No, no, not night but death;
Was it needless death after all?
For England may keep faith
For all that is done and said.
We know their dream; enough
To know they dreamed and are dead;
And what if excess of love
Bewildered them till they died?
I write it out in a verse—
MacDonagh and MacBride
And Connolly and Pearse
Now and in time to be
Wherever green is worn,
Are changed, changed utterly:
A terrible beauty is born.

An Irish Airman foresees his Death

I know that I shall meet my fate
Somewhere among the clouds above;
Those that I fight I do not hate,
Those that I guard I do not love;
My country is Kiltartan Cross,
My countrymen Kiltartan's poor,
No likely end could bring them loss
Or leave them happier than before.
Nor law nor duty bade me fight,
Nor public men, nor cheering crowds,
A lonely impulse of delight
Drove to this tumult in the clouds;
I balanced all, brought all to mind,
The years to come seemed waste of breath,
A waste of breath the years behind
In balance with this life, this death.

Sailing to Byzantium

That is no country for old men. The young
In one another's arms, birds in the trees,
—Those dying generations—at their song,
The salmon-falls, the mackerel-crowded seas,
Fish, flesh, or fowl, commend all summer long
Whatever is begotten, born, and dies.
Caught in that sensual music all neglect
Monuments of unaging intellect.

An aged man is but a paltry thing,
A tattered coat upon a stick, unless
Soul clap its hands and sing, and louder sing
For every tatter in its mortal dress,
Nor is there any singing school but studying
Monuments of its own magnificence;
And therefore have I sailed the seas and come
To the holy city of Byzantium.

O sages standing in God's holy fire
As in the gold mosaic of a wall,
Come from the holy fire, perne in a gyre,
And be the singing-masters of my soul.
Consume my heart away; sick with desire
And fastened to a dying animal
It knows not what it is; and gather me
Into the artifice of eternity.

Once out of nature I shall never take
My bodily form from any natural thing,
But such a form as Grecian goldsmiths make
Of hammered gold and gold enamelling
To keep a drowsy Emperor awake;
Or set upon a golden bough to sing
To lords and ladies of Byzantium
Of what is past, or passing, or to come.

A Prayer for my Daughter

Once more the storm is howling, and half hid
Under this cradle-hood and coverlid
My child sleeps on. There is no obstacle
But Gregory's wood and one bare hill
Whereby the haystack- and roof-levelling wind
Bred on the Atlantic, can be stayed;
And for an hour I have walked and prayed
Because of the great gloom that is in my mind.

I have walked and prayed for this young child an hour
And heard the sea-wind scream upon the tower,
And under the arches of the bridge, and scream
In the elms above the flooded stream;
Imagining in excited reverie
That the future years had come,
Dancing to a frenzied drum,
Out of the murderous innocence of the sea.

May she be granted beauty and yet not
Beauty to make a stranger's eye distraught,

Or hers before a looking-glass, for such,
Being made beautiful overmuch,
Consider beauty a sufficient end,
Lose natural kindness and maybe
The heart-revealing intimacy
That chooses right, and never find a friend.

Helen being chosen found life flat and dull
And later had much trouble from a fool,
While that great Queen, that rose out of the spray,
Being fatherless could have her way
Yet chose a bandy-leggèd smith for man.
It's certain that fine women eat
A crazy salad with their meat
Whereby the Horn of Plenty is undone.

In courtesy I'd have her chiefly learned;
Hearts are not had as a gift but hearts are earned
By those that are not entirely beautiful;
Yet many, that have played the fool
For beauty's very self, has charm made wise
And many a poor man that has roved,
Loved and thought himself beloved,
From a glad kindness cannot take his eyes.

May she become a flourishing hidden tree
That all her thoughts may like the linnet be,
And have no business but dispensing round
Their magnanimities of sound,
Nor but in merriment begin a chase,
Nor but in merriment a quarrel.
O may she live like some green laurel
Rooted in one dear perpetual place.

My mind, because the minds that I have loved,
The sort of beauty that I have approved,
Prosper but little, has dried up of late,
Yet knows that to be choked with hate
May well be of all evil chances chief.
If there's no hatred in a mind
Assault and battery of the wind
Can never tear the linnet from the leaf.

An intellectual hatred is the worst,
So let her think opinions are accursed.
Have I not seen the loveliest woman born
Out of the mouth of Plenty's horn,
Because of her opinionated mind
Barter that horn and every good
By quiet natures understood
For an old bellows full of angry wind?

Considering that, all hatred driven hence,
The soul recovers radical innocence
And learns at last that it is self-delighting
Self-appeasing, self-affrighting,
And that its own sweet will is Heaven's will;
She can, though every face should scowl
And every windy quarter howl
Or every bellows burst, be happy still.

And may her bridegroom bring her to a house
Where all's accustomed, ceremonious;
For arrogance and hatred are the wares
Peddled in the thoroughfares.
How but in custom and in ceremony
Are innocence and beauty born?
Ceremony's a name for the rich horn,
And custom for the spreading laurel tree.

JAMES ELROY FLECKER
1884-1915

The Old Ships

I have seen old ships sail like swans asleep
Beyond the village which men still call Tyre,
With leaden age o'ercargoed, dipping deep
For Famagusta and the hidden sun
That rings black Cyprus with a lake of fire;
And all those ships were certainly so old—
Who knows how oft with squat and noisy gun,
Questing brown slaves or Syrian oranges,
The pirate Genoese
Hell-raked them till they rolled
Blood, water, fruit and corpses up the hold.
But now through friendly seas they softly run,
Painted the mid-sea blue or shore-sea green,
Still patterned with the vine and grapes in gold.

But I have seen,
Pointing her shapely shadows from the dawn
And image tumbled on a rose-swept bay,
A drowsy ship of some yet older day;
And, wonder's breath indrawn,
Thought I—who knows—who knows—but in that same
(Fished up beyond Aeaea, patched up new
—Stern painted brighter blue—)
That talkative, bald-headed seaman came
(Twelve patient comrades sweating at the oar)
From Troy's doom-crimson shore,
And with great lies about his wooden horse
Set the crew laughing, and forgot his course.
It was so old a ship—who knows—who knows?
—And yet so beautiful, I watched in vain
To see the mast burst open with a rose,
And the whole deck put on its leaves again.

RUPERT BROOKE

1887-1915

The Old Vicarage, Grantchester

CAFÉ DES WESTENS, BERLIN

Just now the lilac is in bloom,
All before my little room;
And in my flower-beds, I think,
Smile the carnation and the pink;
And down the borders, well I know,
The poppy and the pansy blow. . . .
Oh! there the chestnuts, summer through,
Beside the river make for you
A tunnel of green gloom, and sleep
Deeply above; and green and deep
The stream mysterious glides beneath,
Green as a dream and deep as death.
—Oh, damn! I know it! and I know
How the May fields all golden show,
And when the day is young and sweet,
Gild gloriously the bare feet
That run to bathe . . .
            Du lieber Gott!

Here am I, sweating, sick, and hot,
And there the shadowed waters fresh
Lean up to embrace the naked flesh.
Temperamentvoll German Jews
Drink beer around;—and *there* the dews
Are soft beneath a morn of gold.
Here tulips bloom as they are told;
Unkempt about those hedges blows
An English unofficial rose;
And there the unregulated sun
Slopes down to rest when day is done,

And wakes a vague unpunctual star,
A slippered Hesper; and there are
Meads towards Haslingfield and Coton
Where *das Betreten*'s not *verboten*. . . .

εἴθε γενοίμην . . . would I were
In Grantchester, in Grantchester!—
Some, it may be, can get in touch
With Nature there, or Earth, or such.
And clever modern men have seen
A Faun a-peeping through the green,
And felt the Classics were not dead,
To glimpse a Naiad's reedy head,
Or hear the Goat-foot piping low: . . .
But these are things I do not know.
I only know that you may lie
Day long and watch the Cambridge sky,
And, flower-lulled in sleepy grass,
Hear the cool lapse of hours pass,
Until the centuries blend and blur
In Grantchester, in Grantchester. . . .
Still in the dawnlit waters cool
His ghostly Lordship swims his pool,
And tries the strokes, essays the tricks,
Long learnt on Hellespont, or Styx;
Dan Chaucer hears his river still
Chatter beneath a phantom mill.
Tennyson notes, with studious eye,
How Cambridge waters hurry by. . . .
And in that garden, black and white
Creep whispers through the grass all night,
And spectral dance, before the dawn,
A hundred Vicars down the lawn;
Curates, long dust, will come and go
On lissom, clerical, printless toe;
And oft between the boughs is seen
The sly shade of a Rural Dean. . . .
Till, at a shiver in the skies
Vanishing with Satanic cries,
The prim ecclesiastic rout
Leaves but a startled sleeper-out,

Grey heavens, the first bird's drowsy calls,
The falling house that never falls.

God! I will pack, and take a train,
And get me to England once again!
For England's the one land, I know,
Where men with Splendid Hearts may go;
And Cambridgeshire, of all England,
The shire for Men who Understand;
And of *that* district I prefer
The lovely hamlet, Grantchester.
For Cambridge people rarely smile,
Being urban, squat, and packed with guile;
And Royston men in the far South
Are black and fierce and strange of mouth;
At Over they fling oaths at one,
And worse than oaths at Trumpington,
And Ditton girls are mean and dirty,
And there's none in Harston under thirty,
And folks in Shelford and those parts
Have twisted lips and twisted hearts,
And Barton men make Cockney rhymes,
And Coton's full of nameless crimes,
And things are done you'd not believe
At Madingley, on Christmas Eve.
Strong men have run for miles and miles,
When one from Cherry Hinton smiles;
Strong men have blanched, and shot their wives
Rather than send them to St. Ives;
Strong men have cried like babes, bydam,
To hear what happened at Babraham.
But Grantchester! ah, Grantchester!
There's peace and holy quiet there,
Great clouds along pacific skies,
And men and women with straight eyes,
Lithe children lovelier than a dream,
A bosky wood, a slumbrous stream,
And little kindly winds that creep
Round twilight corners, half asleep.
In Grantchester their skins are white,
They bathe by day, they bathe by night;

The women there do all they ought;
The men observe the Rules of Thought.
They love the Good; they worship Truth;
They laugh uproariously in youth;
(And when they get to feeling old,
They up and shoot themselves, I'm told) . . .

Ah God! to see the branches stir,
Across the moon at Grantchester!
To smell the thrilling-sweet and rotten
Unforgettable, unforgotten
River-smell, and hear the breeze
Sobbing in the little trees.
Say, do the elm-clumps greatly stand,
Still guardians of that holy land?
The chestnuts shade, in reverend dream,
The yet unacademic stream?
Is dawn a secret shy and cold
Anadyomene, silver-gold?
And sunset still a golden sea
From Haslingfield to Madingley?
And after, ere the night is born,
Do hares come out about the corn?
Oh, is the water sweet and cool
Gentle and brown, above the pool?
And laughs the immortal river still
Under the mill, under the mill?
Say, is there Beauty yet to find?
And Certainty? and Quiet kind?
Deep meadows yet, for to forget
The lies, and truths, and pain—oh! yet
Stands the Church clock at ten to three?
And is there honey still for tea?

Heaven

Fish (fly-replete, in depth of June,
Dawdling away their wat'ry noon)
Ponder deep wisdom, dark or clear,
Each secret fishy hope or fear.

Fish say, they have their Stream and Pond;
But is there anything Beyond?
This life cannot be All, they swear,
For how unpleasant, if it were!
One may not doubt that, somehow, Good
Shall come of Water and of Mud;
And, sure, the reverent eye must see
A purpose in Liquidity.
We darkly know, by Faith we cry,
The future is not Wholly Dry.
Mud unto mud!—Death eddies near—
Not here the appointed End, not here!
But somewhere, beyond Space and Time,
Is wetter water, slimier slime!
And there (they trust) there swimmeth One
Who swam ere rivers were begun,
Immense, of fishy form and mind,
Squamous, omnipotent, and kind;
And under that Almighty Fin,
The littlest fish may enter in.
Oh! never fly conceals a hook,
Fish say, in the eternal Brook,
But more than mundane weeks are there,
And mud, celestially fair;
Fat caterpillars drift around,
And Paradisal grubs are found;
Unfading moths, immortal flies,
And the worm that never dies.
And in that Heaven of all their wish,
There shall be no more land, say fish.

The Dead

Blow out, you bugles, over the rich Dead!
   There's none of these so lonely and poor of old,
But, dying, has made us rarer gifts than gold.
   These laid the world away; poured out the red
Sweet wine of youth; gave up the years to be
   Of work and joy, and that unhoped serene,
That men call age; and those that would have been,

Their sons, they gave, their immortality.
Blow, bugles, blow! They brought us, for our dearth,
    Holiness, lacked so long, and Love, and Pain.
Honour has come back, as a king, to earth,
    And paid his subjects with a royal wage;
And Nobleness walks in our ways again;
    And we have come into our heritage.

THOMAS STEARNS ELIOT
1888 – 1965.

Preludes

I

The winter evening settles down
With smell of steaks in passageways.
Six o'clock.
The burnt-out ends of smoky days.
And now a gusty shower wraps
The grimy scraps
Of withered leaves about your feet
And newspapers from vacant lots;
The showers beat
On broken blinds and chimney-pots,
And at the corner of the street
A lonely cab-horse steams and stamps.
And then the lighting of the lamps.

II

The morning comes to consciousness
Of faint stale smells of beer
From the sawdust-trampled street
With all its muddy feet that press
To early coffee-stands.
With the other masquerades
That time resumes,
One thinks of all the hands
That are raising dingy shades
In a thousand furnished rooms.

III

You tossed a blanket from the bed,
You lay upon your back, and waited;
You dozed, and watched the night revealing
The thousand sordid images
Of which your soul was constituted;

They flickered against the ceiling.
And when all the world came back
And the light crept up between the shutters
And you heard the sparrows in the gutters,
You had such a vision of the street
As the street hardly understands;
Sitting along the bed's edge, where
You curled the papers from your hair,
Or clasped the yellow soles of feet
In the palms of both soiled hands.

IV

His soul stretched tight across the skies
That fade behind a city block,
Or trampled by insistent feet
At four and five and six o'clock;
And short square fingers stuffing pipes,
And evening newspapers, and eyes
Assured of certain certainties,
The conscience of a blackened street
Impatient to assume the world.

I am moved by fancies that are curled
Around these images, and cling:
The notion of some infinitely gentle
Infinitely suffering thing.

Wipe your hand across your mouth, and laugh,
The worlds revolve like ancient women
Gathering fuel in vacant lots.

Morning at the Window

They are rattling breakfast plates in basement kitchens,
And along the trampled edges of the street
I am aware of the damp souls of housemaids
Sprouting despondently at area gates.

The brown waves of fog toss up to me
Twisted faces from the bottom of the street,
And tear from a passer-by with muddy skirts
An aimless smile that hovers in the air
And vanishes along the level of the roofs.

La Figlia che Piange

O quam te memorem virgo . . . O dea certe!

Stand on the highest pavement of the stair—
Lean on a garden urn—
Weave, weave the sunlight in your hair—
Clasp your flowers to you with a pained surprise—
Fling them to the ground and turn
With a fugitive resentment in your eyes:
But weave, weave the sunlight in your hair.

So I would have had him leave,
So I would have had her stand and grieve,
So he would have left
As the soul leaves the body torn and bruised,
As the mind deserts the body it has used.
I should find
Some way incomparably light and deft,
Some way we both should understand,
Simple and faithless as a smile and shake of the hand.
She turned away, but with the autumn weather
Compelled my imagination many days,
Many days and many hours:
Her hair over her arms and her arms full of flowers
And I wonder how they should have been together!
I should have lost a gesture and a pose.
Sometimes these cogitations still amaze
The troubled midnight and the noon's repose.

The Hollow Men

'Mistah Kurtz—he dead'

We are the hollow men
We are the stuffed men
Leaning together
Headpiece filled with straw. Alas!
Our dried voices, when
We whisper together
Are quiet and meaningless
As wind in dry grass
Or rats' feet over broken glass
In our dry cellar

393

Shape without form, shade without colour,
Paralysed force, gesture without motion;

Those who have crossed
With direct eyes, to death's other Kingdom
Remember us—if at all—not as lost
Violent souls, but only
As the hollow men
The stuffed men.

II

Eyes I dare not meet in dreams
In death's dream kingdom
These do not appear:
There, the eyes are
Sunlight on a broken column
There, is a tree swinging
And voices are
In the wind's singing
More distant and more solemn
Than a fading star.

Let me be no nearer
In death's dream kingdom
Let me also wear
Such deliberate disguises
Rat's coat, crowskin, crossed staves
In a field
Behaving as the wind behaves
No nearer—

Not that final meeting
In the twilight kingdom

III

This is the dead land
This is cactus land
Here the stone images
Are raised, here they receive
The supplication of a dead man's hand
Under the twinkle of a fading star.

Is it like this
In death's other kingdom
Waking alone
At the hour when we are
Trembling with tenderness
Lips that would kiss
Form prayers to broken stone.

IV

The eyes are not here
There are no eyes here
In this valley of dying stars
In this hollow valley
This broken jaw of our lost kingdoms
In this last of meeting places
We grope together
And avoid speech
Gathered on the beach of the tumid rive r

Sightless, unless
The eyes reappear
As the perpetual star
Multifoliate rose
Of death's twilight kingdom
The hope only
Of empty men.

V

Here we go round the prickly pear
Prickly pear prickly pear
Here we go round the prickly pear
At five o'clock in the morning.

Between the idea
And the reality
Between the motion
And the act
Falls the Shadow
          For Thine is the Kingdom

Between the conception
And the creation
Between the emotion
And the response
Falls the Shadow
        Life is very long

Between the desire
And the spasm
Between the potency and existence
Between the essence
And the descent
Falls the Shadow
        For Thine is the Kingdom

For Thine is
Life is
For Thine is the

    This is the way the world ends
    This is the way the world ends
    This is the way the world ends
    Not with a bang but a whimper.

Journey of the Magi

'A cold coming we had of it,
Just the worst time of the year
For a journey, and such a long journey:
The ways deep and the weather sharp,
The very dead of winter.'
And the camels galled, sore-footed, refractory,
Lying down in the melting snow.
There were times we regretted
The summer palaces on slopes, the terraces,
And the silken girls bringing sherbet.
Then the camel men cursing and grumbling
And running away, and wanting their liquor and women,
And the night-fires going out, and the lack of shelters,
And the cities hostile and the towns unfriendly
And the villages dirty and charging high prices:

A hard time we had of it.
At the end we preferred to travel all night,
Sleeping in snatches,
With the voices singing in our ears, saying
That this was all folly.

Then at dawn we came down to a temperate valley,
Wet, below the snow-line, smelling of vegetation;
With a running stream and a water-mill beating the darkness,
And three trees on the low sky,
And an old white horse galloped away in the meadow.
Then we came to a tavern with vine-leaves over the lintel,
Six hands at an open door dicing for pieces of silver,
And feet kicking the empty wine-skins.
But there was no information, and so we continued
And arrived at evening, not a moment too soon
Finding the place; it was (you may say) satisfactory.

All this was a long time ago, I remember,
And I would do it again, but set down
This set down
This: were we led all that way for
Birth or Death? There was a Birth, certainly,
We had evidence and no doubt. I had seen birth and death,
But had thought they were different; this Birth was
Hard and bitter agony for us, like Death, our death.
We returned to our places, these Kingdoms,
But no longer at ease here, in the old dispensation,
With an alien people clutching their gods.
I should be glad of another death.

Marina

Quis hic locus, quae regio, quae mundi plaga?

What seas what shores what grey rocks and what islands
What water lapping the bow
And scent of pine and the woodthrush singing through the fog
What images return
O my daughter

Those who sharpen the tooth of the dog, meaning
    Death
Those who glitter with the glory of the hummingbird, meaning
    Death
Those who sit in the stye of contentment, meaning
    Death
Those who suffer the ecstasy of the animals, meaning
    Death
  Are become unsubstantial, reduced by a wind,
A breath of pine, and the woodsong fog
By this grace dissolved in place

  What is this face, less clear and clearer
The pulse in the arm, less strong and stronger—
Given or lent? more distant than stars and nearer than the eye

  Whispers and small laughter between leaves and hurrying
    feet
Under sleep where all the waters meet.
Bowsprit cracked with ice and paint cracked with heat.
I made this, I have forgotten
And remember.
The rigging weak and the canvas rotten
Between one June and another September.
Made this unknowing, half conscious, unknown, my own.
The garboard strake leaks, the seams need caulking.
This form, this face, this life
Living to live in a world of time beyond me; let me
Resign my life for this life, my speech for that unspoken,
The awakened, lips parted, the hope, the new ships.

  What seas what shores what granite islands towards my
    timbers
And woodthrush calling through the fog
My daughter.

WILFRED OWEN
1893-1918

Anthem for Doomed Youth

What passing-bells for those who die as cattle?
　Only the monstrous anger of the guns.
　Only the stuttering rifle's rapid rattle
Can patter out their hasty orisons.
No mockeries for them; no prayers or bells,
Nor any voice of mourning save the choirs,—
The shrill, demented choirs of wailing shells;
And bugles calling for them from sad shires.

What candles may be held to speed them all?
　Not in the hands of boys, but in their eyes
Shall shine the holy glimmer of good-byes.
　The pallor of girls' brows shall be their pall;
Their flowers the tenderness of patient minds,
And each slow dusk a drawing-down of blinds.

Greater Love

Red lips are not so red
　As the stained stones kissed by the English dead.
Kindness of wooed and wooer
Seems shame to their love pure.
O Love, your eyes lose lure
　When I behold eyes wounded in my stead!

Your slender attitude
　Trembles not exquisite like limbs knife-skewed,
Rolling and rolling there
Where God seems not to care;
Till the fierce love they bear
　Cramps them in death's extreme decrepitude.

Your voice sings not so soft,—
Though even as wind murmuring through raftered loft,—
Your dear voice is not dear,
Gentle, and evening clear,
As theirs whom none now hear
Now earth has stopped their piteous mouths that coughed.

Heart, you were never hot,
Nor large, nor full like hearts made great with shot;
And though your hands be pale,
Paler are all which trail
Your cross through flame and hail:
Weep, you may weep, for you may touch them not.

VIOLET JACOB
1863-1946

Tam i' the Kirk

O Jean, my Jean, when the bell ca's the congregation
  Owre valley an' hill wi' the ding frae its iron mou',
When a'body's thochts is set on his ain salvation,
    Mine's set on you.

There's a reid rose lies on the Buik o' the Word afore ye
  That was growin' braw on its bush at the keek o' day,
But the lad that pu'd yon flower i' the mornin's glory,
    He canna pray.

He canna pray; but there's nane i' the Kirk will heed him
  Whaur he sits sae still his lane at the side o' the wa',
For nane but the reid rose kens what my lassie gi'ed him,
    It an' us twa!

He canna sing for the sang that his ain hert raises,
  He canna see for the mist that's afore his een,
And a voice drouns the hale o' the psalms an' the paraphrases,
    Cryin' 'Jean, Jean, Jean!'

MARION ANGUS
1866-1946

Think Lang

Lassie, think lang, think lang,
Ere his step comes ower the hill.
Luve gi'es wi' a lauch an' a sang,
An' whiles for nocht but ill.

Thir's weary time tae rue
In the lea-lang nicht yer lane
The ghaist o' a kiss on yer mou'
An sough o' win' in the rain.

Lassie, think lang, think lang,
The trees is clappin' their han's,
The burnie clatterin' wi' sang
Runs ower the blossomy lan's.

Luve gi'es wi' a lauch an' a sang,
His fit fa's licht on the dew.
Oh, lass are ye thinkin' lang,
Star een an' honey mou'?

JOHN BUCHAN

1875-1940

Fisher Jamie

Puir Jamie's killed. A better lad
  Ye wadna find to busk a flee
Or burn a püle or wield a gad
  Frae Berwick to the Clints o' Dee.

And noo he's in a happier land.—
  It's Gospel truth and Gospel law
That Heaven's yett maun open stand
  To folk that for their country fa'.

But Jamie will be ill to mate;
  He lo'ed nae müsic, kenned nae tünes
Except the sang o' Tweed in spate,
  Or Talla loupin' ower its linns.

I sair misdoot that Jamie's heid
  A croun o' gowd will never please;
He liked a kep o' dacent tweed
  Whaur he could stick his casts o' flees.

If Heaven is a' that man can dream
  And a' that honest herts can wish,
It maun provide some muirland stream,
  For Jamie dreamed o' nocht but fish.

And weel I wot he'll up and speir
  In his bit blate and canty way,
Wi' kind Apostles standin' near
  Whae in their time were fishers tae.

yett, *gate*   linns, *waterfalls*   speir, *ask*
        blate, *self-conscious*   canty, *happy*

He'll offer back his gowden croun
   And in its place a rod he'll seek,
And bashfu'-like his herp lay doun
   And speir a leister and a cleek.

For Jims had aye a poachin' whim;
   He'll süne grow tired, wi' lawfu' flee
Made frae the wings o' cherubim,
   O' castin' ower the Crystal Sea. . . .

I picter him at gloamin' tide
   Steekin' the backdoor o' his hame
And hastin' to the waterside
   To play again the auld auld game;

And syne wi' saumon on his back,
   Catch't clean against the Heavenly law,
And Heavenly byliffs on his track,
   Gaun linkin' doun some Heavenly shaw.

     linkin', *hurrying*

CHRISTOPHER M. GRIEVE
('HUGH McDIARMID')
1892

The Bonnie Broukit Bairn

Mars is braw in crammasy,
Venus in a green silk goun,
The auld mune shaks her gowden feathers,
Their starry talk's a wheen o blethers,
Nane for thee a thochtie sparin,
Earth, thou bonnie broukit bairn!
—But greet, an in your tears ye'll droun
The haill clanjamfrie!

The Watergaw

Ae weet fornicht i' the yow-trummle
I saw yon antrin thing,
A watergaw wi' its chitterin licht
Ayont the on-ding;
An I thocht o' the last look ye gied
Afore ye deed!

There was nae reek i' the laverock's house
That nicht—an nane i' mine;
But I hae thocht o' that foolish licht
Ever sin syne;
An I think that mebbe at last I ken
What your look meant then.

Broukit, *neglected*   crammasy, *crimson*
clanjamfrie, *collection*   watergaw, *rainbow*   fornicht, *early evening*
yow-trummle, *a cold spell after sheep shearing when the sheep are trembling*
antrin, *rare*   chitterin, *shivering*   on-ding, *downpour*
laverock, *lark*

405

Munestruck

When the warl's couped roun' as a peerie
That licht-lookin craw o' a body, the mune,
Sits on the fower cross-win's
Peerin a' roun.

She's seen me—she's seen me—an' straucht
Loupit clean on the quick o' my hert.
The quhither o' cauld gowd's fairly
Gien me a stert.

An the roarin o' oceans noo
Is peerieweerie to me:
Thunner's a tinklin a bell: an' Time
Whuds like a flee.

Crowdieknowe

Oh to be at Crowdieknowe
When the last trumpet blaws,
An see the deid come loupin owre
The auld grey wa's.

Muckle men wi' tousled beards,
I grat at as a bairn,
'll scramble frae the croodit clay
Wi' feck o swearin.

An glower at God an a' his gang
O' angels i' the lift
—Thae trashy bleezin French-like folk
Wha gar'd them shift!

Fain the weemun-folk'll seek
To mak them haud their row
—*Fegs, God's no blate gin he stirs up*
The men o' Crowdieknowe!

couped, *overturned*   quhither, *beam*
    peerieweerie, *diminished to the faintest sound*
whuds, *moves fast*   flee, *fly*   lift, *sky*   blate, *timid*

Frae anither Window in Thrums

Here in the hauf licht waitin' till the clock
Chops: while the winnock
Hauds me as a serpent hauds a rabbit
Afore it's time to grab it
—A serpent faded to a shadow
In the stelled een its een ha'e haud o'

Here in the daurk, while like a frozen
Scurl on Life's plumm the lozen
Skimmers—or goams in upon me
Wan as Dostoevski
Glowered through a wudden dream to find
Stavrogin in the corners o' his mind,

—Or I haud it, a 'prentice snake, and gar
Heaven dwine to a haunfu' haar
Or am like cheengeless deeps aneth
Tho' ice or sunshine, life or death,
Chequer the tap; or like Stavrogin
Joukin his author wi' a still subtler grin. . . .

And yet I canna for the life o' me see
That I'd write better poetry
If like the feck o' Scots insteed
I read the books they read
And drew my thochts o' God and Man
Frae Neil Munro and Annie Swan!

Fu' weel I ken I would mak verses which
'Ud notably enrich
'Oor Scots tradition'—in the minds
O' ministers and hinds;
And fain I'd keep as faur frae that
As Proust frae Johnnie Gibb—that's flat!

chops, *strikes*	winnock, *window*	stelled, *fixed*
scurl, *dry scab*	lozen, *window pane*	skimmers, *flickers*
goams, *gazes wildly*	wudden, *mad*	dwine, *dwindle*
feck, *most*	hinds, *farm servants*	

Can I get faurer frae't than here
Whaur a' life's fictions disappear
And I'm left face to face wi' nocht
But sicna drab splash as brocht
My like to be, to mak' wi't what I can,
Back at the stert whaur a' began?

WILLIAM SOUTAR
1898-1943

The Gowk

Half doun the hill, whaur fa's the linn,
Far frae the flaught o' fowk,
I saw upon a lanely whin
A lanely singin' gowk:
Cuckoo, cuckoo;
And at my back
The howie hill stude up and spak:
Cuckoo, cuckoo.

There was nae soun': the loupin' linn
Hung frostit in its fa':
Nae bird was on the lanely whin
Sae white wi' fleurs o' snaw:
Cuckoo, cuckoo;
I stude stane still
And saftly spak the howie hill:
Cuckoo, cuckoo.

CECIL DAY LEWIS
1904

The Conflict

I sang as one
Who on a tilting deck sings
To keep their courage up, though the wave hangs
That shall cut off their sun.

As storm-cocks sing,
Flinging their natural answer in the wind's teeth,
And care not if it is waste of breath
Or birth-carol of spring

As ocean-flyer clings
To height, to the last drop of spirit driving on
While yet ahead is land to be won
And work for wings

Singing I was at peace,
Above the clouds, outside the ring:
For sorrow finds a swift release in song
And pride its poise.

Yet living here,
As one between two massing powers I live
Whom neutrality cannot save
Nor occupation cheer.

Nor such shall be left alive:
The innocent wing is soon shot down,
And private stars fade in the blood-red dawn
Where two worlds strive.

The red advance of life
Contracts pride, calls out the common blood,
Beats song into a single blade,
Makes a depth-charge of grief.

Move then with new desires,
For where we used to build and love
Is no man's land, and only ghosts can live
Between two fires.

Will it be so again?

Will it be so again
That the brave, the gifted are lost from view,
And empty scheming men
Are left in peace their lunatic age to renew?
Will it be so again?

Must it be always so
That the best are chosen to fall and sleep
Like seeds, and we too slow
In claiming the earth they quicken, and the old usurpers reap
What they could not sow?

Will it be so again—
The jungle code and the hypocrite gesture?
A poppy wreath for the slain
And a cut-throat world for the living? that stale imposture
Played on us once again?

Will it be as before—
Peace, with no heart or mind to ensure it,
Guttering down to war
Like a libertine to his grave? We should not be surprised:
  we knew it
Happen before.

Shall it be so again?
Call not upon the glorious dead
To be your witnessess then.
The living alone can nail to their promise the ones who said
It shall not be so again.

Seen from the Train

Somewhere between Crewkerne
And Yeovil it was. On the left of the line
Just as the crinkled hills unroll
To the plain. A church on a small green knoll—
A limestone church,
And above the church
Cedar boughs stretched like hands that yearn
To protect or to bless. The whole

Stood up, antique and clear
As a cameo, from the vale. I swear
It was not a dream. Twice, thrice, had I found it
Chancing to look as my train wheeled round it.
But this time I passed,
Though I gazed as I passed
All the way down the valley, that knoll was not there,
Nor the church, nor the trees it mounded.

What came between to unsight me? . . .
But suppose, only suppose there might be
A secret look in a landscape's eye
Following you as you hasten by,
And you have your chance—
Two or three chances
At most—to hold and interpret it rightly
Or it is gone for aye.

There was a time when men
Would have called it a vision, said that sin
Had blinded me since to a heavenly fact.
Well, I have neither invoked nor faked
Any church in the air,
And little I care
Whether or no I shall see it again.
But blindly my heart is racked

When I think how, not twice or thrice,
But year after year in another's eyes
I have caught the look that I missed to-day
Of the church, the knoll, the cedars—a ray

Of the faith, too, they stood for,
The hope they were food for,
The love they prayed for, facts beyond price—
And turned my eyes away.

Cornet Solo

Thirty years ago lying awake,
Lying awake
In London at night when childhood barred me
From livelier pastimes, I'd hear a street-band break
Into old favourites—'The Ash Grove', 'Killarney'
Or 'Angels Guard Thee'.

That was the music for such an hour—
A deciduous hour
Of leaf-wan drizzle, of solitude
And gaslight bronzing the gloom like an autumn flower—
The time and music for a boy imbrued
With the pensive mood.

I could have lain for hours together,
Sweet hours together,
Listening to the cornet's cry
Down wet streets gleaming like patent leather
Where beauties jaunted in cabs to their revelry,
Jewelled and spry.

Plaintive its melody rose or waned
Like an autumn wind
Blowing the rain on beds of aster,
On man's last bed: mournful and proud it complained
As a woman who dreams of the charms that graced her,
In young days graced her.

Strange how those yearning airs could sweeten
And still enlighten
The hours when solitude gave me her breast.
Strange they could tell a mere child how hearts may beat in
The self-same tune for the once-possessed
And the unpossessed.

Last night, when I heard the cornet's strain,
It seemed a refrain
Wafted from thirty years back—so remote an
Echo it bore: but I felt again
The prophetic mood of a child, too long forgotten,
Too lightly forgotten.

Sketches for a Portrait

Consider the boy that you were, although you would hardly
Recognize him if you met him, even in his old haunts—
The well-shaved lawn or the Rip Van Winkle forest,
With the slag-tip reek acrid as youth's resentments
Tainting their green, or the mellow South West town
That spoke to him words unheeded but unforgotten—
Even in the haunts where he was most himself,
If a chaos can be a self: there perhaps least of all,
So deceptive are youth's environs, so quick to promise
What is not in your power, to fall in with caving moods.
But question the boy that you were, for you have no other
Clue to the man you are, to the heart divided

*Green boy, green boy, who walk through the furzes
Unsinged, and undevoured through the dandelions,
Tell me your secret*

              I am one who peered
In every stranger's face for my identity,
In every mirror for a family likeness,
In lakes and dewdrops for the antiself,
I stunned myself upon their shallow eyes
Like a chaffinch slamming against a windowpane,
Until at last I learned to use my blindness.
I hung upon their words, and they always broke
Like the old rope they were, letting me down
Into a pit where lidless poisoners coiled:
So was I trained to climb on my thread.
Love I desired, but the father I loved and hated
Lived too much in me, and his images of me
Fretted a frame always outgrowing them:

I went into the wilderness bearing all
My faults and his ambitions on my head.
  Solitude then was my métier. I wore it
As an invisible cloak, or a glass cloche
To save from nibbling teeth and clodhopper boots.
And focus the sun's eye on my sullen growth.
I kept my solitude as a young girl guards
Virginity yet wishes it away,
Impatient of the blossom cloud that endears her.
The bee forces the blossom. I knew the weak
Involuntary spasms of consent. . . .
I wished to commit myself to the irretrievable
As a bee is committed to the bell, or a suicide
Already half way from the parapet, to the river:
But the river whisked away and the flower turned nasty.
Or perhaps I was a coward.

> *Green boy, green boy,*
> *What did the lawn teach, what did the Rip Van Winkle*
> *Forest say, and the mellow South West town?*

  Resilience first, release perhaps, the lawn.
Morning brought tears and daisies, afternoon
A tennis party. Athletic clergymen. Flannels—
The uniform of a class, of a way of thinking,
Or of not thinking: as I looked for a lost ball
In the laurels, they smirched with pit-grime. It was good—
The sensual leap, the stinging drive and return
Of the blood, conflict without relationship.
I preferred singles—the world, such as it was,
Where I wanted it, on the run, with a net between us.
  Winters, I walked much alone, rubbing my thoughts
Together, and prayed for a spark and imagined a forest
My tinderbox. Around me, sodden bracken:
Overhead, interlocked branches snickering.
A roar from a distant pithead as the cage dropped
Like a stone into the well of an orphic mystery.
Otherwise the forest was silent: birdless; nymphless;
Oaks hollow as history; morose and regimented
Conifers; birches with the hauteur of fashion plates
  And the silence said something, something about a wish
To be rooted, a wish profounder than roots, more insidious:

But the whirring wheels at the pithead, 'Stay on the surface,
You were not made to dip your hand in darkness
Or hew at the mystery's face': and the lawn replied,
'There is coal beneath us, everywhere coal, the dream
Of the deep sleep of forests, so sleep and dream':
And the oaks, 'We are hollow with unfulfilled desire—
Hurry, all is not the same in a thousand years.'
  So I returned to school, a kaleidoscope
Of shaken images, arguments jangling like glass.
And the wise grey South West town claimed me, calmed me
With the sedatives of routine, the balm of multitude.
Snatches of wisdom borne on a wet wind
Like bells or wood smoke or ancestral memories—
Borne from the high, dry plateaux of reason, weathered
To a romantic tone: and the god was reborn
In the echo. Words unheeded but unforgotten.
Call no man happy. . . . Our actions burst like spray
Upon a reef, nevertheless we must act. . . .
Know yourself. . . . But knowing, do not presume
To swerve or sweeten what is foreordained. . . .
For the heart, magnanimity; for the mind, good sense;
For the soul, a natural piety; for fate,
A stoic's bending steel. . . . Nothing too much.
Pinnacles of a drowned, four-square age broke surface
Between the waking bell and the afternoon wicket—
Temperate isles in a distempered sea,
Isles of the blessed, a landfall for my tossed dreams.

  Green boy, green boy, tell me your dreams

                                              Sit here
On the harbour wall with me. Look down at the water
Swaying, impassive, transparent, evasive:
Motiveless swaying, vibrantly motionless,
Rumpling the olive-green and slate-blue boulders
Fathomed below, and glossing the seaweed
To hair hyacinthine of marble statuary.
Look at the seabrow, puckered in sunlight,
Jigged over by millions of sparklers for ever
Quenched, re-illumined: and beyond the fireworks
A swell, a haze, a forever encroaching
Receding question. Such were my daydreams.
Dare you interpret them? Had we not better

Turn round to the castles of sand and the starfish
Sunbathers? return to our spade and bucket?
  Sleepwalking with the tides, unskilled to dive
Into the heart of my images, I practised
Words like a secret vice: words perpetually
Flung-up, encroached on, crumbling, superseded,
Real to me as wet sand to a child's fingers,
More real than the quaking asphalt of the sea front
Or the rook-babble of bathers. Oh, innocent vice—
Could everything be reduced to a form of words!
But they were only a guesswork map of the terrain
Where soon I should have to fight; or else a petition
To be exempted. The love I feared and longed for
Would come in out of the sea, a terrible sun
Thrusting aside my screen of words, and pin me
To the sand like a starfish, and pick my dreams
And bleach my fears and make my dry words live.

  So, when he met a girl in the forest, he knew her
A nymph. His random casts had found a quarry.
The dead wood woke with her, she dappled the night wood
With carillons of noon, siftings elusive
Of light from the fountain of all truth and legend.
Pursuing then, he quickened his solitude
With a thousand images of her—images
More real to him than the fugitive flesh that awoke them.
Charmed life of a green boy, threading the maze
But alone no longer! The eyes and claws drew back
Deeper into the shade, biding their time.
Was he hunter or hunted? He cared not. The pursuit led
Out of the forest, over the lawn, past pitheads
Where steam puffed out in a squall of imprecation,
Through smoke-rings in college rooms and the blackened circles
Of picnic fires, across the common and
The garden, and over the moon, with a coursed hare's
Demented doublings and the closed circuit
Of the electric hare—a thousand repetitions
Of a routine immemorial, each unique,
While the horn hummed like autumn in the blood
Always a field before him or behind him.
Till at last they came to the verge of the sea, where hunter
And hunted face the effacing and are one.

WYSTAN H. AUDEN

1907

It's no use raising a Shout

Its no use raising a shout.
No, Honey, you can cut that right out.
I don't want any more hugs;
Make me some fresh tea, fetch me some rugs.
Here am I, here are you:
But what does it mean? What are we going to do?

A long time ago I told my mother
I was leaving home to find another:
I never answered her letter
But I never found a better.
Here am I, here are you:
But what does it mean? What are we going to do?

It wasn't always like this?
Perhaps it wasn't, but it is.
Put the car away; when life fails,
What's the good of going to Wales?
Here am I, here are you:
But what does it mean? What are we going to do?

In my spine there was a base;
And I knew the general's face:
But they've severed all the wires,
And I can't tell what the general desires.
Here am I, here are you:
But what does it mean? What are we going to do?

In my veins there is a wish,
And a memory of fish:
When I lie crying on the floor,
It says, 'You've often done this before.'
Here am I, here are you:
But what does it mean? What are we going to do?

A bird used to visit this shore:
It isn't going to come any more.
I've come a very long way to prove
No land, no water, and no love.
Here am I, here are you:
But what does it mean? What are we going to do?

Get there if you can

Get there if you can and see the land you once were proud
to own

Though the roads have almost vanished and the expresses
never run:

Smokeless chimneys, damaged bridges, rotting wharves and
choked canals,

Tramlines buckled, smashed trucks lying on their side across
the rails;

Power stations locked, deserted, since they drew the boiler
fires;

Pylons falling or subsiding, trailing dead high-tension wires;

Head-gears gaunt on grass-grown pit-banks, seams abandoned
years ago;

Drop a stone and listen for its splash in flooded dark below.

Squeeze into the works through broken windows or through
damp-sprung doors;

See the rotted shafting, see holes gaping in the upper floors;

Where the Sunday lads come talking motor bicycle and girl,

Smoking cigarettes in chains until their heads are in a whirl.

Far from there we spent the money, thinking we could well
afford,

While they quietly undersold us with their cheaper trade
abroad;

At the theatre, playing tennis, driving motor cars we had,
In our continental villas, mixing cocktails for a cad.

These were boon companions who devised the legends for
  our tombs,
These who have betrayed us nicely while we took them to
  our rooms.

Newman, Ciddy, Plato, Fronny, Pascal, Bowdler, Baudelaire,
Doctor Frommer, Mrs. Allom, Freud, the Baron, and
  Flaubert.

Lured with their compelling logic, charmed with beauty of
  their verse,
With their loaded sideboards whispered 'Better join us, life is
  worse,'

Taught us at the annual camps arranged by the big business
  men
'Sunbathe, pretty, till you're twenty. You shall be our servant
  then.'

Perfect pater. Marvellous mater. Knock the critic down who
  dares—
Very well, believe it, copy, till your hair is white as theirs.

Yours you say were parents to avoid, avoid then if you please
Do the reverse on all occasions till you catch the same disease.

When we asked the way to Heaven, these directed us ahead
To the padded room, the clinic and the hangman's little shed.

Intimate as war-time prisoners in an isolation camp,
Living month by month together, nervy, famished, lousy,
  damp.

On the sopping esplanade or from our dingy lodgings we
Stare out dully at the rain which falls for miles into the sea.

Lawrence, Blake and Homer Lane, once healers in our English
  land;
These are dead as iron for ever; these can never hold our hand.

Lawrence was brought down by smut-hounds, Blake went
  dotty as he sang,
Homer Lane was killed in action by the Twickenham Baptist
  gang.

Have things gone too far already? Are we done for? Must
    we wait
Hearing doom's approaching footsteps regular down miles of
    straight;

Run the whole night through in gumboots, stumble on and
    gasp for breath,
Terrors drawing close and closer, winter's landscape, Fox's
    death;

Or, in friendly fireside circle, sit and listen for the crash
Meaning that the mob has realised something's up, and start
    to smash;

Engine-drivers with their oil-cans, factory girls in overalls
Blowing sky-high monster stores, destroying intellectuals?

Hope and fear are neck and neck: which is it near the course's
    end
Crashes, having lost his nerve; is overtaken on the bend?

Shut up talking, charming in the best suits to be had in town,
Lecturing on navigation while the ship is going down.

Drop those priggish ways for ever, stop behaving like a stone:
Throw the bath-chairs right away, and learn to leave ourselves
    alone.

If we really want to live, we'd better start at once to try;
If we don't, it doesn't matter, but we'd better start to die.

A. E. Housman

No one, not even Cambridge, was to blame;
—Blame if you like the human situation—
Heart-injured in North London, he became
The leading classic of his generation.

Deliberately he chose the dry-as-dust,
Kept tears like dirty postcards in a drawer;
Food was his public love, his private lust
Something to do with violence and the poor.

In savage footnotes on unjust editions
He timidly attacked the life he led.
And put the money of his feelings on

The uncritical relations of the dead,
Where purely geographical divisions
Parted the coarse hanged soldier from the don.

Look, Stranger

Look, stranger, at this island now
The leaping light for your delight discovers,
Stand stable here
And silent be,
That through the channels of the ear
May wander like a river
The swaying sound of the sea.

Here at the small field's ending pause
Where the chalk wall falls to the foam, and its tall ledges
Oppose the pluck
And knock of the tide.
And the shingle scrambles after the suck-
ing surf, and the gull lodges
A moment on its sheer side.

Far off like floating seeds the ships
Diverge on urgent voluntary errands;
And the full view
Indeed may enter
And move in memory as now these clouds do,
That pass the harbour mirror
And all the summer through the water saunter.

LOUIS MACNEICE
1907

Spring Voices

The smaller householder now comes out warily
Afraid of the barrage of sun that shouts cheerily,
Spring is massing in force, birds wink in air,
The battlemented chestnuts volley green fire,
The pigeons banking on the wind, the hoots of cars,
Stir him to run wild, gamble on horses, buy cigars;
Joy lies before him to be ladled and lapped from his hand—
Only that behind him, in the shade of his villa, memories
    stand
Breathing on his neck and muttering that all this has
    happened before,
Keep the east wind out, cast no clout, try no unwarranted
    jaunts untried before,
But let the spring slide by nor think to board its car
For it rides West to where the tangles of scrap-iron are;
Do not walk, these voices say, between the bucking clouds
    alone.
Or you may loiter into a suddenly howling crater, or fall,
    jerked back, garrotted by the sun.

Rugby Football Excursion

Euston—the smell of soot and fish and petrol;
Then in the train jogging and jogging,
The sheaf of wires from pole to pole beside us
Dogging the fancy northward

And waking to board the *Hibernia*—Bass and Guinness,
Bull-necks and brogues and favours
And Kerry-coloured girls; the whole excursion
Savours of twelve years back

423

Back to my adolescence, back to Ireland,
'Ilkla Moor b'at a't' from Midland voices,
And Wicklow apricot in early sunshine
Rejoices what was jaded.

Horse-cabs and outside cars—the ballyhoo for trippers—
And College Park reposeful behind the railings;
Emphatic old ladies' voices in a lounge lamenting
Failings of health and budgets.

Lansdowne Road—the swirl of faces, flags,
Gilbert and Sullivan music, emerald jerseys;
Spire and crane beyond remind the mind on furlough
Of Mersey's code and Rome's.

Eccentric scoring—Nicholson, Marshall and Unwin,
Replies by Bailey and Daly;
Rugs around our shins, the effortless place-kick
Gaily carving the goal-posts.

Then tea and toast with the Fellows and Bishops in a huge
Regency room in the warmth of a classic assurance
Looking on Stephen's Green where they blew up George the
    Second—
Endurance of one-way thinking.

And then a walk through Dublin down the great
Grey streets broad and straight and drowned in twilight,
Statues of poets and Anglo-Irish patriots—
High lights of merged traditions.

Junkshops, the smell of poverty, pubs at the corner,
A chimney on fire and street on street of broken
Fanlights over the doors of tenement houses—
Token of the days of Reason.

In a frame from Sir Isaac Newton the dusk of Ireland
Bathes the children whipping their tops on the cobbles
Or swinging by ropes from a lamp post while a cripple
Hobbles like a Hogarth sketch.

These I must leave, rejoin the beery trippers
   Whose other days prefer to-day delirious
Packing the bar on the boat, while a sapphire pinhead
   Sirius marks Dun Laoghaire.

Autumn Journal—X

And so return to work—the M.A. gown,
   Alphas and Betas, central heating, floor-polish,
Demosthenes on the Crown
   And Oedipus at Colonus.
And I think of the beginnings of other terms
   Coming across the sea to unknown England
And memory reaffirms
   That alarm and exhilaration of arrival:
White wooden boxes, clatter of boots, a smell
   Of changing-rooms—Lifebuoy soap and muddy flannels—
And over all a bell
   Dragooning us to dormitory or classroom,
Ringing with a tongue of frost across the bare
   Benches and desks escutcheoned with initials;
We sat on the hot pipes by the wall, aware
   Of the cold in our bones and the noise and the bell
      impending.
A fishtail gas-flare in the dark latrine;
   Chalk and ink and rows of pegs and lockers;
The War was on—maize and margarine
   And lessons on the map of Flanders.
But we had our toys—our electric torches, our glass
   Dogs and cats, and plasticine and conkers,
And we had our games, we learned to dribble and pass
   In jerseys striped like tigers.
And we had our make-believe, we had our mock
   Freedom in walks by twos and threes on Sunday,
We dug out fossils from the yellow rock
   Or drank the Dorset distance.
And we had our little tiptoe minds, alert
   To jump for facts and fancies and statistics
And our little jokes of Billy Bunter dirt
   And a heap of home-made dogma.

The abbey chimes varnished the yellow street,
　　The water from the taps in the bath was yellow,
The trees were full of owls, the sweets were sweet
　　And life an expanding ladder.
And reading romances we longed to be grown up,
　　To shoot from the hip and marry lovely ladies
And smoke cigars and live on claret cup
　　And lie in bed in the morning;
Taking it for granted that things would still
　　Get better and bigger and better and bigger and better,
That the road across the hill
　　Led to the Garden of Eden;
Everything to expect and nothing to deplore,
　　Cushy days beyond the dumb horizon
And nothing to doubt about, to linger for
　　In the halfway house of childhood.
And certainly we did not linger, we went on
　　Growing and growing, gluttons for the future,
And four foot six was gone
　　And we found it time to be leaving
To be changing school, sandstone changed for chalk
　　And ammonites for the flinty husks of sponges,
Another lingo to talk
　　And jerseys in other colours.
And still the acquiring of unrelated facts,
　　A string of military dates for history,
And the Gospels and the Acts
　　And logarithms and Greek and the Essays of Elia;
And still the exhilarating rhythm of free
　　Movement swimming or serving at tennis,
The fives-courts' tattling repartee
　　Or rain on the sweating body.
But life began to narrow what was done—
　　The dominant gerundive—
And Number Two must mimic Number One
　　In bearing, swearing, attitude and accent.
And so we jettisoned all
　　Our childish fantasies and anarchism;
The weak must go to the wall
　　But strength implies the system;
You must lose your soul to be strong, you cannot stand
　　Alone on your legs or your own ideas;

The order of the day is complete conformity and
    An automatic complacence.
Such was the order of the day; only at times
    The Fool among the Yes-men flashed his motley
To prick their pseudo-reason with his rhymes
    And drop his grain of salt on court behaviour.
And sometimes a whisper in books
    Would challenge the code, or a censored memory some-
        times,
Sometimes the explosion of rooks,
    Sometimes the mere batter of light on the senses.
And the critic jailed in the mind would peep through the grate
    And husky from long silence, murmur gently
That there is something rotten in the state
    Of Denmark but the state is not the whole of Denmark;
And a spade is still a spade
    And the difference is not final between a tailored
Suit and a ready-made
    And knowledge is not—necessarily—wisdom;
And a cultured accent will not alone provide
    A season ticket to the Vita Nuova;
And there are many better men outside
    Than ever answered roll-call.
But the critic did not win, has not won yet
    Though always reminding us of points forgotten;
We hasten to forget
    As much as he remembers.
And school was what they always said it was,
    An apprenticeship to life an initiation,
And all the better because
    The initiates were blindfold;
The reflex action of a dog or sheep
    Being enough for normal avocations
And life rotating in an office sleep
    As long as things are normal.
Which it was assumed that they would always be;
    On that assumption terms began and ended;
And now, in 1938 A.D.,
    Term is again beginning.

The Conscript

Being so young he feels the weight of history
Like clay round his boots; he would, if he could, fly
In search of a future like a sycamore seed
But is prevented by his own Necessity,
His own yet alien, which, whatever he may plead,
To every question gives the same reply.

Choiceless therefore, driven from pillar to post,
Expiating his pedigree, fulfilling
An oracle whose returns grow less and less,
Bandied from camp to camp to practise killing
He fails even so at times to remain engrossed
And is aware, at times, of life's largesse.

From camp to camp, from Eocene to chalk,
He lives a paradox, lives in a groove
That runs dead straight to an ordained disaster
So that in two dimensions he must move
Like an automaton, yet his inward stalk
Vertically aspires and makes him his own master.

Hence, though on the flat his life has no
Promise but of diminishing returns,
By feeling down and upwards he can divine
That dignity which far above him burns
In stars that yet are his and which below
Stands rooted like a dolmen in his spine.

STEPHEN SPENDER

1909

I think continually

I think continually of those who were truly great.
Who, from the womb, remembered the soul's history
Through corridors of light where the hours are suns
Endless and singing. Whose lovely ambition
Was that their lips, still touched with fire,
Should tell of the Spirit clothed from head to foot in song.
And who hoarded from the Spring branches
The desires falling across their bodies like blossoms.

What is precious is never to forget
The essential delight of the blood drawn from ageless springs
Breaking through rocks in worlds before our earth.
Never to deny its pleasure in the morning simple light
Nor its grave evening demand for love.
Never to allow gradually the traffic to smother
With noise and fog the flowering of the spirit.

Near the snow, near the sun, in the highest fields
See how these names are fêted by the waving grass
And by the streamers of white cloud
And whispers of wind in the listening sky.
The names of those who in their lives fought for life
Who wore at their hearts the fire's centre.
Born of the sun they travelled a short while towards the sun,
And left the vivid air signed with their honour.

The Pylons

The secret of these hills was stone, and cottages
Of that stone made,
And crumbling roads
That turned on sudden hidden villages.

Now over these small hills they have built the concrete
That trails black wire:
Pylons, those pillars
Bare like nude, giant girls that have no secret.

The valley with its gilt and evening look
And the green chestnut
Of customary root
Are mocked dry like the parched bed of a brook.

But far above and far as sight endures
Like whips of anger
With lightning's danger
There runs the quick perspective of the future.

This dwarfs our emerald country by its trek
So tall with prophecy:
Dreaming of cities
Where often clouds shall lean their swan-like neck.

The Landscape near an Aerodrome

More beautiful and soft than any moth
With burring furred antennae feeling its huge path
Through dusk, the air-liner with shut-off engines
Glides over suburbs and the sleeves set trailing tall
To point the wind. Gently, broadly, she falls
Scarcely disturbing charted currents of air

Lulled by descent, the travellers across sea
And across feminine land indulging its easy limbs
In miles of softness, now let their eyes trained by watching
Penetrate through dusk the outskirts of this town
Here where industry shows a fraying edge.
Here they may see what is being done.

Beyond the winking masthead light
And the landing-ground, they observe the outposts
Of work: chimneys like lank black fingers
Or figures frightening and mad: and squat buildings
With their strange air behind trees, like women's faces

Shattered by grief. Here where few houses
Moan with faint light behind their blinds
They remark the unhomely sense of complaint like a dog
Shut out and shivering at the foreign moon.

In the last sweep of love, they pass over fields
Behind the aerodrome, where boys play all day
Hacking dead grass: whose cries, like wild birds,
Settle upon the nearest roofs
But soon are hid under the loud city.

Then, as they land, they hear the tolling bell
Reaching across the landscape of hysteria
To where, larger than all the charcoaled batteries
And imaged towers against that dying sky,
Religion stands, the church blocking the sun.

An Elementary School Classroom in a Slum

Far far from gusty waves, these children's faces.
Like rootless weeds the torn hair round their paleness.
The tall girl with her weighed down head. The paper-
seeming boy with rat's eyes. The stunted unlucky heir
Of twisted bones, reciting a father's gnarled disease,
His lesson from the desk. At back of the dim class,
One unnoted, sweet and young: his eyes live in a dream
Of squirrels' games, in tree room, other than this.

On sour cream walls, donations. Shakespeare's head
Cloudless at dawn, civilised dome riding all cities.
Belled, flowery, Tyrolese valley. Open-handed map
Awarding the world its world. And yet, for these
Children, these windows, not this world, are world,
Where all their future's painted with a fog,
A narrow street sealed in with a lead sky,
Far far from rivers, capes, and stars of words.

Surely Shakespeare is wicked, the map a bad example
With ships and sun and love tempting them to steal—
For lives that slyly turn in their cramped holes
From fog to endless night? On their slag heap, these children

431

Wear skins peeped through by bones and spectacles of steel
With mended glass, like bottle bits on stones.
All of their time and space are foggy slum
So blot their maps with slums as big as doom.

Unless, governor, teacher, inspector, visitor,
This map becomes their window and these windows
That open on their lives like crouching tombs
Break, O break open, till they break the town
And show the children to the fields and all their world
Azure on their sands, to let their tongues
Run naked into books, the white and green leaves open
The history theirs whose language is the sun.